100 SCIENCE LESSONS

C000120021

YEAR 2

Scottish Primary 3

Published by Scholastic Ltd,
Villiers House,
Clarendon Avenue,
Leamington Spa,
Warwickshire CV32 5PR

© **Scholastic Ltd 2001**
Text © Carole Creary and Gay Wilson 2001

1 2 3 4 5 6 7 8 9 0   1 2 3 4 5 6 7 8 9 0

Series Consultant
Peter Riley

Authors
Carole Creary
Gay Wilson

Editor
Irene Goodacre

Assistant Editor
David Sandford

Series Designers
David Hurley
Joy Monkhouse

Designers
Anna Oliwa
Paul Cheshire

Cover photography
Martyn Chillmaid

Illustrations
Ann Kronheimer

British Library Cataloguing-in-Publication Data
A catalogue record for this book is available from the British Library.

ISBN 0-439-01803-X

The right of Carole Creary and Gay Wilson to be identified as the Authors of this work has been asserted by them in accordance with the Copyright, Designs and Patents Act 1988.

All rights reserved. This book is sold subject to the condition that it shall not, by way of trade or otherwise, be lent, hired out or otherwise circulated without the publisher's prior consent in any form of binding or cover other than that in which it is published and without a similar condition, including this condition, being imposed upon the subsequent purchaser.

No part of this publication may be reproduced, stored in a retrieval system, or transmitted, in any form or by any means, electronic, mechanical, photocopying, recording or otherwise, without the prior permission of the publisher. This book remains copyright, although permission is granted to copy those pages indicated as photocopiable for classroom distribution and use only in the school which has purchased the book, or by the teacher who has purchased the book, and in accordance with the CLA licensing agreement. Photocopying permission is given for purchasers only and not for borrowers of books from any lending service.

Teachers should consult their own school policies and guidelines concerning practical work and participation of children in scientific experiments. You should only select activities which you feel can be carried out safely and confidently in the classroom.

Acknowledgements
The National Curriculum for England 2000
© The Queens Printer and Controller of HMSO. Reproduced under the terms of HMSO Guidance Note 8.
The National Curriculum for Wales 2000
© The Queens Printer and Controller of HMSO. Reproduced under the terms of HMSO Guidance Note 10.

Contents

Introduction

100 Science Lessons is a series of year-specific teachers' resource books that provide a wealth of lesson plans and photocopiable resources for delivering a whole year of science teaching, including differentiation and assessment.

The series follows the QCA *Science Scheme of Work* in the sequencing of topics. However, instead of having six or seven units as in the QCA scheme, the book for each year contains eight units. These units are the familiar topics: 1. Ourselves, 2. Animals & plants, 3. The environment, 4. Materials, 5. Electricity, 6. Forces & motion, 7. Light & sound, 8. Earth & beyond. They appear in the same order in every book, but have sub-titles which describe the emphasis of the work in that year. For example, in this book Unit 1 is Ourselves: Keeping Healthy.

By having eight units, this resource builds on the QCA scheme to accommodate the demands of the curricula for Wales, Scotland and Northern Ireland. It also creates opportunities to visit each topic in every year: after visiting a topic in synchrony with the QCA scheme, you can make a further visit the following year for extension or consolidation of the previous year's work. The grid on page 208 shows how the topics are mapped out through the whole series.

Each unit is divided into a number of lessons, ending with an assessment lesson. The organisation chart at the start of each unit shows the objectives and outcomes of each lesson, and gives a quick overview of the lesson content (Main activity, Group activities, Plenary). The statements from the national curricula for England, Wales, Scotland and Northern Ireland (given in the grids on pages 198–207) provide the basis for the lesson objectives used throughout the book.

ORGANISATION (14 LESSONS)

	OBJECTIVES	MAIN ACTIVITY	GROUP ACTIVITIES	PLENARY	OUTCOMES
LESSON 1	● To know that light sources are used in different ways.	Revise Y1/P2 work on light sources. Discuss the use of light sources.	Consider and record how many lights there are at home. Write a story or poem about what it would be like without any light.	Discuss the uses of light and share the children's writing.	● Can recognise different uses of light sources.
LESSON 2	● To know that light cannot pass through some materials and that is how shadows are created.	Investigate and have fun with shadows.	Investigate which materials make shadows. Draw silhouettes.	Discuss findings. Identify the silhouettes.	● Can explain that a shadow forms due to light being blocked.

LESSON PLANS

Each lesson plan is divided into four parts: Introduction, Main activity, Group activities and Plenary. In many of the lessons, the introduction is supported by background information and a vocabulary list that will help in delivering the lesson and support assessment of the work. The lesson introduction sets the context for the work; the Main activity features direct whole-class or group teaching, and may include instructions on how to perform a demonstration or an experiment in order to stimulate the children's interest and increase their motivation. There is then usually a choice of Group activities to engage groups of children. (In those lessons where a whole-class investigation takes place, there is a single Group activity related to this.) Advice on differentiation and formative assessment linked to this work is provided. Finally, there are details of a Plenary session.

About 70% of the lesson plans in this book, including those for the assessment lessons, are presented in full detail. Many of these are followed by outlines for closely related extension of the lesson; these plans are presented as grids for you to develop. They contain the major features of the detailed lesson plans, allowing you to plan for progression and assessment.

Detailed lesson plans

The lessons in this book have been designed to encourage and develop the children's investigative skills. Children at this stage are not expected to carry out a fair test without a great deal of help, though they may be able to recognise when a test is not fair. It is, however, important that they begin to understand the process and practise the skills of making predictions, planning a fair test, choosing appropriate resources, collecting data and drawing conclusions. Even lessons that focus on knowledge and understanding are approached in an investigative way through questioning, in order to develop the children's thinking skills. Careful observation and the use of secondary sources are also encouraged as ways of gaining science knowledge.

Objectives

The objectives of the lessons are derived from the statements in all the UK science curriculum documents. They are stated in a way that helps to focus each lesson plan and give a unique theme to each unit. At least one objective for each lesson is derived from the statements related to content knowledge. In addition, there may be objectives relating to scientific enquiry; but you may choose to replace these with others to meet your needs and the skills you wish the children to develop. The relationship of the curriculum statements to the coverage of each unit's lessons is indicated in the grids on pages 198–207.

Wherever relevant, the focus of each unit coincides with that of the matching unit in the QCA *Science Scheme of Work*. However, we have not distinguished in the lesson objectives which content is specific to any one curriculum, and have left it to your professional judgement to identify those activities that are best suited to the age and ability of your class and to the minimum requirements spelled out in your local curriculum guidance. If you wish to check whether a particular activity cross-references directly to your curriculum, please refer to pages 198–207.

Resources and Preparation

The Resources section provides a list of everything you will need to deliver the lesson, including any of the photocopiables presented in this book. Preparation describes anything that needs to be done in advance of the lesson, such as preparing cards for a game or making ice cubes. As part of the preparation for all practical work, you should consult your school's policies concerning the use of plants and animals in the classroom, so that you can select activities for which you are confident to take responsibility. The ASE publication *Be Safe!* gives useful guidance on what things are safe to use in the classroom.

Background

The Background section provides relevant facts and explanations of concepts to support the lesson. In some cases, the information provided may go beyond what the children need to learn at Year 2/Primary 3; but you may find this further knowledge valuable in helping you to avoid reinforcing any misconceptions the children may have.

Vocabulary

Each fully detailed lesson plan has an associated vocabulary list, containing words that should be used by the children in discussing and presenting their work, and in their writing. The words relate both to scientific enquiry and to knowledge and understanding.

It is important that children develop their scientific vocabulary in order to describe their findings and observations and to explain their ideas. Whenever a specialist word is used, it should be accompanied by a definition, as some children in the class may take time to understand and differentiate the meanings of words such as 'hibernate', 'habitat' and 'migrate'.

Introduction

The lesson introductions contain ideas to get each lesson started and to 'set the scene'. You may also wish to draw on the Background or make links with other lessons in your scheme of work.

Main teaching activity

This section presents a direct, whole-class (or occasionally group) teaching session to follow the Introduction. This will help you to deliver the content knowledge outlined in the lesson objectives to the children before they start their group work. It may include guidance on discussion, or on performing one or more demonstrations or class investigations to help the children understand the work ahead.

The relative proportions of the lesson given to the Introduction, Main teaching activity and Group activities vary. If you are reminding the children of their previous work and getting them on to their own investigations, the group work may dominate the lesson time; if you are introducing a new topic or concept, you might wish to spend all, or most, of the lesson engaged in whole-class teaching.

Group activities

The Group activities are very flexible. Some may be best suited to individual work, while others may be suitable for work in pairs or larger groups. In the detailed lesson plans, there are usually two Group activities provided for each lesson. You may wish to use one after the other; use both together, to reduce demand on resources and your attention; or, where one is a practical activity, use the other for children who complete their practical work successfully and quickly. Some of the Group activities are supported by a photocopiable sheet.

The Group activities may include some writing. These activities are also aimed at strengthening the children's science literacy, and supporting their English literacy skills. They may involve writing labels and captions, developing scientific vocabulary, writing about or recording investigations, presenting data, explaining what they have observed, or using appropriate secondary sources. The children's mathematical skills are also developed through number and data-handling work in the context of science investigations.

Differentiation

For each of the lessons, where appropriate, there are suggestions for differentiated work for the more able and less able children in the class. Differentiated Group activities are designed so that all the children who perform these tasks can make a contribution to the Plenary session. At this stage many of the activities are suitable for all abilities, with children contributing at their own level.

Assessment

Each lesson includes advice on how to assess the children's success in the activities against the lesson objectives. This may include questions to ask or observations to make to help you build up a picture of the children's developing ideas and plan future lessons. A separate summative assessment lesson is provided at the end of each unit of work.

Plenary

This is a very important part of the lesson. It is important not to let it get squeezed out by mistiming other activities in the lesson. Suggestions are given for drawing the various strands of the lesson together in this session. If an investigation has been tried, the work of different groups can be compared and evaluated. The scene may be set for another lesson, or the lesson objectives and outcomes may be reviewed.

Homework

On occasions, small tasks may be suggested for the children to do at home. These are tasks such as completing an exercise timetable for a week or counting the number of light sources at home.

Outcomes
These are statements related to the objectives; they describe what the children should have achieved through the lesson.

Links to other units or lessons
The lesson may be linked to other lessons in the same unit to provide progression or reinforce the work done, or it may be linked to other units or lessons elsewhere in the book. You may like to consider these links in planning your scheme of work – for example, linking Lesson 12 (about animals producing young that grow into adults) in Unit 1: Keeping healthy with Lesson 15 (about how animals reproduce and change as they grow older) in Unit 2: Growing up.

Links to other curriculum areas
These are included where appropriate. They may include links to subjects closely related to science, such as technology or maths, or to content and skills in subjects such as art, history or geography.

Lesson plan grids
These short lesson plans, in the form of a grid, offer further activity ideas to broaden the topic coverage. As the example below shows, they have the same basic structure as the detailed lesson plans. They lack the Introduction, Background and Vocabulary sections, but these are supported by the previous and related detailed lesson plans. Notes suggesting a Main activity and Group activities are provided for you to develop. There are no photocopiable sheets linked to these lesson plans.

LESSON 3

Objectives	● To know that an occasional meal that is not well balanced does no harm. ● To produce a simple block graph.
Resources	Flip chart or board, large squared paper for making block graphs, pencils.
Main activity	Ask the children to tell you about some of their favourite party foods. List them on the flip chart. Ask: *Are they healthy or not?* Remind the children that less healthy foods are not bad for them, they should just eat them in moderation. Discuss the fact that an occasional meal that is not well balanced does no harm if their overall diet is a healthy one. The occasional special treat is also allowed! Make a block graph of favourite party foods.
Differentiation	All the children should be able to take part in this activity.
Assessment	Note which children are able to make a block graph and interpret the data. Question the children to find out if they understand that the occasional unbalanced meal does no harm if their overall diet is healthy.
Plenary	Look at the graph with all the children. Ask them to interpret the data. Ask: *Which is the favourite party food? Which is the least favourite?*
Outcomes	● Know that an occasional meal that is not well balanced does no harm. ● Know that some foods should be eaten in moderation. ● Can produce and interpret a simple block graph.

RESOURCES
Photocopiable sheets

Photocopiable sheets are an integral part of many of the lessons and are
found at the end of the relevant unit, marked with the 'photocopiable' symbol:
They may provide resources, a means of recording (including writing or drawing) or activities
(such as ordering).

Classroom equipment and space

A wide range of resources are needed for the lessons in this
book. However, every attempt has been made to restrict the
list to resources that will be readily available to primary
schools. You may wish to borrow some items from the science
department of your local secondary school.

Each lesson plan includes a resources list. When you have
planned which lessons you wish to use, you could make up
your own resources list for the term's or year's work.
Encourage your colleagues to do the same for other years, so
that you can compare lists, identify times when there may be
a high demand for particular resources and make adjustments
as necessary.

ICT

Many of the lessons in this book can be enhanced by the use
of ICT. As new products are entering the market all the time,
few are specified in this book. However you may like to plan
your ICT work under these headings:

Interactive programs

These are available for the younger children in the school, and
some are useful to reinforce early skills with older children:

- *My World* series from Semerc (includes *All About Ourselves, Skeleton* and *Healthy Eating*)
- *My Amazing Human Body* from Dorling Kindersley.

Information retrieval

Some children may be starting to find information from secondary sources, including CD-ROMs.
Where this is the case, it is important that the children have a focus for their enquiries, that the
materials offered are at an appropriate level, and that the task of information retrieval is
sufficiently challenging.

Visual recordings

A visual record of an investigation may be made by taking photographs (with a conventional or
digital camera) or recording an activity with a video camera, and storing the information on the
computer for use in a presentation. Visual records should be annotated to provide a complete
record, not just a picture of the children's experiences.

Desktop publishing
Some children may be able to design and produce booklets of their work using their own written material, graphs, charts, photographs and information retrieved from other sources.

Presentations
Presentations may be made using video sequences that have been recorded during an investigation with a digital or video camera.

ASSESSMENT

The assessments in this book indicate the likely progress of children in Year 2/Primary 3. The statements relate specifically to work in this book, and are arranged in groups to reflect different levels. In this year's work, it is expected that most children will achieve National Curriculum Level 2/Scottish Level B; but some may not progress so well and achieve only Level 1 or W/working towards Scottish Level A. Others may progress further in some aspects to achieve Level 3/Scottish Level C.

You may find it useful to determine what the children already know before embarking on each unit. If appropriate, look at the previous book in the series, find the corresponding unit and check with your colleagues what work has been covered. Talk to the children about what they know, and use the results to plan differentiated activities and provide materials as you teach the unit.

The last lesson in every unit focuses on summative assessment. This assessment samples the content of the unit, focusing on its key theme(s); its results should be used in conjunction with other assessments you have made during the teaching of the unit. The lesson comprises one or two activities which may take the form of photocopiable sheets, a 'question and answer' session or practical activities. This will give you an idea of how the children are progressing relative to an average expectation of Level 2 attainment in England/Level B in Scotland by the end of Year 2/Primary 3. You may wish to start the assessment lesson by reviewing the vocabulary learned in the unit with the children.

A sample of the children's work from the assessment lessons in this book, kept in a general portfolio, will be very useful in supporting your teacher assessment judgments.

SUPPORT FOR PLANNING

Developing your scheme of work

This book is planned to support the QCA *Science Scheme of Work* and the statements of the UK national curricula. In planning your school scheme of work, you may wish to look at the units in this book or throughout the series along with those of the QCA scheme. You may also wish to address the objectives in your curriculum planning more directly to those of the curriculum documents. The grids on pages 198–207 show how the statements of the national curricula for knowledge and understanding and science enquiry for England, Wales, Scotland and Northern Ireland provide the basis for the lesson objectives used throughout the eight units in this book. In the grids, each statement is cross-referenced to one or more lessons to help with curriculum planning.

Planning progression

The Series topic map on page 208 shows the focus of each of the units in the books in this series, to help you work out your plan of progression. By looking at the grids of curriculum coverage on pages 198–207, and the organisation chart for each unit, you can plan for progression through the year and from one year to the next, covering the whole of the work needed for Reception and Key Stages 1–2/Primary 1–7.

You may choose to use all or most of the lessons from the units in this book in their entirety, or make a selection to provide a 'backbone' for your own curriculum planning and supplement this with lessons you have already found successful from other sources. The pages in this book are perforated and hole-punched, so you can separate them and put them in a planning file with other favourite activities and worksheets.

TEACHING SCIENCE IN YEAR 2/PRIMARY 3

The units in this book introduce children to the work in the national curricula, and build on the early learning work done in Year 1/Primary 2. It is expected that most children will attain NC Level 2/Scottish Level B as they work through this book, though some may still be working towards this level and some may attain Level 3/Level C in some areas.

An underlying theme of this book is the application of science knowledge to our everyday world. As the children are maturing, this approach allows them to consider the ways in which science can alter our everyday life. This should help them see that it is important to know about science (to become scientifically literate) and to form opinions that, in future, can help in the sensible development of their world. This idea is only introduced in this book, but should help to prepare the children for work in later years on this topic.

A brief description of the unit contents follows, to show more specifically how the themes are developed:

● **Unit 1: Ourselves** focuses on 'Keeping healthy', including knowledge of the main external parts of the human body, the purpose of the senses, hygiene, healthy teeth, the importance of food and water and the need for a healthy, balanced diet.

● **Unit 2: Animals & plants** focuses on 'Growing up'. It looks at the difference between animals and plants and begins to sort and classify them into different groups. The children learn that animals change and reproduce as they grow older and that flowering plants produce seeds.

● **Unit 3: The environment** focuses on 'Life in habitats'. The children learn that a habitat is a small part of the environment and that living things in a habitat depend on each other. They learn that it is important to care for the environment and show respect for living things.

● **Unit 4: Materials** focuses on 'Materials and change'. It looks at the properties and characteristics of a range of materials. The children learn about the uses of some everyday materials and how they can be changed by heating and cooling.

● **Unit 5: Electricity** focuses on 'Making circuits', looking at the different ways in which we use electricity. The children learn how to make a simple circuit and control the flow of electricity with a switch.

● **Unit 6: Forces and motion** focuses on 'Making things move'. Children learn that actions such as stretching, squeezing, squashing, twisting and turning can be explained as pushes and pulls. They also learn about the force of friction.

● **Unit 7: Light and sound** focuses on 'Properties and uses'. The children learn about the formation of shadows and the different ways in which we use light and sound. They investigate making a range of sounds and learn that sounds get fainter as they travel away from the source.

● **Unit 8: Earth and beyond** focuses on 'The Sun and the seasons'. The children learn about the apparent movement of the Sun across the sky. They learn about the Moon reflecting sunlight. They use weather recordings to see the pattern of the seasons.

Keeping healthy

ORGANISATION (17 LESSONS)

	OBJECTIVES	MAIN ACTIVITY	GROUP ACTIVITIES	PLENARY	OUTCOMES
LESSON 1	To know that food can be put into different groups. To understand that a knowledge of food groups can help us to build healthy diets.	Allocate foods to different groups. Assess a healthy diet. Know that humans also need water. (Revision from Y1/P2.)	Make giant faces and list some foods found in each of the main food groups on the tongues. Devise a healthy, balanced main course that includes all the food groups.	Discuss how humans need different foods and water to stay alive and healthy.	Can arrange food into groups. Can show how knowledge of food groups can help to build a healthy diet. Can state that food and water are needed to stay alive.
LESSON 2	To know how to arrange a meal into food groups.	Look at a meal brought into school and sort into food groups.	Devise healthy menus for a week.	Discuss the menus and healthy eating.	Can arrange the food in a meal into food groups. Can assess how healthy a meal is.
LESSON 3	To know that an occasional meal that is not well balanced does no harm. To produce a simple block graph.	Discuss 'party food' for birthdays or other special occasions. Make a block graph.		Interpret the data on the graph.	Know that an occasional meal that is not well balanced does no harm. Know that some foods should be eaten in moderation. Can produce and interpret a simple block graph.
LESSON 4	To know that regular exercise is needed to maintain good health. To know the difference between exercise and inactivity.	Discuss how regular exercise is needed for health. Observe changes in the body during exercise.	Complete a personal exercise timetable. Choose a favourite form of inactivity and write about it.	Discuss the need for exercise and a balance between activity and inactivity.	Can explain why exercise is needed. Can describe the changes in the body caused by exercise. Can describe the difference between exercise and inactivity.
LESSON 5	To know that enough and regular sleep is needed for good health.	Keep a diary of bedtimes to help understand the need for rest and sleep.		Consider the importance of sleep.	Know that a certain amount of sleep is needed every night for good health.
LESSON 6	To know that the mouth needs care and attention to keep it healthy.	Discuss oral hygiene, with a talk from an expert, if possible.	Write and decorate a letter to the Tooth Fairy. Write an oral hygiene poem.	Discuss how to keep teeth and mouths healthy.	Can describe the care needed to keep teeth and gums healthy.
LESSON 7	To know that the skin needs to be kept clean for good health.	Discuss the importance of keeping clean and the dangers of dirty skin. Learn how to wash hands properly.	Investigate who needs really clean hands. Write hygiene rules.	Review and prioritise the hygiene rules.	Can describe how to care for the skin and keep it clean.
LESSON 8	To know that the skin needs to be kept clean for good health.	Observe how dirty hands can be.		Groups report back on their discussion on dirty hands.	Understand how dirty the skin gets and why it needs to be kept clean.
LESSON 9	To know that people who are ill take medicines to help them.	Talk about medicines and safety. Learn about the appropriate use of syringes.	Compare the packaging of sweets and drugs. Design packaging for a medicine with warnings.	Discuss safety issues of medicines.	Know that medicines are drugs that can be dangerous if they are not taken as instructed. Know that children should only take medicines under adult supervision. Can explain that people take medicines to keep them well or make them better.

ORGANISATION (17 LESSONS)

	OBJECTIVES	MAIN ACTIVITY	GROUP ACTIVITIES	PLENARY	OUTCOMES
LESSON 10	● To know that some household substances are dangerous.	Talk about substances that must not be touched or played with. Discuss hazard symbols and safe storage.	Sort labels with hazard symbols. Write about safe storage for dangerous household substances.	Talk about dangerous substances and how they can be kept safe.	● Can identify dangerous household substances. ● Can suggest ways in which dangerous household substances might be kept away from children.
LESSON 11	● To know that humans are more like each other than other animals.	Look at the similarities and differences between different humans, and humans and animals.	Research another animal and say why it is different from a human. Note similarities and differences between yourself and a partner.	Discuss the differences between humans and animals.	● Know that there are more similarities between humans than there are between humans and other animals. ● Can identify similarities and differences between humans and other animals.
LESSON 12	● To know that animals (including humans) produce young which grow into adults. ● To know that different animals mature at different rates.	Comparing human and animal growth more closely. If possible, keeping butterfly or moth pupae in the classroom.	Match and name more unusual animals and their young. Sort out animals that need care or are independent from birth.	Talk about the names of animals and their babies. Discuss the ways that different animals grow and develop.	● Can compare the growth of some animals with that of humans. ● Can match parent to offspring. (Revision from Y1/P2.)
LESSON 13	● To know that young humans need care while they are growing up.	Interview a parent about how to care for children of different ages.		Make a list of ways that parents care for children.	● Can describe some of the ways in which young humans need care as they grow up.
LESSON 14	● To know that humans are similar in some ways and different in others.	Look at differences which help us to recognise people. Listen to a tape and identify voices.	Fill in a fingerprint card and go on to make fingerprint pictures. Decorate a measured ribbon with 'facts about me'. Display in size order.	Talk about similarities and differences.	● Can identify ways in which people are similar and different. ● Know that people can be grouped in many different ways.
LESSON 15	● To know that appearance may change but that people can still be recognised.	Face painting and hairdressing.		Discuss ways in which people who have been disguised can still be recognised.	● Can describe some of the ways in which appearance can be changed, but people can still be recognised.
LESSON 16	● To know that our appearance changes over time.	Read, and discuss the 'Seven Ages of Man'.	Draw pictures of people at seven different ages. Create a portrait of what you will look like when you are old.	Discuss how people change with age.	● Can recognise that the appearance of humans changes over time. ● Can describe some of the changes.

	OBJECTIVES		ACTIVITY 1	ACTIVITY 2
ASSESSMENT 17	● To know that food can be put into different groups. ● To know that some household substances are dangerous.		Sort food into groups. Explain the need for a balanced diet.	Identify household substances that are dangerous and need to be stored safely.

LESSON 1

OBJECTIVES
● To know that food can be put into different groups.
● To understand that a knowledge of food groups can help us to build healthy diets.

RESOURCES

Main teaching activity: A story such as *The Giant Jam Sandwich* by John Vernon (Picture Piper) or possibly versions of traditional stories such as: 'The Magic Porridge Pot', 'The Gingerbread Boy', 'The Enormous Pancake' or 'The Enormous Turnip'. A flip chart or board with columns headed: 'Fruit and vegetables'; 'Meat, fish, eggs and dairy products'; 'Cereals'; 'High energy foods'; a collection of foods including a small range from each food group, such as: meat, eggs, milk, cereals (including bread) and fruit and vegetables. Include some processed foods such as crisps (which can be high in salt and fat) and sweets (which are high in sugar).
Group activities: 1. A3 copies of photocopiable page 34 (see also diagram overleaf), for the children to write their foods on; drawing and colouring materials; collage materials such as wool, wood shavings and hole punch circles to create features such as hair, spots and freckles; scissors, adhesive. **2.** One A4 sheet of stiff paper or light card for each child, writing and drawing materials.

PREPARATION

On the flip chart draw four columns. Head these with the names of the main food groups: 'Fruit and vegetables'; 'Meat, fish, eggs and dairy products'; 'Cereals'; 'High energy foods'.

BACKGROUND

It is difficult to divide food into exact categories since many foods contain significant amounts of more than one type of ingredient. At this stage the foods are being divided into four main groups: fruit and vegetables (containing mostly sugars, carbohydrates, minerals and other trace elements); meat, fish, eggs and dairy products (containing mainly proteins and fats); cereals (containing mainly carbohydrates, minerals and trace elements); high energy foods such as sweets, crisps and chocolate (containing mainly sugars, salts and fats).

Children should be encouraged not to view some foods as 'bad'. Instead they need to appreciate that it is important to eat a balanced diet that contains items from all the food groups. Ideally, they should be eating large amounts of fruit and vegetables and cereals, and medium amounts of proteins and fats. Sweets, sugars and salt should be eaten in moderation. Vegetarians and vegans also need protein in their diets but will obtain this from dairy products, or nuts and pulses.

> ### Vocabulary
> fruit, vegetables, cereals, starch, processed, balanced, healthy, energy, high-energy

INTRODUCTION

There is a wealth of food-related stories or songs that could be used as initial stimulation for this lesson. Read *The Giant Jam Sandwich* or sing 'Food Glorious Food' from the musical *Oliver*. Remind the whole class that they talked about food and their favourite meals in Year 1/Primary 2 and that food and water are needed to stay alive.

MAIN TEACHING ACTIVITY

Gather the whole class around you. Ask a few children to tell you some of the things that they ate for breakfast, lunch and their evening meal yesterday. Make a list of these foods on the flip chart under the main food group headings (Fruit and vegetables; Meat, fish, eggs and dairy products; Cereals; High energy foods). Add what you had for your own meals yesterday. (This is a good opportunity to add to any lists if, for example, the children's list is short on fruit and vegetables.) Look at the lists with the children and talk about the fact that all foods can be grouped in this way. Ask the children: *Can anyone think of another food that could go in the fruit and vegetable list?*

Add their suggestions to the lists. Then ask: *Does anyone think that any of these foods are bad for you? Can a food be bad for you?* Tell the children that no food is bad for you unless you eat too much of it and talk about the need for a balanced diet. Explain to them that in order to balance our diet and keep healthy we need to eat a large amount of fruit and vegetables, a medium amount of things like meat, fish and dairy products and a large amount of cereals. Sweets, chocolate and salt are all right if they are eaten in small amounts. Remind them that we also need to drink, and that water is an important part of our diet too.

Look at the collection of foods together and ask the children to name them. Can they sort them into the correct groups? Ask: *Where do we put the processed foods such as the crisps? Although they are made from a vegetable, they are not the fresh vegetable and have been made into something else. They sometimes contain a lot of salt and fat so we should not eat too many of them.*

GROUP ACTIVITIES

1. Give each child a copy of the 'Giant face' sheet on photocopiable page 34. Ask them to draw the face of a greedy giant (male or female). Tell them that they should draw a big mouth, slightly open so that they can cut out the tongue and stick it in the right place (see diagram opposite). They should then list some foods found in each of the main food groups on the tongue. They can now finish off their faces by using the collage materials to make the giant's face as horrid as possible! These could form the basis of a class display.

2. Ask each child to devise a healthy, balanced main course, including all the food groups. Give each child an A4 sheet of stiff paper or light card. Ask them to decorate their sheet with pictures of any foods they have included.

DIFFERENTIATION

1. More able children will be able to list several foods (possibly including some that were not mentioned in the Main teaching activity) in each group. Less able children may draw pictures of one or two foods in each group. Some may need to explain their pictures to you.

2. Some children will need help writing their words. Some may draw pictures. More able children may be able to label each food in their meal with the name of the food group to which it belongs.

ASSESSMENT

Check the children's work to assess whether they have listed foods correctly under the various groups. Does the main course that they have devised contain at least one food from each main group?

PLENARY

Read out the names of some of the foods the children have listed in their work and ask the class which group each food belongs to. Add these to the list made on the flip chart in the Main teaching activity. Ask the children to tell you why it is important to know about foods and which group they belong to. Ask them to tell you again what else humans need to stay alive and healthy (water).

OUTCOMES

● Can arrange food into groups.
● Can show how knowledge of food groups can help to build a healthy diet.
● Can state that food and water are needed to stay alive.

LESSON 2

OBJECTIVE

● To know how to arrange a meal into food groups.

RESOURCES

Main teaching activity: A packed lunch, including something from all the food groups but making sure that the meal is not well-balanced, for example: jam sandwich, cold sausages, chocolate bar, crisps, yoghurt, apple, cake, sweets; large sheets of paper on which to write the names of the food groups, cards on which to write the children's suggestions.

Group activity: Writing materials; painting, drawing or collage materials for decorating the menu sheets.

BACKGROUND

For this activity, it is best not to use the children's packed lunches, but to provide one of your own. The contents of children's lunch boxes can be a sensitive issue; children of this age are not responsible for what is sent to school for them to eat, although the contents of lunch boxes often become more healthy during and after the class has learned about healthy eating. Children need to know that a good balanced diet is necessary to maintain good health and growth and that there are no bad foods, just some that we should eat or drink in moderation. They should also be aware of the need to drink in order to replace fluids lost through excretion (sweating and urinating) and that they should drink lots of water and not just sweet or fizzy drinks. Any discussions on food and nutrition should be handled sensitively – some children may come to school without breakfast, others may only have one meal a day. Some children have little choice and may have to eat whatever they can find in the house that day. Others may be given too many crisps, sweets and fizzy drinks. Young children need to learn about healthy eating, but should not be made to feel guilty when they have no say in what is given to them.

Vocabulary

healthy, balanced, food groups, excretion

INTRODUCTION

Remind the whole class about what they learned in the last lesson. Ask: *Can anyone remember the food groups that we were talking about?* Write the names of the groups on individual sheets of paper and lay them down where the children can see them.

MAIN TEACHING ACTIVITY

Ask the whole class if they can remember which food groups we should eat freely (fruit and vegetables and cereals) and which we should eat in moderation (meat, fish, eggs, dairy produce). Ask: *What types of food should we eat only small amounts of?* (Crisps, sweets, chocolate, and anything with large amounts of fat, sugar or salt.) With the children, look at the packed lunch you have brought in. Ask them to sort the various foods into the appropriate groups and place them on the relevant sheets of paper. When this is done say: *We have some things in each of the food groups but is this a healthy meal?* (No.) Explain that this is because there are too many sweet and fatty things and not enough fruit and vegetables. Talk to the children about how the meal could be changed or improved to make it more balanced. Ask for their ideas on what could be added or removed to turn the meal into a healthy one. Add these items by drawing them or writing their names on cards and placing these on the correct sheet. Take away the foods that the children suggest should be removed. Look at the result with the children and ask if the meal is now a healthy one.

GROUP ACTIVITY

Sort the children into seven groups with one child who is able to scribe in each group. Provide writing and drawing materials to create menu sheets, then ask each group to think of a healthy menu for one day. Remind them, before they begin, that they should have at least one thing from every food group for lunch and tea, but that breakfast may be slightly different. It should still be healthy, and may be a good opportunity to have some of the milk they need for strong teeth and bones. Be sensitive to any children who have a food allergy. Each child in the group could then select one of the foods or courses to illustrate and add it to the menu sheet that the group has devised. The menus could then be put together to make a class 'Healthy Menu Book', with the addition of decorated covers.

DIFFERENTIATION

All the children should be able to take part in this activity.

ASSESSMENT

Use the children's work to assess whether they have understood the difference between a balanced and an unbalanced meal. Ask them what is meant by a healthy meal.

PLENARY

Ask the groups to tell the rest of the class what they have put into their day's menu. Discuss each day with the children. If they ate like that for a week would their diet be really healthy? Is anything missing? Should anything be added?

OUTCOMES

- Can arrange the food in a meal into food groups.
- Can assess how healthy a meal is.

LESSON 3

Objectives	● To know that an occasional meal that is not well balanced does no harm. ● To produce a simple block graph
Resources	Flip chart or board, large squared paper for making block graphs, pencils.
Main activity	Ask the children to tell you about some of their favourite party foods. List them on the flip chart. Ask: *Are they healthy or not?* Remind the children that less healthy foods are not bad for them, they should just eat them in moderation. Discuss the fact that an occasional meal that is not well balanced does no harm if their overall diet is a healthy one. The occasional special treat is also allowed! Make a block graph of favourite party foods.
Differentiation	All the children should be able to take part in this activity.
Assessment	Note which children are able to make a block graph and interpret the data. Question the children to find out if they understand that the occasional unbalanced meal does no harm if their overall diet is healthy.
Plenary	Look at the graph with all the children. Ask them to interpret the data. Ask: *Which is the favourite party food? Which is the least favourite?*
Outcomes	● Know that an occasional meal that is not well balanced does no harm. ● Know that some foods should be eaten in moderation. ● Can produce and interpret a simple block graph.

LESSON 4

OBJECTIVES

- To know that regular exercise is needed to maintain good health.
- To know the difference between exercise and inactivity.

RESOURCES

Main teaching activity: The hall, large PE equipment.
Group activities: 1. A copy of photocopiable page 35 for each child, pencils, coloured highlighter pens. **2.** Writing and drawing materials.

Vocabulary

exercise, energetic, active, inactive, regular, muscle, fit, abdominal

BACKGROUND

The human body is designed to be active and needs regular exercise in order to maintain good health. Children are becoming less and less active and their overall health is suffering as a consequence. This is not only due to the popularity of activities such as watching television and sitting for long periods in front of a computer, it is also because children are often driven to school and kept indoors because of parents' fears for their safety. PE at school may be the only regular physical activity some children get. Muscle tone is lost when there is insufficient use (this

includes the heart). Sufficient, regular exercise also helps to burn off any excess calories.

INTRODUCTION

Remind the children about the lessons on moving their bodies that they had in Year 1/Primary 2. Ask them what they can remember. Ask: *Does anyone know what 'exercise' means and what it does for our bodies?*

MAIN TEACHING ACTIVITY

Before you begin the physical part of the lesson, talk to all the children about the fact that the body is designed to be active and that we need to take regular exercise in order to keep healthy. Tell them that we need to use our muscles to keep them strong and make them stronger. Ask what sort of things we are doing when we exercise our bodies and what sort of exercise the children enjoy (running, cycling or skating, for example). Find out whether the children think they have any exercise at school. Do they realise that the various aspects of school PE are exercise? Ask whether they think they are getting exercise when they are out on the playground. (Only if they are moving about.)

Begin the physical part of the lesson with a vigorous warm-up, asking the children to change the way they are moving and the parts of the body they are using when you call out: *Change!* Ask the children to stop once they are well warmed-up, and to close their eyes and think about their bodies. *What is different about your body since you started moving? Are you warmer, are you out of breath, do you feel thirsty, do you feel more energetic than when you started the lesson?*

Move on to the large apparatus, asking the children as they work to think about the muscles that they are using and developing. Stop the class occasionally and ask individual children to say which muscles they have been using (leg, arm or abdominal). At the end of the lesson, ask the children if they know the difference between being active and inactive. Ask them to tell you some of the inactive things that they do regularly. (Watching television, playing on the computer, working at their desks, sitting quietly listening to a story.)

GROUP ACTIVITIES

1. Give each child a copy of photocopiable page 35. Ask them to complete their own exercise diary for one week, including all the exercise they get both at home and at school. Remind the children what exercise is and help to get them started by mentioning a few possibilities such as walking, cycling or swimming. Talk to them about the fact that exercise needs to be regular in order to be properly beneficial and ask them to highlight with a coloured highlighter pen any forms of exercise that they do regularly (such as school PE).
2. Ask the children, as individuals, to make a list of the inactive things they do regularly. These are likely to include watching television, listening to stories or playing on the computer. They should then select their favourite and write a few lines or a poem about why they enjoy what they have chosen. Remind the children that being inactive some of the time is a good thing as long as they are getting sufficient exercise to keep their bodies fit. They could illustrate their work and make a class book or display.

DIFFERENTIATION

1. More able children may want to calculate the number of hours they spend doing exercise for each day or each week. Less able children may need a list of suggestions of possible types of exercise to help them.
2. More able children could go on to write about more than one thing that they enjoy. Less able children may need to draw pictures and label them.

ASSESSMENT

Use the children's work to assess whether they understand what exercise is and whether they are able to identify regular exercise. Note which children understand the difference between being active and inactive.

PLENARY

Use the children's work as a basis for discussing what they have learned. Remind them that we need to exercise regularly in order to say healthy and fit. Ask: *What changes did you notice in yourselves after you had been exercising?* Talk about the difference between being active and inactive. Make sure that the children understand that inactivity is not wrong and that there should be a balance between taking exercise and enjoying inactive pursuits.

OUTCOMES

- Can explain why exercise is needed.
- Can describe the changes in the body caused by exercise.
- Can describe the difference between exercise and inactivity.

LINKS

Maths: making a timetable.
Literacy: writing a poem.

LESSON 5

Objective	● To know that enough and regular sleep is needed for good health.
Resources	Paper, card for diary covers, writing and drawing materials.
Main activity	Ask the children why we need to sleep. Do they understand that we all need a certain amount of sleep every night to keep us healthy, and that our bodies and our brains need proper rest in order to help them grow and develop? Talk about the effects of too little sleep. (Tiredness, lack of concentration, even grumpiness!) Ask the children to keep a bedtime diary (for one or two weeks, or whatever time period suits the unit of work you are doing). They could decorate the cover with appropriate pictures and illustrate each page.
Differentiation	More able children could add the time they get up every morning to their diaries and calculate the number of hours they spend sleeping each day or each week.
Assessment	During the Plenary session ask the children why they need to sleep. *Why is it important to get enough, regular sleep?*
Plenary	Talk to the children about the earlier discussion and the importance of sleep. What happens if they don't get enough, regular sleep? (They feel tired during the day and find it more difficult to concentrate.) When the children have completed their bedtime diaries, use these as the basis for a further Plenary session to reinforce what has been learned.
Outcome	● Know that a certain amount of sleep is needed every night for good health.

LESSON 6

OBJECTIVE

- To know that the mouth needs care and attention to keep it healthy.

RESOURCES

Main teaching activity: A copy of the poem 'Oh I wish I'd looked after my teeth' by Pam Ayres, from *Pam Ayres – The Works* (BBC Books). A collection of artefacts such as large sets of teeth, toothbrushes, toothpaste containing fluoride and appropriate leaflets. You may be able to borrow some, or all, of these from your local Community Dental Health Service, who may also be willing to send a member to talk to the children.
Group activities: 1. Paper and writing materials for a letter; appropriate materials for making 3D Tooth Fairies to stick to the letters (see diagram, opposite). These might include: old-fashioned wooden pegs for bodies, pipe cleaners for arms, gauze, net, cellophane or acetate (for wings), matchsticks and tiny gold and silver stars (for wands), lace, chiffon or coloured lining fabric (for dresses or shirts and trousers), wool or raffia (for hair), sequins and/or glitter (for decoration), adhesive. **2.** Poem, as for the Main teaching activity; writing and drawing materials.

PREPARATION

Get in touch with your local Community Dental Health Service to find out if they can help with resources or personnel. If they agree to send someone, make sure that you talk to them about the age of the children and how they are going to present what they say. You should also look at any resources or paperwork in advance to make sure that they are suitable and check if you need to augment it in any way.

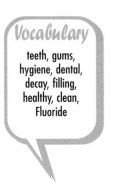

Vocabulary

teeth, gums, hygiene, dental, decay, filling, healthy, clean, Fluoride

BACKGROUND

Although the health of children's teeth has greatly improved in recent years, oral hygiene is still not as universal and meticulous as it could be. There are families where not every member has an individual toothbrush and where cleaning teeth is not part of an everyday routine. Although children need to be made aware of the importance of caring for their teeth and oral hygiene, the subject should be approached in a sensitive way. When you are six it is not always up to you whether you have your own toothbrush or not. Fluoride toothpaste has been a major factor in the reduction of dental caries and most brands of toothpaste now contain fluoride. The current advice is that teeth should be brushed regularly and kept clean, but not after every meal. The acid produced after eating in the localised area round the teeth etches the enamel, and brushing at that time may cause extra wear. It is best to clean teeth before breakfast and before going to bed, or at least an hour after eating. Eating crunchy foods does nothing to help clean the teeth, although eating a piece of cheese after a meal does help, as cheese contains a substance that neutralises the acid that causes tooth decay.

INTRODUCTION

Reading the Pam Ayres poem 'Oh I wish I'd looked after my teeth' with the whole class gathered around you, would be a stimulating way to start this lesson. A discussion about the best way to look after teeth can then take place without personalising it.

MAIN TEACHING ACTIVITY

Gather the children around you, and ask them all to give you a big smile so that you can see their teeth. Smile back! Ask the children why teeth are important and what we do with them. (We need them to chew our food, but they also help us to form our words properly and keep the shape of our mouths.) Ask: *Does anyone know what we need to do to help keep our teeth and gums really healthy?* (Clean them regularly with fluoride toothpaste, eat a healthy, balanced diet (including milk), don't suck sweets last thing before you go to sleep at night and so on.) Show the children the resources that you have and, with the large teeth and toothbrush, demonstrate how to clean the teeth properly (working up and down and getting right to the back teeth).

Discuss with the children how looking after the teeth and eating a healthy diet can help to prevent tooth decay. Ask if any of them have been to the dentist and what the dentist did. *Did they look carefully at all your teeth and tell you how to look after them?* Try to instil the idea that going to the dentist is a good thing and is a vital part of looking after their teeth. Most children will have had a good experience at the dentist and may have been given a badge and a picture to colour to show how good they have been. Some children could recount such visits, but nip any horror stories in the bud! Ask the children if any of them have started to lose their baby teeth. Remind them that the new teeth that come through when the baby teeth have gone have to last them for the rest of their lives and need to be taken care of. If you have a visitor from the Community Dental Health Service allow time for him or her to talk to the children and answer questions before you move on to the Group activities.

GROUP ACTIVITIES

1. Write individual letters to the Tooth Fairy telling him or her about the rules for keeping teeth and gums clean and healthy. Before they begin ask the children to remind you of the things you have talked about in the main lesson and some of the rules they will need. Ask the children to make and stick a 3D model of a tooth fairy onto the corner of their letter. The letters could then form the basis of a class display. Tell the children that the Tooth Fairy doesn't like collecting decayed teeth!
2. Read the Pam Ayres poem again and ask the children to write a funny poem about looking after teeth.

DIFFERENTIATION

1. More able children will be able to list several rules such as: regular cleaning, using fluoride toothpaste, eating a healthy diet and drinking a certain amount of milk, making regular visits to the dentist for a check-up, and so on. Less able children may manage one or two rules and some pictures. Less able children are more likely to need adult help with their Tooth Fairy model.
2. All the children should be able to do this activity, although some will write shorter poems or draw pictures.

ASSESSMENT

Check the children's work to find out whether they have understood how to take care of their teeth and gums.

PLENARY

Ask the children to tell you some of the ways in which they can help to keep their teeth and mouths healthy. Ask some of the children to read their letters or poems.

OUTCOME

● Can describe the care needed to keep teeth and gums healthy.

LINKS

Literacy: writing a poem, writing sets of rules, writing a letter.

LESSON 7

OBJECTIVE

● To know that the skin needs to be kept clean for good health

RESOURCES

Main teaching activity: A flip chart, board or large sheet of paper to note points from the discussion; a washing-up bowl of warm water, soap, a clean white towel or paper towel; class display of toiletries; pomander (see Preparation, below) made from a small orange studded with a quantity of cloves and tied with a length of ribbon.
Group activities: 1. Simple reference books and CD-ROMs, paper and pencils, drawing and collage materials. **2.** Writing materials.
Plenary: Flip chart, large sheet of paper, scissors, felt-tipped pens.

PREPARATION

About two weeks before the lesson, make the pomander (see diagram below). This gives the pomander time to dry out a bit before use. It will last for several years once it has thoroughly dried out.

Vocabulary

skin, hygiene, health, clean, wash, bacteria, germs

BACKGROUND

The dangers of a lack of hygiene, and of passing bacteria from one person to another, are well known, particularly in relation to touching others or handling food. A recent survey has shown that, in spite of all the reminders, a high proportion of people still do not wash their hands after visiting the toilet. It is therefore very important that children, from a young age, are made aware of the dangers. Germs are easily passed from one person to another through touching each other with unwashed hands. We can also harm ourselves by putting dirty hands into our mouths and ingesting
bacteria that can cause a range of illnesses. Unwashed skin begins to smell and can become infected and sore.

Push some cloves into the rind of an orange, trying to cover the whole surface. In a small bowl, mix together 2 tablespoons of orris root, and add some cinnamon, nutmeg and lemon or orange oil, then roll the orange around in the mixture. Then cut a piece of ribbon, about 1m in length. Place the middle of the ribbon at the top of the fruit, and tie it round the package as if you were tying a parcel. Tie a bow at the top to hang the pomander from.

INTRODUCTION

Gather all the children around you and ask: *Who thinks they know why it is important to keep clean?* In this way you will find out about the children's own ideas and be able to build on them during the discussion.

MAIN TEACHING ACTIVITY

Talk to the children about the dangers of a lack of hygiene and the importance of regular bathing and washing. Tell them about some of the possible results of not keeping clean, building on some of the things they have mentioned in the Introduction. As well as leaving germs on our dirty hands and maybe getting an upset stomach, we would also become very smelly if we didn't wash. Eventually our skin would become infected and sore.

Show the children the pomander, pass it around and let them smell it. Ask: *What do you think it is?* Explain that long ago people didn't know about the benefits of washing properly and keeping clean, so everyone was very smelly. Rich people carried pomanders, like this one, around with them so that they had something nice to smell instead of the horrible smell of other people and the dirt everywhere. Tell the children that, at that time, people also used perfumes to try to make them smell better, but perfume is not enough to make you smell nice if you are dirty.

Show the children the collection of toiletries and explain that we still use perfumes today, but that they smell much nicer when put on to a clean body. Ask the children if they recognise any of them and what they are used for. Ask: *Who knows why we should be particularly careful to wash our hands thoroughly after visiting the toilet?* Tell the children that they might get sick from the germs on their hands if they put them in their mouths, and that if they touch other people they might spread the germs and make them sick too.

Ask the children to mime how they would wash their hands. Then use the bowl of water, and the soap to show the children how to wash their hands really well and dry them thoroughly on the towel. Remind them that washing properly all over every day is the best way to keep our skin clean and healthy and help prevent germs from spreading.

GROUP ACTIVITIES

1. Put the children into groups of about four and ask them, using reference books and CD-ROMs, to find out about people who need to have really clean hands to do their work. (People who handle food, for example on the delicatessen counter in the supermarket, butchers, bakers, cooks, waiters, doctors, nurses.) Each group could select one or two of these people, make a large drawing or collage of them and write a sentence or two about why they need to have particularly clean hands.

2. Remind all the children about the discussions in the Main teaching activity and ask them (in groups of about four, with one child in each group acting as scribe) to think of, and write down, as many sensible hygiene rules as they can. Tell them that they will then, as a class, decide which are the most important rules and turn them into a class display.

DIFFERENTIATION

1. More able children may be able to write a little more about the people that they have chosen. Others may just label their drawing with the occupation of the person and tell you why it is important for them to keep their hands clean.

2. This activity will be accessible to all the children.

ASSESSMENT

During the Plenary session, note which children understand the link between hygiene and health. Are the rules that they have come up with sensible and relevant?

PLENARY

Talking to the whole class, ask the children to read out the rules that they have written in their groups. Make a note of these on a large sheet of paper. Read them through again with the children and talk about which are the most important. (The health and hygiene ones should come before the ones about keeping our work clean, for example.) Number the rules in order of importance. Cut the sheet up to separate the rules and stick them, in order of importance, onto a fresh sheet to display in the classroom.

OUTCOME

● Can describe how to care for the skin and keep it clean.

LINKS

Literacy: writing rules.

LESSON 8

Objective	● To know that the skin needs to be kept clean for good health.
Resources	A bowl or plastic tank of water per group of six, sufficient white paper towels for each child to have one.
Main activity	Try to do this activity at the end of the morning when hands are likely to be grubby! Put the children into groups to share a bowl or tank of water, making sure they have at least one clean white paper towel each. Tell them that they are going to see how dirty their hands are. Ask them to wet their hands in the water, then wipe them thoroughly on the paper towel. Spread out the towels and look at the resulting dirt. Remind them that it is nearly lunchtime and that they are just about to handle food. Ask: *What should you be sure to do before you go to lunch? Why?* Ask them to talk in their groups about all the things they, and other people, do where having dirty hands could cause problems (preparing, cooking and eating food; putting dirty hands in the mouth; doing work that needs to be kept clean such as sewing or drawing). Tell the children that each group is going to report back on their discussion to the whole class.
Differentiation	The main part of this activity is accessible to the whole class, but more able children may report back to the class more effectively.
Assessment	During the Plenary session, as the groups of children report to the class, note those who understand that the skin gets dirty and why it needs to be kept clean for good health.
Plenary	Ask each group to report on their discussion to the whole class. Take this opportunity to reinforce the hygiene rules they created in Lesson 7.
Outcome	● Understand how dirty the skin gets and why it needs to be kept clean.

LESSON 9

OBJECTIVE
● To know that people who are ill take medicines to help them.

RESOURCES

Main teaching activity: A collection of empty pill and medicine bottles and packets; sweet packets, tubes, boxes and wrappers (including throat 'sweets'); syringes without needles (different sizes, if possible); one or two pills that look rather like sweets.
Group activities: 1. Several empty pill bottles and packets, sweet wrappers, packets, tubes and boxes for each group of four; two large sheets of paper or small hoops for each group to sort onto or into. **2.** Writing and drawing materials.

Vocabulary
medicine, drugs, better, well, adult, dangerous, bottles, packets, difference, syringe, disease, illness, safety

BACKGROUND

From a young age children need to be introduced to the fact that medicines are drugs. They are used to make you better when you are ill, or keep you well if you have a condition such as asthma, diabetes or epilepsy. Children should understand that they must only ever take medicines (drugs) from a known and trusted adult. They must also understand that they should never eat anything that they find if they don't know where it has come from, even if it looks very like sweets. It is sometimes thought that young children should not be introduced to syringes but, unfortunately, syringes are found regularly in some school grounds and playgrounds. Children need to be made aware that they should never touch these, that they are very dangerous and that, if they do see them, they should tell an adult at once. On the other hand children may have to go to the doctor for an injection, either for an illness or an

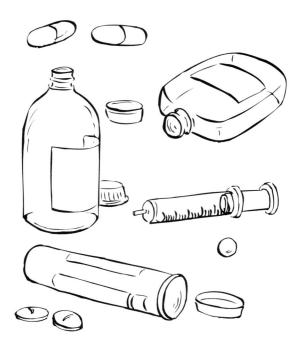

immunisation, and a fear of syringes may turn this into a much more traumatic and stressful experience than it should be. It is therefore also important to show them, and tell them about, the beneficial uses of syringes.

INTRODUCTION

Ask the whole class if they know what medicines are. You will then be able to judge what level their understanding is at and build on their ideas without reinforcing misconceptions.

MAIN TEACHING ACTIVITY

Ask the children when you should take medicines. *What sorts of things do you take medicines for? Does anyone sometimes have a headache and Mummy or Daddy gives you something to make it better? Who has ever had medicine for a cough? Does anyone have to take medicine all the time to keep them well?* (This may create a good opportunity to talk sensitively about people who need to stay on medication for long periods in order to feel well, such as asthmatics or diabetics.)

Ask the children to tell you who should give them medicine. Stress that they should never take medicine from anyone except an adult that they know and trust, or a doctor or nurse. Explain that medicines are drugs that people take when they are ill to make them better, or to keep them well. Add that if they are taken at the wrong time, they can also be dangerous. Show the children the syringes (without needles) and ask: *Can anyone remember going to the doctor or nurse to have an injection? Can you remember what it was for?* Explain to the children that injections can only be given by a doctor or nurse – or a parent at home (to a diabetic child, for example) – to treat, or to stop us catching, an unpleasant disease. Make sure that the children understand that if anyone shows them a syringe, or if they see one anywhere other than at a doctor's or a hospital, they should tell a grown up straightaway. Schools sometimes use syringes as instruments in science or the water tray; the children should know that this is fine.

Show the children the collection of pill bottles and sweet wrappers. Hold up one or two of each and ask the children if they can tell the difference. Show them the tablets that look like sweets and explain that they are not sweets, but strong medicines that could be dangerous for children. Make sure they understand that they should never eat things they find, even if they look like sweets, but should take them to a grown-up. Look at some of the medicine boxes, bottles and wrappers in detail with the children and read out some of the warnings on them. Point out that, although they are called 'sweets', the things that people suck for sore throats are actually medicines and should only be taken by adults. Now look at some of the sweet wrappers and boxes and show the children that the same warnings do not feature on these.

GROUP ACTIVITIES

1. Ask the children (working in groups of about four) to sort the packages, bottles and packets in front of them into two sets – one set of medicines and one of sweets. Children could then write a sentence individually to say why they should always take medicines only from a trusted adult.
2. Working as individuals, ask the children to design a package for a medicine, showing quite clearly that it is a medicine and warning people of the dangers of not following safety rules.

DIFFERENTIATION

1. Less able children may need to tell you the reasons rather than writing a sentence.
2. All the children should be able to do this activity.

ASSESSMENT

Look at the sets when the groups have finished sorting and talk to the children. Note which children know that medicines can be dangerous unless taken under adult supervision, and that people should only take medicines to keep them well or make them better.

PLENARY

Ask the children to tell you when it is safe to take medicines. (When they are ill or to keep them well). *Who should give you medicine? What should you do if you find some pills or medicines?*

OUTCOMES

- Know that medicines are drugs that can be dangerous if they are not taken as instructed.
- Know that children should only take medicines under adult supervision.
- Can explain that people take medicines to keep them well or make them better.

LESSON 10

OBJECTIVE
● To know that some household substances are dangerous.

RESOURCES

Main teaching activity: A collection of empty and well-rinsed household substance containers and packets, including some products that are used in the garden.
Group activities: 1. A copy of photocopiable page 36 for each group of three; a collection of labels from household substance and chemical bottles and packets which contain hazard and warning symbols; the collection of bottles and packets used in the Main teaching activity; scissors, adhesive, writing and drawing materials. **2.** Writing and drawing materials.

PREPARATION

Main teaching activity: Make sure that the empty household substance containers have been thoroughly rinsed.
Group activities: 1. Ensure that any hazard symbols cut from packets have no residue of the substance on them.

BACKGROUND

Every year many children end up in hospital, and some die, from touching or swallowing household and garden chemicals and substances. It is therefore important that children are made aware of these dangers and recognise some of the substances involved. The main symbols that children should be able to identify and understand at this stage are:

 Harmful or **Irritant:** This will damage the skin and is harmful when swallowed. The substances are usually dilute acids or alkalis.

 Toxic: This is used on all poisonous substances. Bleach, cleaning fluids, weed killers and insecticides would be included in this group.

 Highly flammable: This symbol appears mostly on liquids but is also used on some solids and gases that ignite quickly. Included in this group are methylated spirits, turpentine, white spirit, lighter fuel and firelighters.

INTRODUCTION

Remind the children about what they learned in Lesson 9: that medicines can be dangerous if we take them when we don't need them. Tell them that there may be other things in their houses that are very dangerous, and that it is important that children know never to touch or play with these.

MAIN TEACHING ACTIVITY

With the children around you, ask: *Does anyone know what a household substance or household chemical is? Can anyone name one?* If the children are able to name some and you have them, point these out in the collection. Look at the rest of the collection with the children and ask them if they recognise any of the bottles or packets. *Do you have any of these at home? What are they for? Why is it important that they are kept somewhere safe?* Tell the children that these substances are dangerous and that they should never play with them or handle them. Explain that these items should be kept in a very safe place away from children, babies and pets.

Point out the hazard symbols and read some of the hazard warnings on the packets and bottles. Tell them that it is very sad that many children and babies become ill and end up in hospital because they have swallowed or touched household substances or chemicals. Ask: *Can anyone think of good, safe places where dangerous things like bleach, toilet cleaner or weed killer could be kept away from children?* (A high cupboard which is out of the reach of children, a locked cupboard or a locked shed.)

GROUP ACTIVITIES

1. Organise the children into groups of three. Give each group a copy of the sheet of hazard symbols on photocopiable page 36 and a collection of labels from bottles. Cut the symbols from the sheet out to separate them. Ask the children to sort their set of labels into the correct groups to match the symbols. When this has been done ask each child to choose one of the symbols and stick it in their books (or on a sheet of paper). They should then find one or two things from the collection of bottles and packets that carry that symbol, draw these, and write under their drawing what they are.

2. Ask the children to write about a good place for storing dangerous household or garden substances to keep them away from children and pets. Remind them that they talked about this in the Main teaching activity.

DIFFERENTIATION

1. All the children should be able to contribute to the first part of this activity. Some children will be able to choose several substances to match their symbol.
2. More able children could write about more than one safe place to keep household substances.

ASSESSMENT

Ask the children to name a range of dangerous household substances. Use their work to assess whether they can suggest ways in which dangerous substances can be kept away from children and pets.

PLENARY

Talk to the whole class about what they have learned. Ask them to tell you some of the ways in which household substances are dangerous. (They are poisonous, they can damage your skin, they may catch fire.) Read out some of their suggestions for keeping dangerous substances out of the reach of children, babies and pets.

OUTCOMES

● Can identify dangerous household substances.
● Can suggest ways in which dangerous household substances might be kept away from children.

LESSON 11

OBJECTIVE

● To know that humans are more like each other than other animals.

RESOURCES

Main teaching activity: Collections of pictures of different animals (try to include pictures of animals with fur, feathers, scales, tails, trunks, and so on – see photocopiable page 37 for some samples), flip chart or board.
Group activities: 1. Reference books, CD-ROMs, writing materials. **2.** Writing and drawing materials, pictures of a range of different animals.

Vocabulary

same, similar, similarities, different

BACKGROUND

Each type of creature is adapted to its environment and lives and feeds in a particular way. Year 2/Primary 3 children can begin to think about the more obvious differences between species, and identify that all humans are much more similar to each other than they are to any other types of animal. Most animals, including humans, have certain attributes in common (such as possession of eyes and a mouth), but these are not always present. Some burrowing creatures, and others that live in totally dark caves or the depths of the sea, have no eyes. Some species of moth, such as Atlas Moths, have no mouthparts as their lifespan is very short: they emerge, mate and die without the need for feeding.

INTRODUCTION

Remind all the children of the work they did in Year 1/Primary 2 about humans being animals and about the similarities and differences between people.

MAIN TEACHING ACTIVITY

Tell the children to look carefully at their neighbour. Ask: *Who can tell me some of the ways in which humans are all the same as each other*? (We all have a head, a body, two legs, two arms, two eyes and so on.) Make a list of the children's suggestions on the flip chart and add to their list if they have forgotten anything significant. Discuss further similarities between humans that other animals definitely don't have. (Humans can talk to each other in words, they can read and write and make music on musical instruments, they use tools and care for their young for about

16 years from birth.) Say: *Now think of some of the ways in which we are different and tell me what they are.* (We have different-coloured hair, eyes and skin; the shapes of our bodies, faces and features are different.)

Show the children the collection of pictures of animals (there are some pictures on photocopiable page 37 to start you off). Ask them to tell you some of the ways in which they are different from humans. (Some have fur, feathers, scales, tails, fins; some live underwater, some live in trees, some can fly, some lay eggs, many have four legs, some have no legs.) Again discuss any additions to the children's list if necessary. Ask: *Are there any ways in which animals are similar to us?* (They have two eyes, most have two ears, they generally have mouths with teeth in them, some have two legs.) Hold up a picture of a bird and ask two children of different hair colour to come and stand beside you. Say: *Look at the picture of the bird, then look at your two classmates. In what ways is the bird the same as the humans?* (It has two legs and two eyes. It also has ears but you generally can't see them. Some children may know that it is warm-blooded.) *Now tell me ways in which it is different from us.* (It has a beak with no teeth in it, it has wings instead of arms, it has feathers, it can't talk, it lays eggs.)

Tell the children to look at their two classmates again. Point out that their hair colour is different but that in most ways they are very similar. Ask the children: *Are they more like each other than like the bird? Are we all more like each other than the bird?* Repeat this process with one or two more of the animals, pointing out that humans are much more like each other than they are like other animals.

GROUP ACTIVITIES

1. Organise the children into pairs, or groups of three, and give each group a reference book or CD-ROM. Ask them to choose an animal and then find out as many things about it as they can that make it different from humans. They should also note if there are any similarities. Tell the children to record what they find out in note form to remind them of what they have learned, because they are going to report back to the rest of the class.

2. Put the children in pairs. If possible place a boy with a girl, or pair children with different-coloured hair, eyes and so on. Ask the children to look at each other very carefully. (They could draw pictures of each other, including as much detail as possible.) They should then write down in two columns as many differences and similarities between them as they can think of. (They should include things like the ability to talk, walk on two legs and so on). *Are there more similarities than differences?* Give each pair a picture of an animal and ask them to note the similarities and differences between that animal and human beings. *Are there more differences in this case?*

DIFFERENTIATION

1. Some children will need help to use the reference materials and note the things they have found out. You may wish to put them in mixed-ability groups so that they can help each other.

2. More able children will include more subtle similarities and differences in their lists such as language, sense of humour or creative ability. Less able children may concentrate more on physically observable features.

ASSESSMENT

Use the children's work to assess the level of their understanding. During the Plenary session, note those who report clear differences between their given animal and humans.

PLENARY

Remind the children about what they learned in the Main teaching activity. Ask groups to report some of the differences between their animal and humans to the class. *Were there any similarities?* Reiterate the fact that humans are more like each other than they are like other animals.

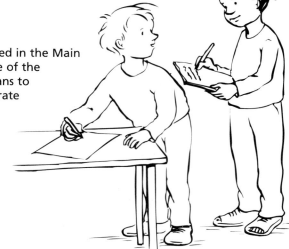

OUTCOMES

● Know that there are more similarities between humans than there are between humans and other animals.

● Can identify similarities and differences between humans and other animals.

LESSON 12

OBJECTIVES

● To know that animals (including humans) produce young which grow into adults.
● To know that different animals mature at different rates.

RESOURCES

Main teaching activity: If possible, obtain butterfly and moth larvae or pupae and observe them in the classroom as they develop and emerge. (See Preparation and Background, below.)
Group activities: 1. Pictures of animals and their babies (or use the resources on photocopiable page 37); reference books, dictionaries and CD-ROMs, a copy of photocopiable page 38 for each child, pencils. **2.** A copy of photocopiable page 39 for each child, reference materials as for Group activity 1, pencils.

PREPARATION

Main teaching activity: Kits for rearing butterflies from caterpillars can be obtained from Small-Life Supplies, Station Buildings, Station Road, Bottesford, Notts, NG13 0EB, or from their website: www.small-life.co.uk. The kits include caterpillars, butterfly feeding kit, instruction book and observation chamber. You could also visit a tropical butterfly park if there is one in your local area.
Group activities: 1. If you choose to use the resource page (photocopiable page 37), photocopy one page per group of four (enlarge to A3 if possible). Cut into separate cards and laminate for durability.

Vocabulary
young, grow, care, rate, mature, produce, live birth, mate, womb, offspring, hatch, dependent, independent

BACKGROUND

Animals vary greatly in the amount of time taken for embryos to mature in the womb or egg (from a few weeks for mice to 21 months for elephants), but there is also great variation in the degree of maturity of the young. Kangaroos, for example, give birth to tiny immature creatures that instinctively work their way up the mother's fur into the pouch where they latch on to a nipple and the rest of their development takes place. Baby mice and the young of many other rodents are born pink, blind and hairless, and take time to develop and grow their first coats. Similarly, baby birds are born without their feathers. All these creatures are totally dependent on the care and protection of their parents. Human babies too, although more developed at birth than the creatures mentioned above, rely on adults for everything in order to survive.

In contrast, the young of animals such as horses and deer are able to get to their feet and run almost immediately after birth. This is necessary for their survival in the wild, a world of predators and prey, although they too rely on their mothers for protection and food. The young of most cold-blooded creatures are born fully mature, able to take care of themselves from the moment of birth and generally require no further help from their parents. This applies to creatures such as snakes, lizards, turtles, crocodiles (although some mother crocodiles carry their young down to the water in their mouths when they have hatched), and most fish and crustaceans. Most insects are independent from the time of hatching, although in some instances the mother offers protection for a time – spiders may carry their hatchlings on their backs for a short time after they emerge from the egg.

Young children find it fascinating to observe a butterfly or moth caterpillar changing into a pupae and subsequently emerging (a very different form of growing and maturing from humans). This can be done very easily in the classroom.

INTRODUCTION

With the children around you, remind them of what they learned about animals in Year 1/ Primary 2. Say: *Can anyone tell me about some of the things we learned about animals and their babies, and the ways in which humans (we are animals too) grow and change as they get older?*

MAIN TEACHING ACTIVITY

Ask the children to think about humans and some other animals such as birds, insects, dogs or cats. Remind them that all animals, including humans, are similar in that they all have babies that grow up, grow old and eventually die. Now ask the children to think very carefully. Ask if they can tell you about some of the similarities and differences between this process in humans and in other animals. (Some lay eggs, some give birth to live babies; some are independent at birth and some need to be cared for.) Most animals grow up much more quickly than humans and don't need care for very long. Humans live longer than most animals, although there are some

creatures, such as tortoises, parrots and elephants, that may live as long, or longer, than humans. Ask: *Can anyone tell me about the very different ways that butterflies and frogs grow and develop into adults from the way in which humans grow and get old?* (Their parent lays eggs, they then hatch into caterpillars or tadpoles, butterflies change into pupae and emerge as butterflies, tadpoles grow legs and their bodies change.) Humans are born alive as babies, with their legs and arms in place, they then grow bigger and develop into adults.

Show the class the butterfly kit (if you have one) and tell them that they are going to watch the caterpillars grow and change into pupae, and that the pupae will eventually split and butterflies will emerge. This will only take a few weeks and the caterpillars do not need their parents to look after them while all this happens. Set aside time every few days for the class to look at the butterfly observation chamber and note any differences. Keep a close eye on it yourself, particularly when the butterflies are due to emerge. Hopefully this will happen when the class is in session – the children's excitement and amazement will make all the effort worthwhile!

GROUP ACTIVITIES

1. Organise the children into groups of about four and give each group a set of cards with pictures of adults and babies (possibly cut from photocopiable page 37). Remind them that they matched some adults and babies in Year 1/Primary 2 but that today they are going to match more unusual babies to their parents. Ask them to match each baby to its parent, then give each child a copy of photocopiable page 38 and ask them to complete it by finding out the special names of the baby animals. They should use the reference materials to help them.
2. Give each child a copy of photocopiable page 39. Explain the three groups that the circles represent and ask the children to complete the sheet by copying the name of each animal into the correct circle. Encourage them to use the reference materials.

DIFFERENTIATION

1. Some children may need help in using the reference materials. You may wish to use mixed-ability groups so that the more able can help the less able to find the information.
2. Some children may need help in reading the sheet as they work. Some may prefer to work together to find their information.

ASSESSMENT

Use the children's work to assess their understanding.

PLENARY

Ask the children to tell you some of the things they have learned in this lesson. Go through the adults and babies sheet (page 38) that they used in Group activity 1 and ask the children to tell you the names of the babies as you read out the adults. Ask if anyone found a really unusual name for a baby animal to complete their sheet. Can they tell you some of the similarities and differences in the way that human animals and other animals grow and develop?

OUTCOMES

- Can compare the growth of some animals with that of humans.
- Can match parent to offspring.

LINKS

Unit 2, Lesson 15: to know that animals reproduce and change as they grow older.

LESSON 13

Objective	● To know that young humans need care while they are growing up.
Resources	Pictures of parents, babies and children, flip chart or board, a parent with children of different ages who is willing to talk to the class.
Main activity	Working with the whole class, ask: *How many things can you tell me that parents need to do for their children as they are growing up?* (Feeding, keeping warm, keeping clean, cuddling, talking to and so on.) Ask a parent with older and younger children to visit the classroom and talk about the different things he or she does to look after children of different ages. Before the visit spend some time helping the children to prepare sensible questions and ask the visitor to talk about the care children receive which is not for physical needs, but to help them develop in other ways. (Encouraging them to talk, to read books, to play and do creative things.)
Differentiation	All the children can take part in this activity.
Assessment	During the Plenary session, note those children who contribute sensible suggestions for the list.
Plenary	Ask the children to tell you some of the ways in which parents care for young humans as they are growing up. List these on the flip chart. Encourage the children to talk about types of care that are not just physical. Help the children to complete the list.
Outcome	● Can describe some of the ways in which young humans need care as they grow up.

LESSON 14

OBJECTIVE
● To know that humans are similar in some ways and different in others.

RESOURCES
Main teaching activity: A tape recording of all the children saying the same very short sentence or phrase (see Preparation, below), cassette player, enlarged copy of the key (see Preparation, below), flip chart or board.
Group activities: 1. Washable inks or similar (black for the fingerprint cards and other colours for the pictures); copies of photocopiable page 40, paper for the fingerprint pictures, pictures of pointillist art. **2.** Sufficient paper 'ribbons' that are longer than the children (till rolls are useful for this, or 'ribbons' can be cut from joined sugar paper), writing and drawing materials.

PREPARATION
Make a tape recording of all the children (and you) one by one, saying exactly the same very short sentence or phrase. Make a key that lists the order of people speaking.

Vocabulary

similar, different, features, humans, subtle, obvious, individual, measurement, recognise

BACKGROUND
The fact that all humans usually have the same features (ears, eyes, noses and so on) whatever their race or colour was discussed in Year 1/Primary 2 and visited again in Lesson 11. This lesson can therefore be used to review and reinforce this, and also to concentrate on other less obvious features that are 'the same but different', such as our voices, our teeth, the shape of our faces and whether we have freckles or not. Children should realise that, although the body parts are the same, there are differences, some very much more subtle than others, that enable us all to be recognised as individuals. You can often recognise people from a distance simply by the way they move or by a particular mannerism, for example the way they walk, or the way they use their hands while talking. This lesson also provides a good opportunity to talk sensitively about those of us who might differ in some way or have a disability. Take care not to focus too closely on similarities between parents and children as some children may be adopted, or not living with both biological parents, and may be unaware of this.

INTRODUCTION
Gather the children around you and remind them of what they learned in Year 1/Primary 2 and in Lesson 11 of this unit. Ask: *Can anyone tell me about some ways in which we are all the same and some ways in which we are different?* (We all have two eyes and ears, one nose, hair and two legs; but we are not the same height, and eyes and hair may be different colours.)

MAIN TEACHING ACTIVITY

Ask the children if they can think of something else, less obvious than two eyes, that we all have but that is different. Suggest that we all have skin, but some of us have freckles and some don't. We all have hair, but some is naturally curly and some is not. All of us have teeth, but different people's teeth are different in shape and size. Ask the children to stand up in pairs and look carefully at their partners. What else can they see that is the same, but different? (Perhaps they have different- shaped faces, their hands and feet may be a different size from their partner's, their partner's neck may be longer or shorter than theirs.) Tell the children that all these subtle differences, although we have the same features, enable us to recognise people for who they are. We don't look at other people and mistake one for another – because of these differences we know who they are.

Ask the children to sit down again and listen very carefully to the tape you are going to play. Challenge them to see if they can tell who is speaking (remind them that we all have voices, but they sound different). Ask: *Have you ever answered the phone and recognised who is speaking by their voice even though you couldn't see him or her?* Tell them this is what you are going to try to do now. As the children guess who is speaking, list the suggestions on the flip chart. At the end, pin up the prepared key to the speaking order and run through it with the children. Discuss how accurate they were.

Ask the children to stand up. Remind them that they have been thinking about some of the things that all humans have but that are slightly different so people can be recognised as individuals. Ask them now to think of ways in which they could be grouped, such as: freckles/no freckles; straight hair/curly hair and so on. Each time a suitable group is named, ask the children with the attribute mentioned to join the group. Discuss the fact that the children can be grouped in lots of ways and that they fit into more than one group.

GROUP ACTIVITIES

1. Give each child a copy of the fingerprint card on photocopiable page 40. Ask them to complete the card by putting their fingerprints on it for both their right and left hands. When this is done, ask them to pair up and compare their fingerprints with a partner, looking for

similarities and differences. They could then compare their right hand with their left hand. Ask: *Are there any differences?* Show the children some pointillist pictures and explain that these are done using hundreds and hundreds of little dots. Ask them to make a picture in the same sort of way, using just their fingerprints to make the dots.

2. Sort the children into pairs and give each child a paper ribbon long enough to lie down on. Ask them to take turns to lie down on their ribbons (with their shoes off) while their partner marks where the top of their head and their feet come. They should then cut their ribbon to the correct length, on the marks, so that it shows how tall they are. Each child then writes his or her name very clearly at the top of the ribbon and decorates it with pictures and facts about themselves. It is a good idea to run through some of the appropriate facts that could be put onto the ribbons such as: weight, shoe size, hand span size, circumference of head, colour of skin, eyes or hair. They could also record any achievements such as: 'I can swim', 'I belong to...',and so on. When the ribbons are finished, lay them out on the floor or pin them on the wall in height order. They can then form the basis of a class display.

DIFFERENTIATION

1. All the children should be able to do this activity.
2. More able children should include more subtle facts about themselves on their ribbon. They should also be able to include more accurate measurements. Less able children may fill their ribbon with pictures.

ASSESSMENT

During the Plenary session, ask the children to tell you some of the things that humans all have that are the same, but different. Look for more subtle answers, as detailed above. Ask the children if they remember some of the ways in which they could be grouped.

PLENARY

Talk to the children about what they have learned. Ask them to remind you of some of the less obvious ways in which they are the same, but different. Look at the 'Facts about me' ribbons and discuss them. *Has the shortest child also got the smallest hands and shoe size?* Talk about some of the similarities and differences illustrated by the ribbons.

OUTCOMES

● Can identify ways in which people are similar and different.
● Know that people can be grouped in many different ways.

LINKS

Art: pointillism.

LESSON 15

Objective	● To know that appearance may change but that people can still be recognised.
Resources	Pictures of people with changed appearance (from make-up, different hairstyles, dyed hair); face paints, make-up (adult help would be useful for this); combs, ribbons, hair grips, ponytail holders, wigs, mirrors.
Main activity	Show the pictures to the children and talk to them about the people in them. Some of them are wearing make-up. Do the children think that they can still be recognised? Some have elaborate hairstyles – can they be recognised? Ask the children if they think that their classmates would still recognise them even if they had a different hairstyle or wore make-up. *What about a clown's make-up, or face paints? Would your friends still know you?* Ask the children to change their appearance in some way with the things you have provided.
Differentiation	All children should be able to take part in this activity according to their ability.
Assessment	During the Plenary session ask the children to describe some of the ways in which appearance can be changed but people can still be recognised. Note those children who are able to respond, and the quality of their responses.
Plenary	Gather the children together and look at each other. Ask: *How have people changed their appearance? Can they still be recognised? How?* (Their voices are the same, their faces are the same shape, they move in the same way.)
Outcome	● Can describe some of the ways in which appearance can be changed, but people can still be recognised.

LESSON 16

OBJECTIVE

● To know that our appearance changes over time.

RESOURCES

Main teaching activity: 'The Seven Ages of Man' speech from Shakespeare's *As You Like It*, flip chart or board.
Group activities: 1. A copy of photocopiable page 41 for each child, writing and drawing materials. **2.** Plastic mirrors, paper; drawing, colouring or painting materials (depending on how you wish to approach this activity).

BACKGROUND

Some of the differences and changes in the appearance of human beings are very obvious, others are much less so. Discuss some of these more subtle differences with the children as the lesson progresses. Babies have round faces and snub noses because their complete bone structure has yet to develop. They have snub noses to make suckling easier. Their heads are quite large in proportion to their bodies as heads grow less, proportionally, during development than other parts of the body, such as the limbs. Although some babies are born with thick hair, they often lose most of it in the first few weeks of life so, generally, babies have less hair than a fully grown adult. Other changes in bodies are due to puberty and hormonal differences, such as the growth of body and facial hair in young men, and the development of genitalia and breasts. Other changes as people age are also due to hormonal changes or 'wear and tear' – hair loss in men and thinning hair in women; the skin becomes less elastic and develops more wrinkles. Other changes, such as the tendency for everything to sag are due, in part, to the effects of gravity, as well as wear and tear!

INTRODUCTION

Remind the children of the work on ageing that they did in Year 1/Primary 2. Ask: *What do you remember about some of the things we talked about?* (How they had grown from babyhood to the age of 5 or 6 and about different stages in the human life cycle.) Say: *Now we are going to think about how people's appearance changes as they grow old.*

MAIN TEACHING ACTIVITY

Read 'The Seven Ages of Man' speech from *As You Like It* by William Shakespeare and help the children to identify the stages described. Ask them what stages they think a human being goes through from birth to death, and list these on the flip chart, leaving room to note the children's ideas about appearance next to, or under, each stage. Possibilities include: baby, toddler, schoolboy or girl (children may want to say 'infant' and 'junior'), teenager, young adult, parent, granny or grandpa, very old person. Help the children to make a full list if they leave any out. Read through the list again and ask them to think about the different stages that they have identified. Take each stage in turn and say: *Think about some of the people you know at this stage. What do they look like? How will they have changed when they get to the next stage?* Remind the children to focus on how people look at the various stages of their lives, not on what they can or can't do, which was the focus in Year 1/Primary 2. (Babies and toddlers have very round faces, no lines, little snub noses and sometimes a little hair. Later the shape of the face is less round, the nose becomes more prominent, the head is a smaller proportion of the height and people have more hair. Later still lines begin to appear, people may stoop, the hair becomes thinner again and may go grey or white. See Background, above, for further ideas.) Write the children's ideas about appearance against each stage.

GROUP ACTIVITIES

1. Give each child a copy of photocopiable page 41. Ask them to draw a picture of a person at each of the stages showing the differences in appearance. Ask them to write one or two differences under, or near, each picture.
2. Ask the children to think of a very old person that they know, and what they look like. Say: *Now look carefully at yourself in the mirror and try to imagine what you may look like when you are very old too. Draw what you think you will look like then.* Remind the children of some of the things listed against 'very old person' in the Main teaching activity.

DIFFERENTIATION

1. Some children may be able to write more than one or two things about each stage that they draw, some may only manage one. Some children may have to explain their pictures to you.
2. All the children should be able to take part in this activity at their own level.

ASSESSMENT

Use the children's completed photocopiable sheets to assess the level of their understanding and note which children are able to respond correctly to questions asked during the Plenary session.

PLENARY

Ask the children to name some of the differences in human appearance during the various stages from birth to old age. (See Main teaching activity.) Hold up some of the children's work and discuss the changes that they have drawn and written about. You may wish some of the children to explain their work to the class.

OUTCOMES

● Can recognise that the appearance of humans changes over time.
● Can describe some of the changes.

LINKS

Unit 2, Lesson 15: animals change as they grow older.

ASSESSMENT

LESSON 17

OBJECTIVES

● To know that food can be put into different groups.
● To know that some household substances are dangerous.

RESOURCES

Assessment activities: 1. A copy of photocopiable page 42 for each child, writing materials.
2. A copy of photocopiable pages 43 and 44 for each child, scissors, adhesive.

INTRODUCTION

Remind the children what they have been learning about in this unit.

ASSESSMENT ACTIVITY 1

Give each child a copy of photocopiable page 42 and read through the sheet with them. Ask them to look at the pictures of different foods and copy the name of each food into the correct food group. Ask them to write a sentence about why it is necessary to eat a balanced diet.

Answers

Fruit and vegetables: lettuce, apple, tomatoes, cabbage.
Meat, fish, eggs and dairy produce: cooked chicken, cheese, eggs, fish, sausages.
High energy: chocolate bar, packet of crisps, bag of sweets.
Cereals: packet of cereal, spaghetti, loaf of bread.
For the writing activity, accept any answer that indicates an understanding that a balanced diet is needed for health and well-being.

Looking for levels

Most children should be able to categorise the foods correctly. Some may have difficulty in recognising that the bread is made from cereal. Some may put the sausages under 'High energy foods'; these children need to be questioned as to their reason for doing this. If they recognise that sausages are very high in fat, this is an acceptable reason. If they also realise that the sausages could be listed under 'Meat, fish, eggs and dairy produce' this indicates a higher level of understanding. More able children will show a clear understanding of the need for a balanced diet. Less able children may have difficulty in explaining this.

ASSESSMENT ACTIVITY 2

Give each child a copy of photocopiable pages 43 and 44 and explain the pictures to them. Ask them to cut the pictures out and stick those that could be dangerous into the high cupboard out of the reach of children, and those that are safe into the low cupboard.

Answers

High cupboard: bottle of pills, bleach, medicine, aerosol, firelighters, weed killer, white spirit, blister pack of pills.
Low cupboard: lemonade, cereal, spaghetti, jar of jam, tin of beans, apples, oranges, basket of pegs.

Looking for levels

Most children should complete the sheet successfully.
Less able children may have difficulty in distinguishing between the bottles of liquid and may not recognise the dangers of aerosols. More able children could be asked to try and add more items to each cupboard.

Giant face

Finish the face to make the hungry giant.

Write your food words on the tongue.
Cut out the tongue and stick it into the mouth.

Name

Exercise diary

Keep a record of all the exercise you do in one week.

Day	At school	At home
Monday		
Tuesday		
Wednesday		
Thursday		
Friday		
Saturday		
Sunday		

Highlight with a coloured pen the exercise you do regularly.

My favourite sort of exercise is _____

_____

UNIT 1 OURSELVES

Hazard symbols

Match your labels to the symbols in the boxes.

 | ## Harmful or irritant

 | ## Toxic

 | ## Highly flammable

Adults and babies resource sheet

UNIT 1 OURSELVES

Adults and babies

The adult is a:	The baby is called a:
Swan	
Deer	
Seal	
Hare	
Kangaroo	
Ladybird	
Fish	
Fly	
Lion	

Can you find two more adult creatures whose babies have a special name to fill in the blank boxes?

Caring for babies

Some babies need caring for completely. Their parents do everything for them.
Some babies only need feeding and protecting.
Some babies are completely independent and may never see their parents.

Care for completely

Feed and protect

Copy the name of each animal into the correct circle.

human	frog
dog	goldfish
deer	cow
horse	kangaroo
cat	ladybird
elephant	monkey
robin	snake
butterfly	mouse

Completely independent

Name

Fingerprint card

Right hand		Left hand	
thumb		little finger	
index finger		ring finger	
middle finger		middle finger	
ring finger		index finger	
little finger		thumb	

Name

Growing older

Draw pictures of a person as they grow older and write a few words to explain how they change.

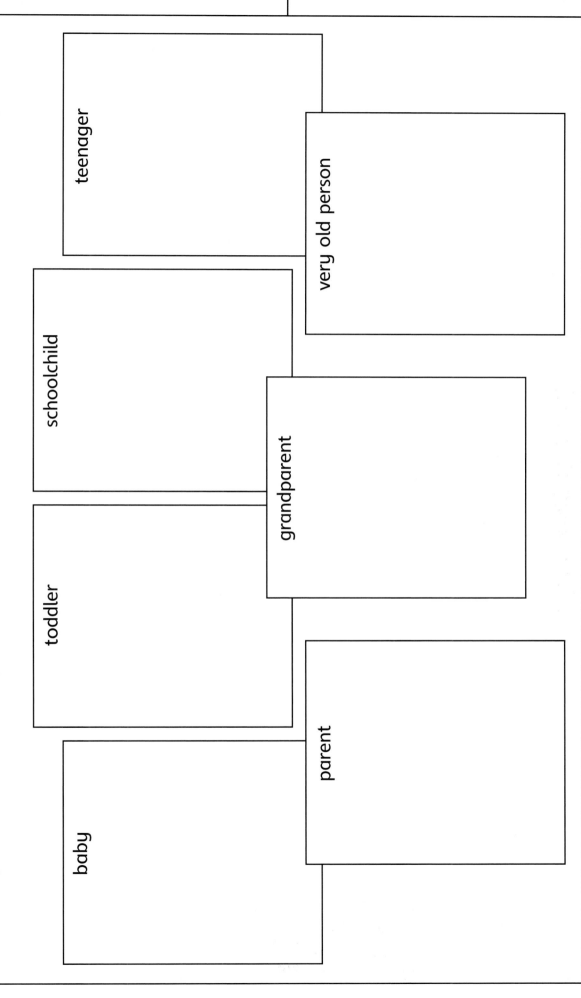

baby

toddler

schoolchild

teenager

parent

grandparent

very old person

UNIT 1 OURSELVES

Keeping healthy

lettuce

cooked chicken

chocolate bar

packet of cereal

loaf of bread

cheese

eggs

packet of crisps

apple

sausages

fish

spaghetti

tomatoes

cabbage

bag of sweets

Write the name of each food in the correct box.

Fruit and vegetables	Meat, fish, eggs and dairy produce

Cereals	High energy foods

Using the back of this sheet write about why it is important to eat a balanced diet.

Growing up

ORGANISATION (16 LESSONS)

	OBJECTIVES	MAIN ACTIVITY	GROUP ACTIVITIES	PLENARY	OUTCOMES
LESSON 1	● To know the difference between an animal and a plant.	Distinguish between plants and animals.	Complete a sheet with differences between plants and animals. Make a mis-match book.	Discuss the differences identified between plants and animals.	● Can distinguish between plants and animals.
LESSON 2	● To know the difference between an animal and a plant.	Farm study or park study.		Look at the similarities and differences between plants and animals.	● Know the difference between an animal and a plant.
LESSON 3	● To sort a group of living things into animals and plants.	Sort pictures of animals and plants and give reasons.	Play animal and plant card games. List and write about plants and animals.	Discuss the differences between plants and animals.	● Can sort out living things into animal and plant groups.
LESSON 4	● To know that plants can be separated into groups (flowering and non-flowering). ● To practise close observation skills.	Look at a range of different flowering and non-flowering plants.	Make a mushroom spore print. Make an observational drawing of a flowering plant.	Discuss and sort flowering and non-flowering plants.	● Can compare the structure of different kinds of plants. ● Can identify a fern and a flowering plant. ● Can make an observational drawing showing some detail.
LESSON 5	● To know that plants can be separated into groups (broad-leaved and conifer).	Compare broad-leaved trees and conifers.		Talk about broad-leaved trees and conifers.	● Can tell the difference between a broad-leaved tree and a conifer.
LESSON 6	● To know how to use secondary sources to find out about plants.	Use reference materials to find out about a particular type of plant.		Children present the information they have found.	● Can present information gained from a secondary source.
LESSON 7	● To know that flowering plants produce seeds.	Examine flowers to find pollen and identify the seed-case.	Look for different seed-heads on flowering plants and make an observational drawing. Set and care for seeds to grow new plants.	Look at the drawings and discuss the seed-heads.	● Know that seeds come from flowering plants.
LESSON 8	● To know that there are many different types of fruits and seeds.	Look at, and compare, a range of fruits and seeds.		Talk about fruits and seeds.	● Know that there are many different kinds of fruits and seeds.
LESSON 9	● To know that different fruits contain different numbers of seeds.	Examine and count the seeds in the seed-heads of different plants.		Discuss the variation in the numbers of seeds produced by different plants.	● Know that different fruits contain different numbers of seeds.
LESSON 10	● To plan and carry out a simple fair test with help. ● To devise, with help, a fair test to investigate the effect of water on the germination of seeds and the growth of seedlings.	Investigate the germination of seeds and the growth of seedlings. Plan, with help, a fair test to see if all seedlings need water.	Groups set up the test with each group using different seeds. Write up the investigation.	Discuss how the test was set up and kept fair. Decide when to check the pots for progress.	● Know that seeds and seedlings need water to germinate and then grow.

ORGANISATION (16 LESSONS)

	OBJECTIVES	MAIN ACTIVITY	GROUP ACTIVITIES	PLENARY	OUTCOMES
LESSON 11	● To plan and carry out, with help, a simple fair test to investigate the effect of light on seedling growth.	Investigate the growth of seedlings. Plan, with help, a fair test to see if all seedlings need light.		Review what is needed to make a fair test and compare the plants.	● Know that seedlings need light for healthy growth.
LESSON 12	● To know that animals can be sorted into groups.	Sort animals into main groups, giving reasons.	Sort out a set of insect pictures giving reasons for sorting. Make a collage picture of an animal for a class picture. Decide which group it belongs to.	Discuss the characteristics of the collage animals and which groups they belong to.	● Can sort animals into groups giving reasons for their groupings.
LESSON 13	● To know how to use secondary sources to find out about a wide range of animals.	Prepare a presentation on an animal using research.		Children present the information they have found.	● Can use secondary sources to find out facts about animals. ● Can present information about animals obtained from secondary sources.
LESSON 14	● To confirm information they have read about animals by observing them.	Make a list of questions and observations to investigate with small creatures such as snails, slugs and worms.		Children explain what they were looking for and what they found.	● Can observe animals guided by information that they have read.
LESSON 15	● To know that animals reproduce and change as they grow older.	Use a Big Book to talk about the life cycle of a frog.	Make a frog wheel on a paper plate to show a frog's life cycle. Use secondary sources to research the life cycle of other small creatures.	Discuss the life cycle of a frog.	● Can describe how some animals change as they grow up.

	OBJECTIVES	ACTIVITY 1	ACTIVITY 2
ASSESSMENT 16	● To know the difference between an animal and a plant. ● To know that animals can be sorted into groups.	Answer questions about plants and animals.	List animals from different groups.

LESSON 1

OBJECTIVE

● To know the difference between an animal and a plant.

RESOURCES

Main teaching activity: Flip chart or board, a healthy pot plant, a small animal (borrow a pet for the day if you do not keep animals at school, or use one of the children).
Group activities: 1. A copy of photocopiable page 63 for each child, writing and drawing materials. **2.** Thick paper or thin card (A4 size) to make the mis-match book, drawing and colouring materials, stapler, scissors.

PREPARATION

Write the questions listed on the right on the flip chart.

Can it see?
Can it talk (make a noise)?
Can it hear?
Can it feel?
Does it eat?
Does it need water?
Can it move?
Does it have babies or lay eggs?
Does it have roots?
Does it live forever?

Vocabulary

animal, plant,
alive, living,
breathe, feed,
grow, reproduce,
die, similarities,
differences

BACKGROUND

Plants and animals have many similarities as well as differences. Children at Year 2/Primary 3 should have enough experience of animals to appreciate that most have eyes and ears, and can feel, taste and smell. Later they will learn that not all animals have the full range of senses and that while plants cannot see in the way that animals do, they are sensitive to light and will move and grow in response to it. Climbing plants appear to 'feel' for the next anchor point on their support.

Animals and plants both reproduce, but in different ways. Animals lay eggs or have babies while plants can reproduce in a number of ways. Most produce seed or spores but some, like strawberry plants, can also reproduce by sending out runners to root and grow into new plants. New plants can also be grown from cuttings taken from a mature plant.

In Year 1/Primary 2 children looked at how plants and animals both need water. Animals also need food, but plants make their own food through the process of photosynthesis. All animals depend ultimately on plants for their food. Many feed directly on plants, while animals that are higher in the food chain eat the plant-eaters.

Animals are obviously more mobile than plants, but plants do move as they grow. Even some cut flowers may be seen to turn towards the light. Many flowers can be seen to open and close with the Sun.

Children may say that animals breathe and plants don't. Plants also need to take in air but they don't breathe in and out visibly as mammals do.

INTRODUCTION

Remind the children that they learned about caring for plants and animals in Year 1/Primary 2. Show them the healthy plant and animal to help them remember.

MAIN TEACHING ACTIVITY

Working with the whole class, look carefully at the plant and ask the children to tell you anything they can about it. You may need to prompt them with questions such as: *Can you tell me the name of each part? How does a plant move? How do we get new plants? What does it eat? Does it need water? Do plants live forever?*

Look now at the animal and ask the children what they know about it, using similar prompt questions. You may also ask: *Can it speak or make a noise? What does it eat? Does it need water?*

Now look at the list of questions on the flip chart and ask them in turn, filling in ticks or crosses in two columns for the plant and the animal as appropriate. Talk about the questions and help the children to decide what main differences they can see between plants and animals. There are, of course, many differences, but the obvious ones for children at this stage are probably those linked to the senses and movement. Some children may understand that animals need food, while plants are able to make their own. There are also many similarities, and some children may be able to start thinking of these. (Plants and animals both need water and air, they grow and go through a life cycle.)

GROUP ACTIVITIES

1. Give each child a copy of photocopiable page 63 and ask them to complete it by writing or drawing five things that distinguish plants and animals.
2. Make a mis-match book. Each child will need two sheets of thick paper or thin card. These should be roughly A4 size. Divide each page into three equal sections on both sides (see diagram, opposite).
Some children may be able

1. Take two A4 sheets of paper which have been ruled into three sections on each side. Fold these in half to make a small booklet.
2. Draw and colour a plant on page 1, a girl or boy on page 3, a tree on page 5 and an animal or bird on page 7.
3. Staple the book together, then cut all the pages into three sections along the marked lines.

to do this for themselves, but you may prefer to mark one page and photocopy it before giving it to the children. Fold each page in half to make a book. On the first page the children should draw a plant, and on the fifth page a tree, keeping the flower or head of the tree in the top section of the page, the stem or trunk in the middle section, and the roots in the bottom section.

On page three they draw a boy or girl and on page seven an animal or bird. This works best if the animal is two-legged, such as an ostrich, so that the head can be kept in the top section, the body in the middle section and the legs and feet in the bottom section. Staple the book together with a staple through each section, then cut each page along the lines into the three sections. The sectioned pages may then be turned to make 'mis-match' creatures which are part-plant and part-animal. The drawings must be positioned similarly on each page.

DIFFERENTIATION

1. All children should be able to attempt this activity, but less able children may not manage to think of five differences.
2. Some of the children should be able to measure and cut their own pages but others may need help to do this or have the pages photocopied for them.

ASSESSMENT

Check the children's work on photocopiable page 63 to assess their understanding.

PLENARY

Go through some of the work that the children have done in Group activity 1, pointing out some of the differences between plants and animals that they have listed. Remind the children about the questions they answered in the Main teaching activity. *Were there any similarities?* Have fun looking at some of the mis-match books!

OUTCOME
- Can distinguish between plants and animals.

LESSON 2

Objective	● To know the difference between an animal and a plant.
Resources	Access to a farm (or wildlife park), camera.
Main activity	You will need to follow your LEA guidelines before arranging a farm visit. Visit a farm and look at the plants and animals there. Point out that cows give milk, sheep provide wool and hens lay eggs. Wheat, oats and corn are grown as food for humans and other animals. If you are visiting a wildlife park, look for animals and their babies, plants in enclosures or gardens, trees in the parkland. Compare the differences between the plants and animals. Back in the classroom the children can record their experiences in various ways, focusing on the differences between the plants and animals that they have seen.
Differentiation	Children may record their observations in different ways. Some may write their own account, while others may contribute pieces of writing or pictures to a group or class book, or simple captions for photographs.
Assessment	Use the children's work to assess their understanding of the differences between plants and animals.
Plenary	Discuss similarities and differences. Animals and plants are both found on a farm, or in a park. Animals need to be fed and looked after. Plants need care but make their own food. Both plants and animals need water. Animals move around the farm or park, but plants stay in the same place. Both plants and animals grow and reproduce, and so on.
Outcome	● Know the difference between an animal and a plant.

LESSON 3

OBJECTIVE

● To sort a group of living things into animals and plants.

RESOURCES

Main teaching activity: Pictures of plants and animals (including mammals, insects, fish, birds and molluscs), two large PE hoops, two large labels.
Group activities: 1. Animal and plant cards made from the pictures on photocopiable pages 64 and 64 (see Preparation, below). **2.** A copy of photocopiable page 66 for each child, pencils.

PREPARATION

Make enough sets of cards from photocopiable pages 64 and 65 to have one set between two. Enlarge the sheets to A3 if possible. When coloured and laminated these will make a useful resource for several activities. Write 'Animal' on one label and 'Plant' on the other; use these to label the hoops.

Vocabulary

plant, animal, kingdom, similarities, differences

BACKGROUND

Many children will think that the animal kingdom consists only of mammals. This activity will help them to understand that insects, spiders, fish, reptiles, birds and humans are all part of the animal kingdom, as well as helping them sort animals from plants. At this stage they do not need to be able to name individual species, although some interested children may become quite knowledgeable in certain areas.

INTRODUCTION

Working with the whole class, remind them of what they learned in Lesson 1. Look at a picture of a mammal and a plant and ask the children to say which is the animal and which the plant. Can they say how they know which is which?

MAIN TEACHING ACTIVITY

One at a time, look at the other pictures you have and ask the children to decide whether they are plants or animals.

Ask for the reasons for their decisions. Put each picture in the appropriately labelled hoop. Gradually build up two sets, one of animals and one of plants. Talk about the things that the animals have in common. They may not all have legs (compare a snail and a spider) but they can move. They all need to eat. Most of them have senses to help them survive. Plants have stems and leaves and are usually green. They may also have flowers and fruits.

GROUP ACTIVITIES

1. Divide the children into groups of four or six and give each group two sets of cards made from the pictures on photocopiable pages 64 and 65. Suggest that they use the cards to play Snap, or a matching game like Pelmanism, where they match two animal cards or two plant cards. Before they can keep them, the children need to say whether their cards are plants or animals.
2. Give each child a copy of photocopiable page 66. Explain that they should write the names of the animals in the gaps and add why they are animals. They then list the plants and write about why they are plants.

DIFFERENTIATION

1. All the children can take part in this activity. Less able children may play with just one set of cards and match just plants or animals. More able children could use the cards to make up their own game.
2. A list of words on the board will help some children to extend their writing.

ASSESSMENT

Observe the children as they play the games, particularly Pelmanism. Are they able to match things from the same kingdom? Use the work from Group activity 2 to assess their understanding.

PLENARY

Look again at the pictures sorted in the Main teaching activity or at some of the writing done in Group activity 2. Discuss the fact that all these things belong to either the plant or animal kingdom, but that although some of the members of those kingdoms may look very different from each other, they still have things in common.

OUTCOME

● Can sort out living things into animal and plant groups.

LINKS

Unit 1, Lesson 11: comparing humans and animals.

LESSON 4

OBJECTIVES

● To know that plants can be separated into groups (flowering and non-flowering).
● To practise close observation skills.

RESOURCES

Main teaching activity: Two or three examples of different flowering plants, two or three ferns, mushrooms, moss; pictures of plants, including a flowering plant (showing seed-heads if possible), ferns and a mushroom.
Group activities: 1. A large open mushroom for each group of three, empty margarine pots or similar, white paper, fine hairspray or pastel fixative, magnifiers. **2.** Flowering plants, drawing and colouring materials, large sheets of paper, fern leaves, small garden sprayer or diffuser containing suitable non-clogging paint.
Plenary: Seeds to match one of the flowering plants.

Vocabulary

fern, flowering, non-flowering, seeds, spores, fungi, gills, reproduce, leaf, flower, stem

BACKGROUND

There is a huge variety of plants on the Earth and, like animals, these can be divided into different groups. Green plants that produce flowers, and then seed, are perhaps the most familiar. But some plants do not have flowers – conifers produce cones that bear the seeds and ferns develop tiny spores (asexual reproductive cells) usually on the underside of their leaves. Many children will be familiar with mushrooms but may not realise that they belong to a family of non-green plants, or fungi, which also reproduce by dispersing millions of tiny spores. Some plants have become highly adapted to their habitats – cacti have spines that are really leaves adapted to lose as little water as possible in the hot dry climates they inhabit.

Children do not need to identify individual plants by name, but should be able to distinguish between, for example, broad-leafed trees and conifers, or flowering plants and ferns.

INTRODUCTION

Gather all the children together and remind them of the things they learned about plants in Year 1/Primary 2. Using a picture, or a flowering pot plant, rehearse the names of the different parts of a plant (leaf, flower and stem).

MAIN TEACHING ACTIVITY

Ask the children to look carefully at the plants you have collected. Look at each one in turn, starting with a flowering plant. Invite one child to point to and identify the different parts – leaf, flower and stem. Ask: *How do we get new plants from this one?* (Seeds develop that will grow into new plants in the right conditions.) Look at another flowering plant and invite a different child to find the same features on the new plant. Depending on the season you may have a plant with some seed-heads on, otherwise use a picture showing the seed-heads or fruits on a flowering plant. Ask: *Why do plants produce fruits and seeds?* (In order to reproduce.)

Look next at a fern. Ask the children which parts they can identify. Ask: *Where are the flowers? Do you think this plant ever has flowers?* Some children, who have not seen ferns before, might think that it does but that they are not out yet. Ask them to look closely to see if they can see any sign of buds forming. You will then need to tell them that this is a special type of plant that does not have flowers, but instead produces tiny spores on the underside of its leaves. Show the children the underside of a fern leaf and talk about how these spores, like seeds, will grow into new plants. Ask the children to sort your small collection of plants into two sets – flowering and non-flowering.

GROUP ACTIVITIES

1. Show the children a mushroom. Tell them that these also use spores to reproduce and that the spores are hidden in the gills under the cap. Sort the children into groups of three and encourage them to use a magnifier to look closely at the gills of their mushroom. Tell them that the spores are difficult to see, but there is a way of getting them out so that you can see them. Remove the stem from an open-capped mushroom and place it, gills down, on a clean piece of white paper. Carefully cover it with a margarine pot or similar so that it is not disturbed and leave it somewhere warm and safe overnight. Next morning, lift the mushroom very gently to reveal the pattern of the gills outlined in tiny spores that have fallen from the cap during the night. A gentle spray of pastel fixative or light hairspray will help to preserve the print.
2. Allow the children to choose to draw either a fern leaf or flowering plant. Suggest that they draw just part of the plant – a leaf or flower or seed-head – very carefully, rather than trying to draw the whole thing. If you have a good supply of fern leaves then try placing the leaves on paper and spraying over them using a hand sprayer or diffuser with suitable paint: this can produce some very effective patterns. Move the leaves and spray again with a different colour. Large sheets done in this way provide an interesting backing for a display. Make sure the children are well protected and supervised when spraying – it may be better to do this activity outdoors!

DIFFERENTIATION

All the children can take part in these activities.

ASSESSMENT

Observe the children as they sort the plants into sets. In Group activity 2, as the children are working, ask them to tell you the difference between a fern and a flowering plant.

PLENARY

Gather together all the plants you have been using and ask for a volunteer to come and sort them into sets of flowering and non-flowering plants. *Can anyone remember what some of the non-flowering plants are called?* (Ferns or fungi.) Ask the children if they can tell you the main difference between the two groups of plants that they have been looking at. (One has flowers, the other doesn't.) Ask the children: *How do the ferns reproduce?* Talk about the spores, how tiny they are and how they are produced in vast quantities. Look at the seeds from which a pot plant might grow. These may be quite small too, but will still be much bigger than the spores produced by the ferns or the mushroom. Look at one of the mushroom spore prints and ask a child from one of the mushroom groups to explain what they have been doing. *How are the mushrooms similar to the ferns?* (They both produce spores instead of seeds.)

OUTCOMES

- Can compare the structure of different kinds of plants.
- Can identify a fern and a flowering plant.
- Can make an observational drawing showing some detail.

LINKS

Art: observational drawing.

LESSON 5

Objective	● To know that plants can be separated into groups (broad-leaved and conifer).
Resources	Small pieces or branches from various conifers and cones. (Beware! Do not use yew, as this is highly poisonous.) Small pieces or branches from broad-leaved trees such as oak, ash, horse chestnut or whatever is available locally; fruit or seeds (or pictures of these) from the selected trees.
Main activity	Look at the specimens and compare and contrast them. Talk about the fact that the broad-leaved trees are a different type of flowering plant. Look at the fruits or seeds from these trees and compare them with the cones. Discuss the fact that most conifers are 'evergreen' and what this means. Introduce the word 'deciduous' and explain what it means. Go outside and see if you can find examples of conifers and broad-leaved trees in the locality. Can the children distinguish between the two?
Differentiation	All the children can take part in this activity.
Assessment	Show the children a piece from a conifer and a piece from a broad-leaved tree and ask if they can name the group to which each belongs.
Plenary	Talk about the two groups of trees you have been looking at and sort the pieces of plant material into two sets. Discuss the fact that there are many different groups in the plant kingdom and these are just two of them.
Outcome	● Can tell the difference between a broad-leaved tree and a conifer.

LESSON 6

Objective	● To know how to use secondary sources to find out about plants.
Resources	Reference books, CD-ROMs, posters and videos about plants; writing and drawing materials, tape recorder and tapes, OHP and transparencies, OHP pens.
Main activity	Ask the children if they can remember the names of the groups of plants they looked at in previous lessons. Remind them that there are lots of different groups and that they are going to try to find out as much as they can about another group. Show them pictures of cacti, carnivorous plants, climbing plants, and so on from the reference materials and ask them find to out as much as they can about a particular group (either of their choice or yours). 　　Work could be presented as a booklet, a newsletter for a gardening club, an audio-tape or a series of slides on an OHP.
Differentiation	Less able children could work together and contribute to a group booklet.
Assessment	Assess the quality of the work produced.
Plenary	Ask different children or groups of children to tell or show the rest of the class what they have found out.
Outcomes	● Can present information gained from a secondary source.

LESSON 7

OBJECTIVE
● To know that flowering plants produce seeds.

RESOURCES

Main teaching activity: An example of a flower and its seed-head (perhaps a rose and rose hip), a cotton bud.
Group activities: 1. Magnifiers, drawing materials, a selection of flowers and seed-heads, available according to season (wallflowers, daffodils, busy lizzies, marigolds, buttercups, rape, sweet peas); small knives for cutting open the seed-heads (the ASE publication *Be Safe!* lists flowers and plants that should be avoided because of their toxicity). The developing seed-heads can be seen best as the flowers begin to die so try to find stems with a mixture of flowers, dying flowers and seed pods. **2.** Plant pots, seeds, compost, labels, newspaper.

BACKGROUND

Not all flowers will automatically produce fruit. This depends on whether the flower was pollinated, and then fertilised.

Vocabulary

seed, pollinate, fertilise, produce, germinate, grow, seed-head, stamens, pollen, ripe, reproduce

Flowers are produced to attract insects, who carry pollen from one flower to another. This is pollination. Pollen grains (which are the male gametes) then grow down through the stigma to fertilise the ova in the ovary of the plant, which is usually found at the base of the flower. As the flower dies, the ovary can be seen to swell with the developing seeds. Children of this age do not need to understand the process of pollination and fertilisation, but it is helpful for them to know that pollen plays a part in the development of seeds. It is, however, important that if the subject is introduced the correct terminology is used. This will avoid the danger of children developing misconceptions.

INTRODUCTION

Ask the children if they know how we get new plants. Remind them about the seeds they grew in Year 1/Primary 2 and ask if they can remember what happened.

MAIN TEACHING ACTIVITY

Working with the whole class, look at a flower and a dead flower head, such as a rose (Rosa Rugosa, the single, bright pink rose often found as hedging, is useful for showing both stamens and ovary (hip). Try to obtain several examples to pass around the class.) Look at the petals and the centre of the flower. You may be able to gather a little pollen from the stamens on a cotton bud to show the children. Explain that pollen has to be taken from one flower to another, usually by insects or the wind, in order to help them produce seeds. Ask the children to look carefully at the bulge behind the flower head and explain to them how this swells into a seed-case. Look further down the stem where the flowers have already died and fallen off and point out that the swelling is much bigger. Ask: *What do you think is inside the case?* Cut the seed-head in half and show the children what is in there. Ask: *Why do plants produce seeds?* (In order to reproduce themselves.) Take the opportunity to reinforce the safety message that they should never eat any seeds or fruits unless they are told that it is safe to do so by a responsible adult.

GROUP ACTIVITIES

1. Working singly or in pairs, give the children examples of other flowers, with both developing and fully developed seed-heads. Ask them to look for a developing seed-head. They should then carefully cut a ripe seed-case open, look for the seeds inside and make an observational drawing.

2. Working in small groups, take some seeds from one of the seed-heads and set them in a pot of compost. Label the pot with the date of sowing and the variety of plant, if known. Ask the children if they can remember how to care for them. (Keep the seeds warm and damp and you should
have some success with germination whatever the time of year.) This will help the children to see that new plants do begin to grow from the seeds produced by flowering plants. Further growth of the plants will depend on the time of year and the type of seeds chosen. If the seeds are of a size that can be counted, the children could keep a record of the number sown and see if they all germinate and form new plants.

DIFFERENTIATION

These activities should be accessible to all the children.

ASSESSMENT

During the Plenary session ask the children if they can explain where seeds come from, and why seeds are necessary.

PLENARY

Look at some of the drawings the children have done. Ask them to describe the flower they have drawn and where they found the developing seed-head. *Were all the plants similar or were some of the seed-cases different shapes?*

Ask: *What will the seeds grow into if you plant them?* Help the children to understand that the seeds will grow into plants similar to those from which the seed came.

OUTCOME

● Know that seeds come from flowering plants.

LINKS

Art: observational drawing.

LESSON 8

Objective	● To know that there are many different types of fruits and seeds.
Resources	A selection of different fruits such as apples, crab apples, pears, peaches, mangoes, papaws, blackberries, raspberries or rose hips; knife.
Main activity	Look at an apple. *Where are the seeds?* Cut the apple in half and look for the seeds. Look at different fruits and their seeds and compare the shapes and sizes of the seeds. Explain to the children that the fruits of some plants are attractive to certain animals. When the animals eat the fruits with the seeds in them they help to disperse the seeds. (Beware! Some fruit, such as blackberries, may stain.) Reinforce the warning that children should not eat any berries or fruits that they find.
Differentiation	All the children can take part in this activity.
Assessment	During the Plenary session ask the children why plants produce fruits.
Plenary	Discuss the fact that each type of plant produces its own particular fruit containing its seed or seeds. Ask the children why they think some seeds are hidden within fruits. Discuss fruits being attractive to animals and that they help to disperse the seeds by eating the fruits and discarding the seeds.
Outcome	● Know that there are many different kinds of fruits and seeds.

LESSON 9

Objective	● To know that different fruits contain different numbers of seeds.
Resources	A collection of fruits or berries such as rose hips, apples, pears, sweet peas, peas, runner beans, broad beans, sycamore seeds, rape or shell-on peanuts; knives, paper, pencils, clear adhesive tape.
Main activity	Working in pairs, give the children different fruits to investigate. Help them to cut the fruits in half and look for the seeds inside. Encourage them to remove the seeds carefully and place them, in a row, on a piece of paper. Cover each row with a strip of clear adhesive tape. Count the seeds and record the type of plant and number of seeds by the side of each strip. Use the information to produce a simple graph. *Which plant produces most seeds?* Avoid plants that have a large number of very small seeds that it is impossible to count.
Differentiation	Very able children could collect information from other groups and begin to think about the average number of pips, for example, in an apple.
Assessment	Ask the children to tell you, from their graph, which fruit has the most seeds and which the least.
Plenary	Discuss the variation in the numbers of seeds produced by different plants. Ask the children if they have any ideas about why some fruits (such as a peach or a mango) have only one seed, while others have many seeds. (Where there is only one seed it tends to be covered in a very hard shell and for this reason it is often discarded rather than eaten with the fruit. Some of the seeds from other fruits that are eaten may actually be chewed and digested, rather than just passing whole through the digestive system before being excreted. These plants need to produce seeds in greater numbers to make sure that at least some will germinate.)
Outcomes	● Know that different fruits contain different numbers of seeds.

LESSON 10

OBJECTIVES
● To plan and carry out a simple fair test with help.
● To devise, with help, a fair test to investigate the effect of water on the germination of seeds and the growth of seedlings.

RESOURCES
Main teaching activity: Flip chart or board.
Group activities: 1. Two small plant pots of a similar size for each group of three or four; compost, water, measuring jugs, newspaper; plant labels (lolly sticks), some marked with coloured tape to indicate the dry pots; two plastic trays labelled 'Wet' and 'Dry' to hold the pots; a variety of seeds such as broad beans, sweet peas, French marigold or radish. **2.** A copy of photocopiable page 67 for each child, pencils.

PREPARATION
Spread some compost out on a tray and leave this in a warm place for two or three days until it is really dry. You will need enough compost to fill half the number of plant pots. Wrap some coloured tape around half of the plant labels so that the pots that are to be kept dry can be distinguished easily.

BACKGROUND

Vocabulary

seeds, seedlings, compost, growth, fair test, predict, temperature, investigation

Children investigated what happened to plants deprived of water and light in Year 1/Primary 2. This lesson aims to reinforce what they learned at that time and help the children to set up a more systematic investigation and begin to think about fair testing. Children at this stage will need lots of help to plan a fair test, and the quality of their thinking and answers will depend greatly on the quality of the questions they are asked.

Make sure that when you are talking to the children you distinguish carefully between seeds that are germinating and seedlings that are growing. Seeds do not grow. They contain sufficient nutrients to sustain them while they germinate and they do not technically begin to grow until they produce their first pair of true leaves and start to photosynthesise. The children do not need to know the details of this but it is helpful if they develop the correct vocabulary.

Make sure that the children know to wash their hands well after handling compost and that any cuts must be covered before they start.

INTRODUCTION
Working initially with the whole class, remind the children of what they learned in Year 1/ Primary 2 about plants needing water and light.

MAIN TEACHING ACTIVITY

This lesson will need to be revisited over the next few weeks to make observations.

Ask the children: *What do plants need in order to grow well?* Write 'water' and 'light' on the flip chart. (Temperature is investigated more fully in Year 3/ Primary 4). Then ask: *Do all plants need these things? How could we find out?* Explain that, to make a test fair, we can only investigate one thing at a time and we have to keep all the other factors in our investigation the same. *This time we are going to investigate if seeds need water to germinate and grow. We are going to work in groups and each group can test a different kind of seed. Each group is going to set two pots of seeds and give one pot water but keep the other pot dry.* Ask: *What will we need to keep the same to make our test fair?*

Look first at the word 'light' on the flip chart. Ask: *How can we make sure all the pots get the same amount of light?* (Put them in the same place.) *What else will we need to keep the same?* (Some children may volunteer things such as: the same sort of plant pots, the same sort of compost, the same number of seeds, set them at the same time, keep them all warm.) As the children make suggestions add them to the list on the flip chart. If suggestions are not forthcoming ask questions such as: *Do you think it matters if we use a different sort of compost in each pot? Do you think it will make a difference if we give some seeds a lot of water and some just a drop?*

Strictly speaking, it is not necessary for the amount of water given to be exactly the same. However, as part of the process of getting the children to understand what a fair test is, it may be a good idea to decide on an equal amount of water for each group to give to their pot. Remember seeds do not respond well to being drowned! How much water you give will depend on the atmosphere and the heat of the classroom. The compost only needs to be kept damp, and you may need to water every day or just alternate days. With the children, feel the compost each day and decide whether to water or not. You may also need to adjust the amount of water you are giving as the investigation progresses, but talk about this and make sure that each group does the same thing.

GROUP ACTIVITIES

1. Divide the children into groups of three or four. Give each group two plant pots, some dry compost and some damp compost and one variety of seed. Fill one pot with dry compost, one with damp compost, and label the pots with the name of the group, the name of the seeds, and whether the pot is to be kept wet or dry. Place all the pots in the wet tray or the dry tray. Water the 'wet' pots using the measured amount of water. (Keep them separate to avoid the dry pots getting watered unintentionally.) Revisit the activity at sensible intervals to check progress.
2. Give each child a copy of photocopiable page 67 to write a simple structured plan of the investigation, completing all but the last section of the sheet. Keep the children's sheets safe so that you can give them out for completion at the end of the investigation.

DIFFERENTIATION

1. All the children should be able to take part in this activity.
2. The 'What are you trying to find out?' section of the sheet could be filled in for some children before the page is copied. Less able children might work together, with an adult to fill in one sheet for the group, recording the children's comments. These sheets will need to be kept safe, and revisited to update observations and record what happened.

ASSESSMENT

Observe how well the children handle the equipment as they set up their investigation. Use the record sheets from Group activity 2 to assess their understanding.

PLENARY

Revise with the children how they set up the investigation and how they tried to keep the test fair. Ask: *What do you think will happen?* Decide together when the pots are to be checked for progress. You will need to gather the children together for a short time to review their

observations at least once each week until the end of the investigation (three or four weeks). You will need a longer session in the final week to compare the plants, draw some conclusions and allow the children to complete their sheets. You should have some reasonably healthy plants in the pots that have been watered, but no growth in the dry pots. Tip the dry pots out on some newspaper to see if you can find the seeds. Unless they have become damp they should be the same as when they were planted. Ask the children why they think they have not germinated and grown. (Seeds need water to germinate and grow.)

OUTCOME

● Know that seeds and seedlings need water to germinate and then grow.

LINKS

Literacy: writing for a purpose.

LESSON 11

Objective	● To plan and carry out, with help, a simple fair test to investigate the effect of light on seedling growth.
Resources	Two small plant pots of a similar size for each group of three or four; compost, a variety of seeds such as broad beans, sweet peas, French marigold and radish; water, measuring jugs, newspaper, plant labels (lolly sticks), a copy of photocopiable page 67 for each child. Each group should set their seeds two weeks before this lesson and keep the compost moist so that they have healthy seedlings to work with. Set a few pots yourself for emergency replacements!
Main activity	As in Lesson 10, help the children to plan a fair test to find out if seedlings need light in order to grow well. Each group sets two similar pots with seeds. Both are given water as needed but one pot is placed in a light place and the other in a dark place. Make observations every other day and record these on photocopiable page 67.
Differentiation	All the children can take part in the investigation but some may need help with recording.
Assessment	Observe the children as they set up the investigation. Use their recording sheets to assess their understanding.
Plenary	Review what is needed to make a fair test. At the end of the investigation, compare the plants grown in the dark with those that have been in the light.
Outcome	● Know that seedlings need light for healthy growth.

LESSON 12

OBJECTIVE
● To know that animals can be sorted into groups.

RESOURCES

Main teaching activity: Pictures or photographs of animals. These should include at least two examples of each animal class: an ant, a butterfly or a bee (insects); a cat, a mouse or a human (mammals); a goldfish, a stickleback or a shark (fish); a robin, a blackbird or an eagle (birds); a frog, a toad or a newt (amphibians); a lizard, a snake or a crocodile (reptiles). You may need to use pictures from reference books in order to get a good range.
Group activities: 1. A copy of photocopiable page 68 for each child, writing and colouring materials, insect reference books. **2.** Collage materials such as pipe cleaners, cotton buds, feathers, shiny paper, gauze, sequins, fabric and so on; adhesive, scissors, soft wire.

PREPARATION

Make a label for each of the animal classes you are going to sort. Prepare a background for a class picture.

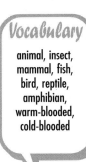

Vocabulary

animal, insect, mammal, fish, bird, reptile, amphibian, warm-blooded, cold-blooded

BACKGROUND

The animal kingdom can be divided and sub-divided indefinitely, but Year 2/Primary 3 children do not need to know subtle divisions. They should be able to distinguish between mammals, birds, fish, insects, reptiles and amphibians, but they are likely to classify spiders as insects (both are members of the phylum Arthropoda), rather than arachnids. (Insects have only six legs while arachnids have eight. Insects have a body divided into three distinct parts – head, thorax and abdomen; arachnids have just two body parts.) Use your professional judgement to decide whether your children are ready to sort spiders from insects or whether it is easier, at this stage, to call them all insects.

   Some children may confuse whales and dolphins (mammals) with sharks (fish). Many children find these animals fascinating so you may want to help them understand the difference. (Whales and dolphins are warm-blooded creatures and need to come to the surface at regular intervals to breathe. They also give birth to live young and suckle them. Fish are cold-blooded and extract oxygen from the water by passing it through their gills; most fish lay eggs.)

INTRODUCTION

Seat the children in a circle and hand out the animal pictures so that the children can hold them up for all to see. Look at the pictures and ask if the children can name any of the animals.

MAIN TEACHING ACTIVITY

Look at a picture of a fish. Ask the children: *Where does it live? What is its skin like? How does it move? What do you think it eats? How does it breathe? What is special about its skin? Can you find another fish in a picture?* Find all the pictures of fish, seat those children together and give them the correct label.

Ask: *Can anyone find a mammal among the pictures?* Some children may be able to identify a mammal but, if not, explain that mammals are warm-blooded, are usually covered in hair or fur (even humans, though it is not so obvious) and give birth to live babies. You may need to get the children to look closely at their arms and legs to persuade them that they are covered in hair. *Can anyone find one now?* Identify the rest of the mammals and seat the children with those pictures together with the appropriate label.

Next look at a picture of an insect. Ask: *How do we know it is an insect?* Help the children to recognise that an insect has six legs. Look for the three parts of the body and explain that insects sometimes have wings, but not always. Again, seat the children with the insect pictures together.

Now ask: *Which other animals have wings?* Most children will be able to identify birds. Ask: *What else is special about birds?* Talk about feathers and how the different colours and patterns of feathers help us to identify what sort of bird it is. Group the birds together and give them their label. Say: *Only two groups left! Does anyone know what they are?* Some children may have learned about reptiles from an interest in dinosaurs. *What is special about them?* (They have scaly skins but these are different from the scales on a fish.) Explain that they are cold-blooded and need to lie in the Sun to warm themselves up before they can move very well. Most of them lay eggs and don't look after their babies. Explain that the last group is called amphibians and that they are very special. They can live on land or in water. *Can you remember from Year 1/Primary 2 how frogs go into the pond to lay their frogspawn and how they sometimes spend the winter at the bottom of the pond?* Look again at the groups and help the children to read the labels and name some of the animals in the group. Can they think of any other creatures that belong to any of the groups?

GROUP ACTIVITIES

1. Give each child a copy of photocopiable page 68. Ask them to circle or colour all the insects they can find in the picture. Tell them they need to look very carefully. There are ten insects. Ask them to find out the names of some of them and write these on the picture.
2. Ask the children to individually make collages of different animals. These could be mounted as part of a class display either as a picture or as separate sets. Try feathers for birds, silver or gold paper scales on fish, cotton bud dragonflies or pipe cleaner insects. Use pieces of soft wire to attach the dragonflies, butterflies and bees to the display so that they seem to hover.

DIFFERENTIATION

1. Less able children may need help in using reference materials to name some insects.
2. All the children should be able to take part in this activity.

ASSESSMENT

Use the photocopiable sheet from the Group activity 1 to assess children's ability to recognise insects. Ask the children if they can name the group that the animal they have made belongs to. Note their responses during the Plenary session.

PLENARY

Look at a few of the collages made by the children and talk about some of the characteristics of that creature. (Birds have beaks and feathers, fish have fins and scales, insects have six legs and three parts to their bodies.) Ask a few volunteers to name their favourite animal. Can they say which group it belongs to and why?

OUTCOME

● Can sort animals into groups giving reasons for their groupings.

LINKS

Art: making 3D models and collages.

LESSON 13

Objective	● To know how to use secondary sources to find out about a wide range of animals.
Resources	Reference books, CD-ROMs, posters and videos about animals; writing and drawing materials, tape recorder and tapes, OHP with transparencies and suitable pens.
Main activity	Working as individuals or pairs, encourage the children to find out about an unfamiliar animal. They could choose an elephant, a crocodile, a shark or an insect, such as a praying mantis or a locust. Their work could be presented as a booklet, a newsletter, an audio tape or a series of slides on an OHP. Tell the children that their presentation should include facts such as which group the animal belongs to, its size, where it usually lives, plus any other interesting information they can find.
Differentiation	Less able children could work together and contribute to a group booklet or presentation.
Assessment	Assess the quality of the work produced.
Plenary	Ask different children or groups of children to tell or show what they have found out.
Outcomes	● Can use secondary sources to find out facts about animals. ● Can present information about animals obtained from secondary sources.

LESSON 14

Objective	● To confirm information they have read about animals by observing them.
Resources	Paper, pencils, clipboards, reference materials about animals that are likely to be found in the local environment; suitable places for the children to hunt and extra adult supervision.
Main activity	The children should use secondary sources to find out about one or two animals and make an observation checklist, such as, for snails: Does the shell always spiral in the same direction? Are they always found in damp places? Do they only eat green leaves? Can the shells be different colours? Are they always the same shape? The children then go out and make observations to check their research.
Differentiation	Most children will need some help in formulating a list and some will need the list to be made for them.
Assessment	Note those children who are able to formulate sensible lists of things to look for. In the Plenary session ask the children to explain their findings.
Plenary	Ask some children to explain what they were looking for and why they chose those points. Did they find what they were looking for? Did they notice anything else?
Outcome	● Can observe animals guided by information that they have read.

LESSON 15

OBJECTIVE
● To know that animals reproduce and change as they grow older.

RESOURCES
Main teaching activity: A Big Book version of *Tadpole Diary* by David Drew (Rigby) or other pictures showing the life cycle of a frog.
Group activities: 1. Paper plates, paper fasteners, scissors, drawing materials. **2.** Reference materials including CD-ROMs (the Insect Lore catalogue contains quite a good selection of appropriate reference materials on this subject, available from Insect Lore, PO Box 1420, Kiln Farm, MK19 6ZH; Tel 01908 563338; www.insectlore-europe.com).

Vocabulary

change, mature,
grow,
metamorphosis,
adult

BACKGROUND
Most animals change as they mature, in size, features and capabilities. Different animals mature at very different rates – this is usually related to their lifespan. Creatures such as butterflies, whose life expectancy is usually only one season, are mature as soon as they emerge from the chrysalis. A mouse, which could expect to live for just a couple of years, reaches maturity in a matter of weeks. Elephants, humans, horses and other animals with a longer lifespan, take several years to reach full maturity.

In Year 1/Primary 2 the children looked at how humans change as they grow older, how features and bodies change shape, how hair changes colour, and that when people grow up they can have babies. Other animals may show similar signs of ageing. Small snub noses allow babies to suckle but, as animals mature and are weaned, their noses often become more prominent. Teeth come and go. Dogs and horses often 'go grey' just like humans. Their shape, however, remains basically the same, although it may be taller, wider or longer.

Some animals change drastically as they grow and mature. Tadpoles look nothing like frogs, and who would guess that the eating machines called caterpillars turn into beautiful, delicate butterflies. The children may have kept some tadpoles in Year 1/ Primary 2 (See *100 Science Lessons: Year 1*, Unit 3, Lesson 15) as part of learning how to care for living things. They could keep some again now to observe the changes in greater detail.

Bear in mind that it is illegal to buy or sell frogspawn or to take it from the wild. It can be taken from a garden pond with the owner's permission. It needs to be kept in a cool position and not on a window ledge in full Sun. Watercress makes quite a good substitute if you can't get pondweed for food. As the tadpoles begin to develop legs they will need extra protein to help their development. They can be given raw meat, but this has hygiene implications. You may find that giving them a little flaked fish food is preferable to hanging small lumps of meat in the water! At this stage, they will also need a rock or stone so that they can climb out occasionally. As soon as the tadpoles become froglets they need to eat insects and should be returned to the pond they came from.

INTRODUCTION
With the whole class together, remind the children about the work they did on ageing in Year 1/ Primary 2. They talked about how people change as they grow older, and that adults can have babies which in turn grow up and have babies of their own. They may have cared for some tadpoles and watched them change.

MAIN TEACHING ACTIVITY

Look at the Big Book *Tadpole Diary,* or the pictures you have. If the children cared for tadpoles last year, ask them what they can remember as you read through the book or look at the pictures. Look at how the tadpoles develop. *What do the tadpoles look like when they first emerge from the spawn?* (Very small with external gills.) *Which legs grow first?* (The back ones.) *How are they different from the front legs?* (The back legs are much longer and stronger.) *How does the shape of the head and body change? What happens to the tail?* (The head and body become longer and more frog-like and the tail gradually disappears, as it is absorbed back into the body.)

If you have tadpoles in the classroom, relate these stages of development to the children and ask: *What stage are they at now? What will happen next?*

GROUP ACTIVITIES

1. Make a 'frog wheel' from paper plates. Each child will need two paper plates and a paper fastener. Divide each plate into six sections (some may need help with this) and from one section of one plate cut a window. On the other plate, draw one stage of the frog's life cycle in each section. (1. frogspawn, 2. tadpole with gills, 3. tadpole without gills, 4. tadpole with back legs, 5. tadpole with back and front legs and reduced tail, 6. froglet.) Fasten the two plates together

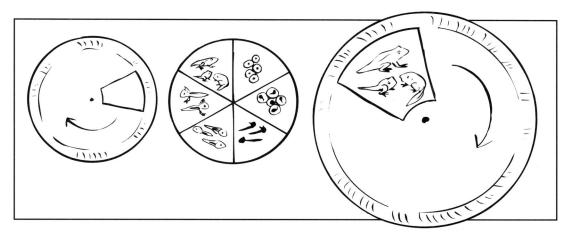

with a paper fastener through the middle so that the top plate can be turned to show the stages of the life cycle in succession (see diagram, above).
2. Work in small mixed-ability groups to use reference materials to find out simple facts about the life cycle of other animals such as dragonflies, moths, bees and wasps.

DIFFERENTIATION

1. All the children can take part in this activity, although some may need help to divide the plate into sections and cut the window from the second plate.
2. All the children can contribute to this activity according to their ability.

ASSESSMENT

Listen to the children as they explain their frog wheels in the Plenary session. Check that they have drawn the stages in the correct order.

PLENARY

Ask one or two children to explain how their frog wheels work, then revise the stages in the life cycle of the frog. Make the point that it is only when the frogs are fully grown that they spawn. Ask the groups to tell the class what they have found out about the life cycle of other animals. Talk about how animals change as they grow older, some more than others, and reiterate that it is only when they are fully grown that they have babies.

OUTCOME

● Can describe how some animals change as they grow up.

LINKS

Literacy: using secondary sources.
Unit 1, Lesson 12: animals produce young that grow into adults.

LESSON 16

OBJECTIVES
● To know the difference between an animal and a plant.
● To know that animals can be sorted into groups.

RESOURCES

Assessment activities: 1. A copy of photocopiable page 69 for each child, pencils. **2.** A copy of photocopiable page 70 for each child, pencils, picture books of animals.

INTRODUCTION

Remind the children that they have been learning about the differences between plants and animals in this unit.

ASSESSMENT ACTIVITY 1

Give each child a copy of photocopiable page 69 and ask them to complete it. Make sure they understand each question, helping them to read where necessary. Tell them that the answer to each question is either 'plants' or 'animals' (or, once, both).

Answers
1. plants, 2. animals, 3. animals, 4. plants, 5. animals, 6. plants, 7. plants, 8. animals, 9. animals, 10. plants and animals.

Looking for levels
Most children will answer about six questions correctly. More able children will get them all right and less able children may manage only three or four correct answers.

ASSESSMENT ACTIVITY 2

Give each child a copy of photocopiable page 70 and help them to read the title of each list. Ask them to write the names of three appropriate animals in each shape. The children could use picture books of animals to give them ideas and help with spellings. The assessment checks that they know which group each animal belongs to.

Answers
This list is not definitive.
Mammals – human, cat, dog, lion, tiger, horse, cow, sheep.
Reptiles – snake, lizard, crocodile, alligator.
Amphibians – frog, toad, newt, salamander.
Birds – robin, blackbird, sparrow, owl, eagle.
Fish – goldfish, cod, plaice, shark.
Insects – ant, woodlouse, ladybird, butterfly, bee, wasp.

Looking for levels
Most children should be able to give at least two examples in each set. More able children will complete each set correctly; some less able children may have difficulty in identifying reptiles and amphibians.

Name

Animals and plants

Draw or write five things in each shape to show how animals and plants are different.

Plants

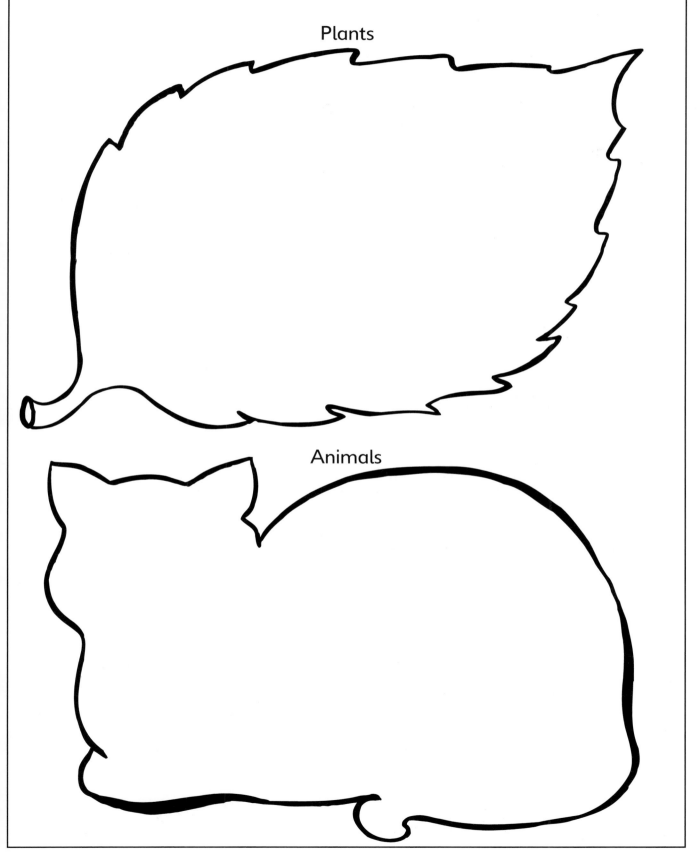

Animals

Snap cards 1

Plant and animal differences

Ladybird   Daffodil   Bird

The _____, _____ and the _____

are all animals because...

The _____, _____ and the _____

are all plants because...

Palm   Starfish   Fern

Snap cards 2

Fair test

What are you trying to find out?

What do you think will happen?

What equipment did you use?

What do you need to keep the same to make your test fair?

What did you find out?

Spot the insect!

Put a ring around all the insects you can find in this picture.
There are ten altogether.

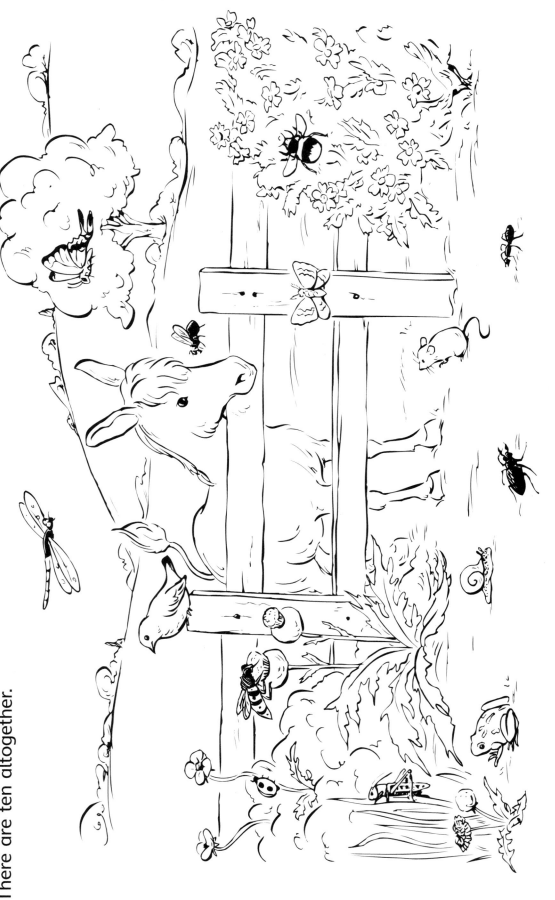

Keeping healthy

A very high cupboard with a lock, out of reach of children.

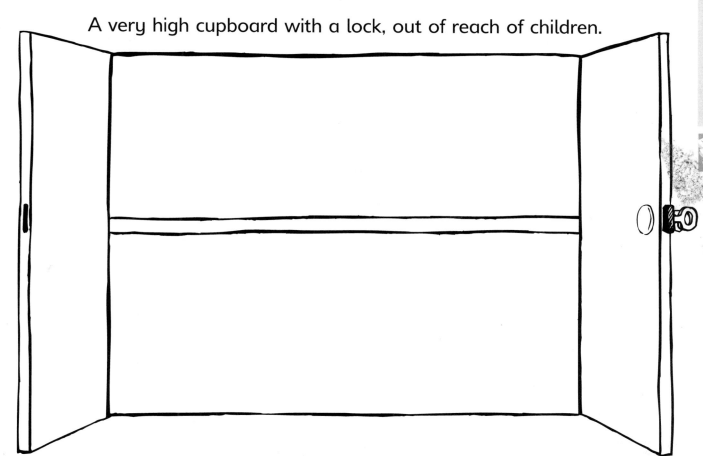

A low cupboard with no lock that children can reach.

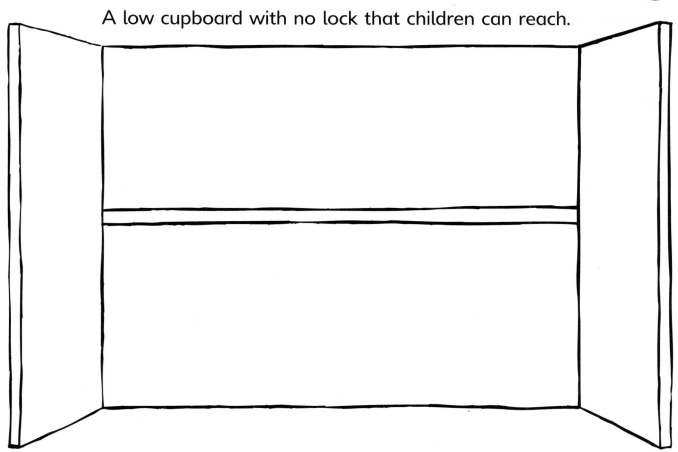

Name

Keeping healthy 2

Cut out the pictures and put each picture in the right cupboard.

Growing up

Write 'plants' or 'animals' in the spaces to make the sentences correct.

1. _____ have leaves.

2. _____ have five senses.

3. _____ eat food.

4. _____ make their own food.

5. Some _____ have babies.

6. Some _____ have flowers.

7. Most _____ produce seeds.

8. _____ can move from place to place.

9. _____ eat plants.

10. Both _____ and _____ grow.

Name

Growing up

Write the names of three animals in each list.

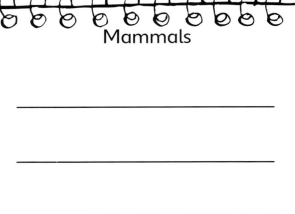

Mammals

_____

_____

_____

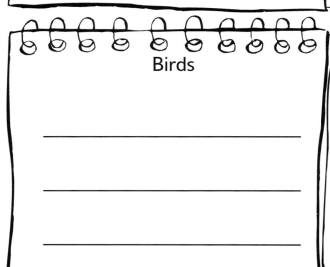

Reptiles

_____

_____

_____

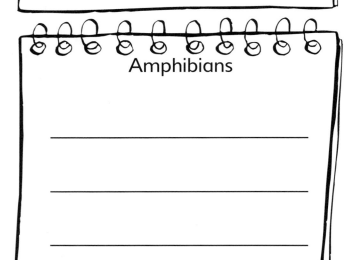

Amphibians

_____

_____

_____

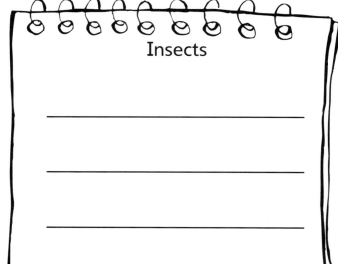

Birds

_____

_____

_____

Fish

_____

_____

_____

Insects

_____

_____

_____

Life in habitats

ORGANISATION (14 LESSONS)

	OBJECTIVES	MAIN ACTIVITY	GROUP ACTIVITIES	PLENARY	OUTCOMES
LESSON 1	● To know the names of some of the plants and animals in the local environment.	Visit the local environment and look for things moving and growing.	Make a class reference book of labelled plants or animals. Find out more about one of the things seen.	Look at the class reference book.	● Can recognise some of the plants and animals in the local environment.
LESSON 2	● To relate life processes to animals and plants found in the local environment.	Look for evidence of feeding or nesting (life processes) in the environment.		Talk about what was seen on the walk.	● Can identify life processes occurring in the environment.
LESSON 3	● To know that plants in the local environment are similar to each other in some ways and different in others.	Compare similarities and differences in plants.	Compare familiar flowers with a different flower. Make a cut-and-paste jigsaw of three plants.	Talk about similarities and differences in plants.	● Can identify the parts of common plants. ● Can compare some common plants.
LESSON 4	● To know that the local environment is divided up into different habitats. ● To know that there are differences and similarities between habitats.	Conduct a habitat survey of the local area (grassland, pond, wood, garden). Compare how much Sun, shade or wind features get. Make a habitat map.	Make a drawing, painting or collage to add to the habitat map. Write a description of, or poem about, a habitat.	Discuss the habitats on the class map.	● Can identify different habitats in the environment. ● Can describe some features of different habitats in the environment.
LESSON 5	● To know some of the plants and animals in a named habitat.	Look at a habitat in detail and record results.		Groups report on the different habitats.	● Can identify some plants and animals found in a particular habitat.
LESSON 6	● To make predictions about what might be found in a different habitat. ● To design a simple chart for collecting information.	Use information from Lessons 4 and 5 to make predictions of what might be found in a different habitat.	Design a chart to take out in Lesson 7. Use reference materials.	Discuss the children's charts.	● Can use previously gathered information to make predictions. ● Can design a simple chart.
LESSON 7	● To investigate a different habitat testing predictions made.	Visit different areas and test predictions.		Discuss what the children found.	● Can make observations to test predictions. ● Can describe how two habitats differ.
LESSON 8	● To know that living things in a habitat, depend on each other.	Look at the relationships between plants and animals.	Make a class habitat display. Draw pictures to show relationships.	Use the habitat display to talk about the different relationships between plants and animals.	● Can give examples of how living things depend on each other in a habitat.
LESSON 9	● To know that some animals use camouflage to help them survive in a habitat.	Discuss origins of, and reasons for, camouflage.	Make camouflage pictures to check effectiveness. Describe, or write a poem about, why animals need camouflage.	Discuss effective camouflage.	● Can explain how camouflage helps animals to survive in a habitat.

ORGANISATION (14 LESSONS)

	OBJECTIVES	MAIN ACTIVITY	GROUP ACTIVITIES	PLENARY	OUTCOMES
LESSON 10	● To understand how camouflage works.	Groups camouflage an object on the school field so that from a distance it appears hidden.		Discuss how camouflage works.	● Can use camouflage to hide an object.
LESSON 11	● To know that plants and animals change in appearance and behaviour with the seasons.	Discuss a year in the life of a tree and its inhabitants.	Make a 'tree' slider which shows the changing seasons. Use reference materials to make a zig-zag book on 'A year in the life of' a chosen animal.	Talk about how things change through the year and how living things depend on each other.	● Can describe how some animals and plants change through the seasons.
LESSON 12	● To know ways in which the environment can be cared for.	Review the habitat visits to consider examples of pollution or abuse and how they could be stopped.	Write a newspaper report about the state of a habitat. Make a set of rules and a poster about protecting the environment.	Discuss ways to care for the environment.	● Can identify ways in which a habitat is damaged. ● Can explain how habitat damage affects things living there. ● Can suggest ways to care for the environment.
LESSON 13	● To know about caring for living things indoors.	Discuss caring for plants, a fish tank, or for pets at home. Care for plants grown from seeds.	Write a simple instruction booklet about caring for a pet. Care for a coleus plant as it grows.	Discuss caring for plants and animals.	● Can describe how to look after living things in the classroom and at home.

	OBJECTIVES	ACTIVITY 1	ACTIVITY 2
ASSESSMENT 14	● To know that living things in a habitat depend on each other. ● To know the names of some of the plants and animals in the local environment.	Link the various dependencies between plants and creatures in a habitat.	Draw and write the names of plants and animals in the local environment.

SAFETY
Many of the lessons in this unit involve taking the children out to investigate the environment. Always consult any school policy regarding this and always visit the proposed site in advance to note any safety issues such as dangerous paths or areas to avoid. If you will be near water you may need extra adults to keep the children safe. Check too that the site is really suitable for your purpose and that you are going to find what you are looking for.

EQUIPMENT
Many of the lessons in this unit require some basic collecting and observation equipment. White plastic trays are useful for collecting both plants and small creatures: pond creatures and other minibeasts show up well and can be observed moving about. Small bug boxes are usually too small to be of any real use, but young children may also find the very large collecting/magnifying boxes difficult to handle. Empty margarine tubs are a good compromise.

Make sure that the children are taught to use a hand lens properly. Magnifiers on stands are useful to place over trays or tubs of specimens, while a stereoscopic microscope (×20) can be an excellent addition to school resources and allow more detailed observations. Pooters are useful for collecting very small creatures, but they should be carefully washed and disinfected between users. Ensure that the gauze over the lower end of the tube that is sucked is in place to avoid an ant going down an unsuspecting throat!

It is important to teach the children how to use and care for equipment properly – this includes making sure that it is cleaned before putting it away so that it is ready for use next time. It also ensures that no poor creature is left imprisoned.

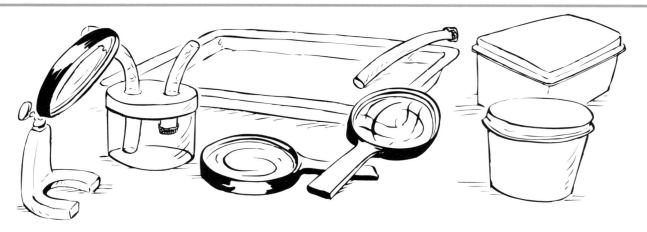

LESSON 1

OBJECTIVE

● To know the names of some of the plants and animals in the local environment.

RESOURCES

Main teaching activity: Reference materials, clipboards, paper, pencils, plastic trays, pooters, small paintbrushes, bug boxes, white trays, magnifiers, empty containers for collecting small creatures, cameras.
Group activities: 1. Specimens collected during the Main teaching activity, magnifiers, reference materials; materials to make a class book: paper, treasury tags or laces. **2.** Reference materials including CD-ROMs.

PREPARATION

Take a walk around your own locality, or the area you are planning to use, to identify some of the common flora and fauna that the children are likely to find. In most cases the emphasis will be on trees and flowers, rather than animals, since creatures are often quite difficult to spot. Make sure that these species are well represented in your reference materials.

Vocabulary

environment, collect, sample, flora, fauna, specimen, minibeast

BACKGROUND

At this stage, it is not necessary for children to know the botanical names of plants, but they should begin to learn the common names of some of the flora and fauna that are found in their locality. They should be able to name, for example, an oak tree or a dandelion. Mosses or lichens rarely have common names so it is easier to settle for 'moss' and 'lichen' in this case.

INTRODUCTION

With the children gathered around you, use some of your reference materials to look at pictures of plants or animals that you might expect to find in the local area.

MAIN TEACHING ACTIVITY

Talk about what the children might expect to see in the local area. Look at the pictures and talk about where the children might see these things. *Can you name any of them? Where might you look for them?* Tell the children that you are all going outside to see how many plants and animals you can identify. Talk about the need to take care of the environment and advise them to collect any samples very carefully. They should take only one leaf from each tree, preferably one that has fallen off. If there are lots of flowers of a particular kind then, again, they may take one, but if there are only one or two then they should draw them or take a photograph. Small creatures, such as snails, might be gently collected and returned to the environment as soon as they are finished with, but make sure that the children know how to use a pooter or paintbrush to collect minibeasts safely.

If the children can name the tree, plant or animal they see, they may not need to collect that particular item, but just make a note or drawing to show that they have seen it. They will need to make sketches or take photographs of any animals, such as rabbits, cats or dogs, since it is obviously not easy to collect them! Divide the children into groups of three or four and provide each group with a clipboard, a plastic tray and any other collecting equipment you think they may need. Go outside and see what you can find.

GROUP ACTIVITIES

1. Back in the classroom, each group should use reference materials to identify any samples brought back. As items are identified, label them and lay them out on the table. Compare the findings of each group.

Ask the children to draw pictures of their finds and collect them together in a class book which could then act as a reference book for other classes, or be used as a comparison for the next year. Any photographs taken could also be used. Make the book with loose pages held together with treasury tags or laces so that extra pages can be added if more things are found.

If you do this lesson in the autumn you could stick dried leaves from the trees directly into the book. If you mount these on card and cover them with sticky-backed plastic they will last for several years. Make sure that any small creatures are returned to their habitats as quickly as possible and that any pots are washed before they are put away.

2. Ask the children to use reference materials, including CD-ROMs, to discover more about some of the samples found in the Main teaching activity and add this information to the class reference book.

DIFFERENTIATION

1. More able children could be encouraged to help organise the class reference book in different sections, or in alphabetical order.

2. Some children may be able to access the Internet to search for information – sites such as the Natural History Museum (www.nhm.ac.uk) are useful. Other children may need help to use the reference books.

ASSESSMENT

Use the children's work to assess their knowledge. During the Plenary session ask them how they would use the class reference book, or how other people could use it. Note those children who can identify pictures of things found in the area.

PLENARY

Look together at the book the children have compiled. Hold up some of the leaves, flowers or creatures that they have included and ask if they can recognise and name any of them. Talk about how they might use the book to identify what things are. Suggest that the book can be added to each time one of the children finds something new in the area.

OUTCOME

● Can recognise some of the plants and animals in the local environment.

LINKS

Literacy: producing a book and organising entries in alphabetical order.

LESSON 2

Objective	● To relate life processes to animals and plants found in the local environment.
Resources	Pictures of the flora and fauna found in Lesson 1, the class reference book made in Lesson 1.
Main activity	Talk about some of the flora and fauna previously found. Can the children remember where they were found? *Did the animals move? How fast? Where were they going? Where did they live? What were they eating? Where were the plants found – in the Sun or in the shade? Where did they seem to grow best? Were there any seeds or new plants?* Go outside again and retrace your steps from Lesson 1, but this time look for seed-heads or baby plants and for signs that plants are growing healthily or struggling (on the side of a path or near a playground). *Are there any baby creatures about?* Look especially for caterpillars or other grubs that will change into moths or butterflies. Can they see holes in leaves where creatures may be feeding?
Differentiation	All the children should be able to take part in this activity, although some may need occasional reminders of what they are looking for!
Assessment	Note those children who contribute sensibly to the Plenary session.
Plenary	Talk about what you saw on the walk. *Did you see evidence of animals eating plants? Were there any signs that plants or animals were reproducing themselves?* (Baby creatures, seeds, young plants.) *Did you find any nests or homes?*
Outcome	● Can identify life processes occurring in the environment.

LESSON 3

OBJECTIVE

● To know that plants in the local environment are similar to each other in some ways and different in others.

RESOURCES

Main teaching activity: Sufficient dandelions, daisies or buttercups, with leaves, for each pair or group of three to have one of each type. Try to obtain one complete plant of each type to show how the leaves are arranged, otherwise use pictures of whole plants. Substitute similar flowers if these are out of season. If you have difficulty finding wild plants locally you could use something like a primula and a pot chrysanthemum. Try to include some of the plants identified by the children in Lesson 1.
Group activities: 1. Writing and drawing materials; flowers for each group (different from those used in the Main teaching activity). If possible, try to find multi-headed flowers such as rosebay willow herb or wallflowers (try hyacinths or bluebells for the more able). **2.** A copy of photocopiable page 89 for each child, scissors, adhesive, colouring materials.

> **Vocabulary**
> leaves, flowers, stem, arrangement, florets, similar, different, variety

BACKGROUND

The Earth holds an enormous variety of plant life and most of us see only a little of it during our lifetimes. As with animals, many plants have basic similarities, but are infinitely different. In this lesson the aim is to encourage the children to look more closely at plants within their environment. This should enable them to see how plants are often quite similar (they have leaves, stems, flowers and so on), but different in the way that the flowers are formed or the way the leaves are shaped and arranged on the stem.

INTRODUCTION

You can use almost any flowers for this lesson but, for ease of explanation, buttercups, dandelions and daisies are being used as examples. Working with the whole class, hold up a daisy. Ask: *Can anyone remember the name of this plant?*

MAIN TEACHING ACTIVITY

Give each pair or group of three a daisy, a buttercup and a dandelion. Ask them to look closely at the daisy. *What colour is it? What are these called?* (Petals.) *What shape are they?* Ask the children to draw the shape of the petals in the air. Now look closely at the buttercup. *What colour is it? What shape are the petals? How is it the same?* (Both flowers have petals and a yellow bit in the centre.) *How is it different?* (The petals are a different colour and shape. A daisy has lots of petals while a buttercup usually has just five.) Now look at the leaves on the daisy.

Show the children the whole plant, or a picture of the plant growing. *What colour are the leaves? What shape are they? Where are they found on the plant?* (Daisy leaves are usually clustered around the base of the plant with the flowers on straight stems above the rosette). Compare these with the leaves on the buttercup. *What colour are they? What shape are they? Can you draw those in the air? Where are they found on the plant?* (Again there may be a rosette of leaves around the base, but other leaves on the stem below the flower. This will depend on the species of buttercup you have. Some types grow quite tall while others put out runners and are lower-growing).

Look now at the dandelion and compare it to the other two plants. The flower is the same colour as the buttercup but it has lots of petals like the daisy. (The 'petals' of a dandelion are actually individual florets, but children at this stage do not need to know this). *The leaves are long, a bit like the daisy, but with a jagged edge, more like the buttercup. They are arranged at the base of the plant like the daisy.* Ask the children: *Do all three plants have leaves?* (Yes.) *Do all three have flowers?* (Yes.) *Do all three have stems?* (Yes.) If possible, go outside to find some of the growing plants and notice how the leaves are arranged.

GROUP ACTIVITIES

1. Give each group another quite different flower to compare with the buttercup, daisy or dandelion. *Does it have just one flower on a stem like the daisy?* Can they identify the petals and say how they are different from the flower they looked at in the Main teaching activity? Ask them to look at the leaves. *What shape are they? How are they arranged on the plant?* The children should draw pictures of each plant and list the similarities and differences. They could press examples of their flowers to add to their work at a later date.
2. Give each child a copy of photocopiable page 89. Ask them to cut out the pieces and stick them on another sheet to make three different flowers. *Do you know, or can you find out, the name of each one?* Ask them to colour them in the appropriate colours.

DIFFERENTIATION

1. More able children could try finding the parts of a bell-shaped flower, such as a hyacinth or bluebell, where the petals are fused.
2. Less able children may need some help using reference materials to identify the flowers.

ASSESSMENT

During the Plenary session, note the children who are able to compare the flowers and tell you some similarities and differences. Use the children's work from the first Group activity to assess their understanding.

PLENARY

Ask some of the groups to explain where they found the petals and leaves on their new flower and how they were the same or different from the one in the Main teaching activity. Ask the children to tell you some similarities that are usually found in flowering plants. *Can you tell me some things that might be different? How do we tell one flower from another?* Say that plants are a bit like people. We all have eyes, noses and mouths but they are all a little different in shape, colour or arrangement so we can tell people apart.

OUTCOMES

● Can identify the parts of common plants.
● Can compare some common plants.

LINKS

Art: observational drawing.

LESSON 4

OBJECTIVES

● To know that the local environment is divided up into different habitats.
● To know that there are differences and similarities between habitats.

RESOURCES

Main teaching activity: Flip chart or board, clipboards and pencils for each group of three, a copy of photocopiable page 90 for each group (plus a few extra), a camera, a prepared display board (see Preparation, below), marker pen or chalk.
Group activities: 1. Drawing, painting and collage materials. **2.** Writing materials or access to a word processor.
Plenary: Pieces of grey or black net (optional).

Vocabulary

habitat, environment, Sun, shade, picture map, identify, specimen

PREPARATION

Visit the area you intend to use to make sure that there are different habitats and that they are safely accessible to the children. Stick large sheets of paper together to cover a display board.

BACKGROUND

At this stage it is important that the children begin to learn how to channel their curiosity, investigate in a more structured and systematic way, and begin to look for cause and effect. All schools are surrounded by different habitats, although some are obviously richer and more

diverse than others. You may already be lucky enough to have a wildlife area that you can use but, if not, a log pile takes up little space and can easily be created in a corner of the school field or playground. A small pond can be made in an old sink or baby bath. If you have a school field, try to arrange for one corner of the grass to be left uncut. You will quickly develop a habitat for grasses, insects and wild flowers.

If none of these options are open to you, churchyards or local cemeteries are often excellent wildlife havens. Local parks are also a possibility if they are not too well-manicured. A local allotment society may be willing to let you investigate a vacant plot, if you ensure that the children respect the cultivated areas. The children began to learn the names of some common plants and animals earlier in this unit. In this lesson they begin to widen their knowledge, but also begin to appreciate that certain plants and animals live in particular places and may be well adapted to particular conditions. At Year 2/Primary 3 it is quite acceptable for the children to use the common names for things – you may even have regional variations in the names of some plants or animals. The children may find some plants or animals that cannot easily be identified. Encourage them to classify these as 'flying insect', 'aquatic insect', 'climbing plant' and so on.

INTRODUCTION

Remind the children that in Year 1/Primary 2 they learned that a habitat is a small part of the environment and is home to particular plants and animals. They looked at a tree and some of its inhabitants.

MAIN TEACHING ACTIVITY

Tell the children that you are going to go outside into a particular area and look for different habitats. Ask if they can think of habitats (places) they might look for. (Sunny or shady places, wet or dry places, places with thick vegetation or very little cover, places with rotting vegetation, hedges, ditches, trees, walls, seashore and so on.) Make a list on the flip chart of some of the habitats you might find in your area.

Divide the class into groups of three or four and give each group a copy of the record sheet on photocopiable page 90 (on a clipboard) and explain to them how to fill it in. In the 'habitat' column they write a very brief description of the habitat (woodpile, corner of field under big tree, pond, and so on). Read through the other columns with them and say that they can just put a tick or a cross, or write something such as 'some shade' or 'very windy'. In the 'plants' and 'animals' columns the children should just note any obvious ones that they recognise. Tell them that you have some extra sheets if they run out of space.

Go outside to the chosen area and explore. As the children are working, take photographs of the habitats they are recording. Back in the classroom, gather the children around the prepared display board and, in a suitable place, mark a significant landmark such as a school wall or fence, a gate or a big tree. Ask the children to say where the habitats they looked at are in relation to this landmark and mark them on the display in order to create a rough map of the area. Don't worry about scale or accuracy, just make sure that the habitats are in roughly the right place.

GROUP ACTIVITIES

1. Ask each small group to do a painting or small collage that could be put on the picture map to illustrate a habitat. Some children might like to draw or paint pictures of other significant things and these could also be included on the map. Add any photographs that are available.
2. Ask the groups to write or word-process a short description of or poem about a habitat, using the information from their record sheets. Encourage the groups to choose different habitats (or choose for them) so that all are covered.

DIFFERENTIATION

1. All the children can contribute to this activity according to their abilities.
2. More able children should be encouraged to contribute more ideas to the group's writing.

ASSESSMENT

Use the work from Group activity 2 to assess the children's understanding. In the Plenary session, note those children who contribute sensibly to the discussion.

PLENARY

Look at the picture map you have created and discuss the features of each habitat. *Was it wet, dry, windy? Can you decide from which direction the Sun was shining? Which areas were in the shade?* (If you have some grey or black net you could, at this point, cut out pieces and stick these over the shady areas to represent the shade.)

OUTCOMES

● Can identify different habitats in the environment.
● Can describe some features of different habitats in the environment.

LINKS

Geography: creating simple maps.

LESSON 5

Objective	● To know some of the plants and animals in a named habitat.
Resources	Collecting equipment such as plastic bags, plastic pots, pooters, small soft paintbrushes, white trays, nets (pond or sweep), magnifiers; a stereo microscope (if available), clipboards, camera, reference materials.
Main activity	Look together at some of the equipment they are going to use and remind the children how to use it. Divide them into their groups from Lesson 4. Tell them not to share pooters and to decide within their groups who will be responsible for each piece of equipment to ensure that nothing is lost or left behind. Remind them to collect any specimens with great care, to make a note of familiar things on their clipboard rather than collecting unnecessary samples, and to pick only one flower and one leaf when there are plenty of plants. They should make a sketch or take a photograph of unusual things that can't be collected. Go out and spend time looking for living things in a particular habitat. Different groups could study different habitats within the same area (under the hedge, on the playing field, in the shade, in the log pile, or any others identified in Lesson 4). Add the lists of any plants and animals that are found to each area of the picture map or make separate group booklets to go with the display.
Differentiation	All the children should be able to take part in this activity.
Assessment	During the Plenary session note those children who can name some of the living things found in a particular habitat.
Plenary	Ask the groups to report back on what they found. Look at the lists. *Were any things common to every habitat?* (There may have been some grass in each one.) *Was there a habitat that had very different things in it?* (Perhaps a pond.)
Outcome	● Can identify some plants and animals found in a particular habitat.

LESSON 6

OBJECTIVES
● To make predictions about what might be found in a different habitat.
● To design a simple chart for collecting information.

RESOURCES
Main teaching activity: Reference materials, writing materials.
Group activities: 1. Paper, pencils, rulers. **2.** Reference materials, including CD-ROMs.

Vocabulary

habitat, specimen, example, prediction, conditions

BACKGROUND
The children studied one particular habitat in Lesson 4 and published their results in a class display. If it is not possible to go to a completely different location for this lesson, ask the children to study a different habitat within the same area. Even if the habitat has to be one that has been studied by a previous groups try to use a section further along the hedge or a different corner of the playing field.

Children need to begin to understand that, although habitats vary infinitely, some of the variations may be very subtle. (A habitat in light shade or sunlight.) Some species of plants and animals may occur in both.

INTRODUCTION
With the children gathered together, remind them of what they did in Lessons 4 and 5.

MAIN TEACHING ACTIVITY
Show the children the collection of appropriate reference books. Tell them that this time, before they go out to look at a different habitat, they are going to try to predict what they might find there. Ask the children to think about what they might find in a very wet area such as a pond. (Frogs, tadpoles, fish, water plants.) Take some suggestions and then ask one of the children to check on the display made in Lesson 4 to see if these are correct. Ask: *Where else might I look to find out what might live in this sort of habitat?* (Reference books or CD-ROMs.) *Can anyone find a book from the collection that might be helpful?*

Now suggest a different type of habitat, perhaps a damp, dark place. *What would you expect to find there?* (Woodlice or slugs but no flowers.) Again consult the display and find any suitable reference books. Continue in this way until you feel that the children understand. Ask the children to work in the same groups as in Lesson 4 and allocate each group a 'new' habit to look at. Ask them to think about the kinds of plants and animals they might find there and make a list of their predictions. Explain that it is not always necessary for them to identify particular species. They may predict 'no flowers' or 'some flowers', but should be able to predict 'frog' or 'tadpole' in a pond habitat.

Suggest that they use the display made in Lesson 4 or any of the reference materials available. You can differentiate by giving less able children a similar habitat to the one they looked at previously, while more able children could look at something very different.

GROUP ACTIVITIES

1. Working in their groups, or individually, ask the children to design a simple chart that they can take out with them to test their predictions. It should list the animals and plants that they think they will find, with a column to say whether they found them or not.
2. Tell the children to check relevant reference materials to familiarise themselves with the new plants and animals they have predicted they might find. This will enable them to recognise them if they do find them.

DIFFERENTIATION

1. Some children may find it easier to try out ideas on a board or flip chart before committing these to paper. Less able children may make only a few predictions and limit themselves to more obvious things.
2. Some children may prefer to do simple drawings or make a few notes to help them remember particular features.

ASSESSMENT

Use the work to assess their ability to design simple charts and make sensible predictions.

PLENARY

Ask the children to show their charts and say how they plan to use them. Look at the lists of creatures they have predicted that they may find and ask the rest of the class if they agree or have any other suggestions. Ask the children why they have predicted finding certain things. (The type of habitat: it is damp and dark so we might find woodlice and slugs; it is hot and dry with long grass so there might be grasshoppers.)

OUTCOMES

- Can use previously gathered information to make predictions.
- Can design a simple chart.

LINKS

Maths: designing simple charts.

LESSON 7

Objective	● To investigate a different habitat, testing predictions made.	
Resources	Collecting equipment such as plastic bags, plastic pots, pooters, small soft paintbrushes, white trays, nets (pond or sweep); magnifiers, a stereo microscope (if available), a camera, reference materials, the children's own charts on clipboards.	
Main activity	Visit the 'new' habitat from Lesson 6 and look for plants and animals. The children should check finds against those they predicted, making a note of any unexpected finds. Collect some samples carefully and take these back to the classroom to look at in more detail, using magnifiers or a stereo microscope if you have one.	
Differentiation	Less able children may look for fewer and more obvious things. They may prefer to work as a group, with one member marking up a group chart.	
Assessment	During the Main teaching activity, note which children are able to use their charts to check their predictions. In the Plenary session ask children to describe differences between the two habitats they have looked at.	
Plenary	Gather the children together and ask which groups found the things they had predicted they would. *Did any group find everything they predicted? Did any group find something totally unexpected?* Ask the children what they based their predictions on. *How did the new habitat differ from the last one you studied?*	
Outcomes	● Can make observations to test predictions. ● Can describe how two habitats differ.	

LESSON 8

OBJECTIVE
● To know that living things in a habitat depend on each other.

RESOURCES

Main teaching activity: Depending on the area you are visiting, you may find extra adult help useful.
Group activities: 1. Drawing and painting materials, fine string, white cotton thread, black tissue, black paint, small egg boxes, pipe-cleaners, collage materials including feathers, green paper, old socks or tights, polystyrene packing chips, rope or twine, scissors, adhesive. **2.** A copy of photocopiable page 91 for each child, simple reference books.

PREPARATION

For Group activity 2 you may wish to make the spider's web before the lesson if you think this is beyond the children's capability.

Vocabulary
depend, rely, survival, food, shelter, support

BACKGROUND

Things usually live in a particular habitat because the climatic conditions suit them or because that is where they find their food source. The climate and soil conditions often govern the type of plants that grow in a particular area and they, in turn, attract other plants and animals looking for food and shelter. Climbing plants depend on their more rigid neighbours for support as they grow. Some animals depend on the plants for food, while others depend on those that have eaten the plants. They, in their turn, may be eaten by larger animals, and so on, right up the food chain.

At this stage children do not need to know about food chains, but they need to know some of the ways in which living organisms depend on each other. The dependency between plants and animals is often a two-way process. Plants provide food for animals but, in return, they may rely upon the animals to disperse their seeds or carry their pollen from one flower to the next. In some cases animal droppings not only help to spread the seed but also provide a rich seed bed in which the new plants can grow.

INTRODUCTION

Remind the children about the work they did in Year 1/Primary 2 when they looked at the things living in a tree and how they depended on each other, or the tree, for their food and shelter.

MAIN TEACHING ACTIVITY

Working with the whole class, ask the children to think about their own families. Their home is their habitat and the members of most families depend upon each other. They depend on Mum or Dad to provide food and shelter. Mum or Dad may rely on them to play with their little brothers or sisters while they are busy. The children may even rely on an older brother or sister to take them to and from school. *Are there any other ways in which the people (the family) living in that particular habitat rely on each other?* (You may have to tread carefully here with regard to the family backgrounds of some of the children.)

Ask the children to think of some of the things that they found when they were looking at particular habitats in the last few lessons. *Can you think of any ways in which the plants or animals there depended on each other? Do you think any of the animals eat any parts of the plants you found there? Do any of the animals eat each other? Might the plants be used for nests, for bedding, or for supporting a web?*

Go outside to look for evidence of plants or animals depending on each other. Look for holes in leaves or ragged edges that show where they have been eaten. Look for twigs supporting spiders' webs or leaves that have little clusters of eggs on the underside. *Are there any flies trapped in the webs?* You may find empty, broken snail shells left by thrushes, or pine-cones nibbled to the core by squirrels. You may find some ivy or honeysuckle which is using a tree to support its upward climb. *Can you see bees or other insects visiting flowers?* The plants provide nectar, but in return depend on the insects to carry pollen from one flower to another. Some relationships may not be so beneficial. Aphids and other such insects may damage plants by sucking their sap or introducing disease, but the aphids also provide a food source for many small birds, such as blue-tits, and ants harvest the sticky honeydew they secrete.

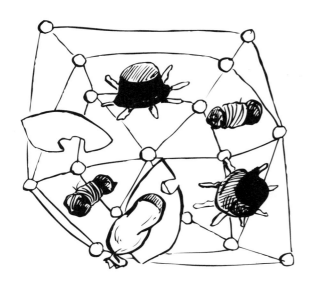

GROUP ACTIVITIES

1. Make a habitat display. In one corner of the room, or on a display board, make a large spider's web from fine string. Make spiders from balls of black tissue, or small egg boxes painted black, with pipe-cleaner legs. Wrap balls of black tissue in white cotton thread to represent captured flies. Cut out giant leaves from green paper and cut holes in the middle or from the edge as if they have been eaten. Stuff old (but clean!) tights or socks to make caterpillars and put these on the leaves. Attach leaves to rope or twine to make a climbing plant. Make a collage picture of a bird (using feathers) eating the caterpillars. Paint some big flowers, using pipe cleaners with pieces of packing material on the ends for the stamens, then make a bee to visit the flower. Be sure to represent any particular evidence you found on the walk. Add labels to show the interdependence of the plants and animals. (For example, the spider needs the tree from which to hang its web.)

2. Give each child a copy of photocopiable page 91 and ask them to complete it using drawings to finish the sentences. The answers are: 1. A (bee) takes pollen from flower to (flower); 2. A spider eats up the (insects); 3. A (squirrel) in the tree eats the berries and scatters the (seeds); 4. A (caterpillar) eats holes in the leaves; 5. An aphid gets honeydew from (an aphid).

DIFFERENTIATION

1. All the children can contribute to this activity. Some children may be able to help make labels.
2. Some children may need to be reminded of what they have seen before they complete the photocopiable sheet. Others may need reference books to check answers they are unsure of.

ASSESSMENT

Use the photocopiable sheet from Group activity 2 to assess the children's understanding. Note those children who contribute new ideas in the Plenary session.

PLENARY

Use the habitat picture to talk about the different relationships between the plants and animals. Ask the children if they can think of any others that might have gone on the display. (Ants and aphids, climbing plants and so on. This will depend on what you have included in your display.)

OUTCOME

● Can give examples of how living things depend on each other in a habitat.

LINKS

Art: models and collage.

LESSON 9

OBJECTIVE

● To know that some animals use camouflage to help them survive in a habitat.

Vocabulary

camouflage, hide, hunt, prey, predator, disguise, protect

RESOURCES

Main teaching activity: Pictures of camouflaged animals (leopards, tigers, stick insects, caterpillars, frogs, toads); camouflage clothing or pictures of soldiers or tanks in camouflage.
Group activities: 1. Thick paper, cardboard tubes, paint, adhesive. **2.** Writing materials.

BACKGROUND

Animals adopt camouflage for various reasons. In some cases it allows them to merge with their surroundings and hide from predators. In other cases a predator may use camouflage to gain an advantage over its prey. All kinds of animals use it – leopards become almost invisible in dappled shade; plaice are mottled to look like the seabed, and stick insects and caterpillars can be indistinguishable from the twigs they are resting on. Most animals are camouflaged to match the surroundings in which they are usually found.

Some animals, like chameleons or people, can change their colouring (or clothing) to match whatever surroundings they happen to be in. All of the above are examples of camouflage by colouring but some animals, such as the stick insect, are also camouflaged by their shape.

INTRODUCTION

Show the children the camouflage clothing or pictures of soldiers in camouflage. Ask: *Why do soldiers wear camouflage?*

MAIN TEACHING ACTIVITY

Many children will be able to tell you that soldiers wear camouflage so that they can't be seen, or so that they can move about without being seen. Look at the soldiers' clothing and talk about what it is like. *Why is it patterned like that?* (Random shapes merge with the light and shade better than regular angular shapes.) *Why have those colours been used?* (They blend with wooded landscapes.) *Would the same colours be used if the soldiers were in the desert or in snow?* (Desert camouflage is a mixture of sandy colours, and whites and greys are used in snowy areas.) Explain that people probably learned how to use camouflage from animals. Some animals need to hide from their enemies (predators), or sometimes they need to hide from other animals that they are hunting (prey). Look at some pictures of well-camouflaged animals. *Can you spot the animal? Why is it camouflaged? Is it hunting or being hunted?*

GROUP ACTIVITIES

1. Give each child a large sheet of thick paper and ask them to paint it in any pattern they choose (stripes, spots, random blobs, checks, and so on). Tell them to cover the whole page. Cut the paper in half and tell them to draw the shape of an animal, fish, bird or insect on the back of one of the pieces and then cut it out. Stick the animal on to a small card roll or small box and then stick this to the other half of the painted paper so that the camouflaged animal is mounted slightly away from the camouflaged background. *Which patterns act as the best camouflage?*
2. Choose an animal and ask children to do a piece of writing to say how camouflage helps it to survive in its habitat.

DIFFERENTIATION

1. Every child should be able to take part in this activity.
2. Some children might like to present their writing in the form of a poem. Less able children may find a word list helpful.

ASSESSMENT

Use the children's work from Group activity 2 to assess their understanding.

PLENARY

Look at the pictures made by the children in Group activity 1 and decide which sort of pattern makes the best camouflage. Ask some of the children to read out their writing or poems. Ask: *How does camouflage help animals to survive in a habitat?*

OUTCOME

● Can explain how camouflage helps animals to survive in a habitat.

LINKS

Literacy: writing poems.

LESSON 10

Objective	● To understand how camouflage works.
Resources	Garden netting, twigs and branches, hay or straw; four stage blocks or other large objects – one for each group (the Headteacher's car would be an interesting challenge). If you are in a 'brick' environment, you may wish to use old sheets that the children can paint appropriately.

Main activity	Take the children out on to the school field, by a hedge if possible. Divide them into four groups and give each group the task of camouflaging their object, using the netting and any other suitable materials they can find.
	    When they have finished, take them all some distance away and ask if they think the objects are well camouflaged. Invite another class to come and see if they can spot the objects.
	    If you have a military base nearby you may be able to persuade someone to come and show you some real camouflage netting.

Differentiation	All the children can take part in this activity.
Assessment	Observe the children as they carry out the task to see who has grasped the idea of making the object blend into the background. Note those children who give sensible answers in the Plenary session.
Plenary	Ask the children how camouflage works. *Why do some animals find it useful or even necessary?*
Outcome	● Can use camouflage to hide an object.

LESSON 11

OBJECTIVE
● To know that plants and animals change in appearance and behaviour with the seasons.

RESOURCES
Main teaching activity: Pictures of trees to act as a stimulus.
Group activities: 1. Thin card, writing and drawing materials, adhesive, sticky tape, scissors, rulers. **2.** Stiff paper or card, reference materials, writing and drawing materials.

PREPARATION
Make a 'tree slider' as an example to show the children in Group activity 1 (see diagram below).

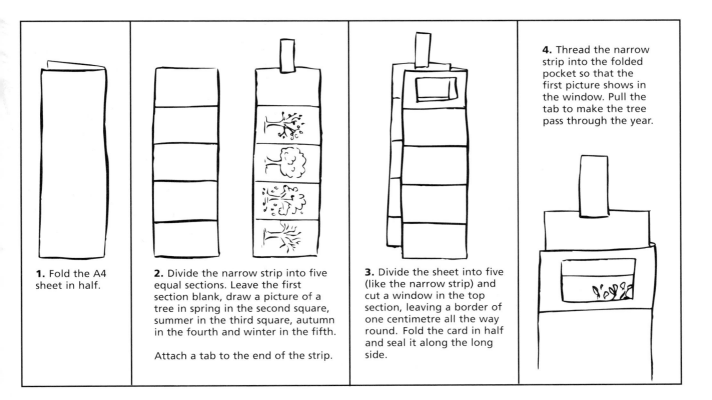

1. Fold the A4 sheet in half.

2. Divide the narrow strip into five equal sections. Leave the first section blank, draw a picture of a tree in spring in the second square, summer in the third square, autumn in the fourth and winter in the fifth.

Attach a tab to the end of the strip.

3. Divide the sheet into five (like the narrow strip) and cut a window in the top section, leaving a border of one centimetre all the way round. Fold the card in half and seal it along the long side.

4. Thread the narrow strip into the folded pocket so that the first picture shows in the window. Pull the tab to make the tree pass through the year.

BACKGROUND

The behaviour or appearance of many plants and animals is affected greatly by climate or day length. Most plants do not grow in the cold, dark days of winter so there are no tender shoots available for slugs, snails and insects to eat. Animals that depend on such things for food are therefore at risk. Some are able to migrate to a warmer climate and some hibernate. Others rely on fat that they have built up during summer and autumn and find what food they can during the winter. In plants the seasonal changes are marked by changes in appearance, while in animals changes in behaviour are most noticeable.

In spring we see new growth on plants, while birds sing their best songs and display their finest feathers in their efforts to find a mate. Many animals produce their young at this time to coincide with the new plant growth or the flush of insects that feed on it. Through the summer, plants continue to grow and animals rear their young, sometimes producing a second brood. Birds that migrated to warmer climes during the winter return to nest and raise their families away from the tropical heat.

Autumn produces a feeding frenzy, with many animals trying to build up their reserves for the leaner months ahead. Birds that prefer to keep warm depart after their short summer visit. The produce from fields and gardens is harvested and the plants, having done their work, die back. The leaves on deciduous trees change colour before falling, leaving the trees as skeletons for the winter. As the temperature drops and the hours of daylight shorten some animals, such as hedgehogs and frogs, find a safe spot in which to hibernate until spring returns. Others, such as squirrels, hide food stores that they can raid during the finer days of winter. Some animals that stay active through the winter may grow a thicker coat to combat the cold, shedding it again when it gets warmer. A few animals, such as the Arctic hare or the stoat, may actually change colour in order to blend in with the snow expected in their northern habitats.

INTRODUCTION

Remind the children of how, in Year 1/Primary 2, they looked at how plants and animals change through the seasons.

MAIN TEACHING ACTIVITY

Ask the children: *Can you tell me what a year in the life of a tree would be like?* (Buds appear in the spring and then the leaves and flowers come out. There are lots of green leaves in the summer and in the autumn the fruits ripen, the leaves change colour and fall off. In the winter it looks dead.)

When the children were looking at a tree in Year 1/Primary 2, they found lots of things living in it. How do they think the changes in the tree affect these creatures? Ask: *What happens to the tree in the spring?* (New shoots and blossom.) *What might like to eat the fresh new leaves?* (Insects such as caterpillars or leaf miners.) *What might visit the blossom looking for food?* (Insects, including bees.) Remind the children of Lesson 8. *Can you remember how the insects are helping the tree?* (They are helping to pollinate the flowers.) *What other animals might visit the tree in the spring?* (Birds, butterflies or moths.) *Why do they need the tree?* (Birds might build a nest in the branches or in a hole in the trunk, or they might just come to eat the insects feeding on the leaves. Butterflies or moths lay eggs under the leaves that provide a food source for the emerging caterpillars.) *What happens to the tree in the summer?* (It continues to grow and get bigger. The fruits start to grow and so do the insects, if they are not eaten first!) *What season comes next?* (Autumn.) *What happens then?* (The fruits ripen and the leaves change colour and fall off.) *Who eats the fruit?* (Birds, insects, squirrels; sometimes humans and other animals if the fruit falls to the ground.) *How does this help the tree?* (It can help to scatter the seed over a wider area.) *What happens next? What season will it be?* (It is winter and the tree becomes dormant.) *What do you think happens to all the things that were living in the tree?* (Many will die off in the cold but eggs laid in the autumn will remain over winter to hatch in the spring. Some creatures will burrow deep into the bark and hibernate. Birds will get food where they can. Squirrels will rely on their fat reserves and hidden food stores.) *Is this where the story of the tree stops?* (No, next it is spring and the story starts all over again.)

GROUP ACTIVITIES

1. Show the children how to make a simple slider and demonstrate how it works. The children may find it easier to create the window if they cut from the edge of the card, cut out the window and then mend the original slit with a small piece of adhesive tape.
Give each child a piece of thin A4 card and a second strip that is slightly narrower than the folded card (see instructions on the previous page).
2. Tell the children to choose a living thing, perhaps a hedgehog, and use reference materials or previous knowledge to make a zig-zag book about a year in its life. Ask them to include information on how it is affected by other animals or plants (lack of slugs and snails for food in the winter).

DIFFERENTIATION

1. All the children can try this activity, but some may need a little help with measuring, cutting and folding. Some children may be able to follow the diagram on page 83.
2. Children who need help with reading may work better with a more able partner. Encourage more able children to add more detail and information to their booklets. They may decide to present their work as a conventional booklet if this allows them more space.

ASSESSMENT

Use the children's work from Group activity 2 to assess their understanding.

PLENARY

Ask some children to demonstrate their tree sliders. Ask others to tell their 'Year in the life of…' stories. Talk about how things change through the year and how living things depend on each other.

OUTCOME

● Can describe how some animals and plants change through the seasons.

LINKS

Technology: making a slider (following instructions).

LESSON 12

OBJECTIVE

● To know ways in which the environment can be cared for.

RESOURCES

Group activities: 1. Writing materials, use of a computer. **2.** Writing and drawing materials, poster-sized paper.

Vocabulary

care, pollution, damage, conservation, destroy, save, wildlife, litter, hazard, risk, graffiti

BACKGROUND

Much of the damage done in the local environment is caused more by thoughtlessness than by deliberate malice. Graffiti is unsightly but may not cause any actual damage to wildlife (unless they are unfortunate enough to be caught in the spray). More damage is caused by people carelessly breaking branches, or dropping litter such as bottles, cans and plastic bags. These are real hazards for small creatures as they can find their way in but often cannot get out again. Broken glass can act as a magnifier and cause grass fires, as well as being a danger to the bare feet of larger animals, including human beings. Discarded fishing lines and nets are hazardous for water birds and fish. Since lead weights on fishing lines have been banned lead poisoning has become less of a hazard for swans.

INTRODUCTION

Ask the children if they know of any areas in the neighbourhood that are not cared for, or an area that is well cared for. (Some villages enter 'Best kept village' competitions and are very well-cared for. Some urban areas have 'clean-up' campaigns to improve the area.)

MAIN TEACHING ACTIVITY

Go back to visit one of the areas you have used previously in this unit. *Is there any graffiti?* Look for any damage to trees and bushes. *Are there any broken branches, or is litter stuck in the branches? Are there any uprooted plants? Are the paths trampled at the edges or are they overgrown?* If there is a pond or stream, ask: *Is it covered in oily scum or is it full of supermarket trolleys and other litter? Have people been riding bikes or motorcycles and churning up the ground? Is there any rubbish tipped in the hedge? Are any litter bins provided? Are they used and, if they are, are they emptied regularly?* Look for evidence that paths have been cleared or pavements mended; hedges or grass cut. *Can you find any other ways in which the area is being cared for?*

Back in the classroom discuss with the children what they have seen and how it might affect the wildlife living in the area. *What could happen to a damaged tree?* (Broken and damaged trees may die and no longer provide food or shelter for animals.) *Why are discarded cans, bottles and plastic bags dangerous for animals?* (Small creatures may get trapped, cows might eat them and die.) *Why do we need to keep streams and ponds fresh?* (Oily scum prevents oxygen entering the water and this can harm any life there. Chemicals can poison it. Trolleys tipped into the water may trap other rubbish that rots and poisons the water.)

GROUP ACTIVITIES

1. As individuals, ask children to write a newspaper report about the state of the area you visited. It may be quite negative if there is a lot of litter or damage, or it may be a very positive report if it is a well-kept area. Your local newspaper might be interested in printing some of these reports.
2. Write a set of rules for caring for the environment, such as: Always put litter in the bin. Don't break fences. Don't draw graffiti. Don't break tree branches. Keep to the paths. Don't pick wild flowers. Help plant trees. Treat wildlife with respect. Each child could make a poster to publicise one particular rule for a class display. A local shop may be interested in displaying some of these.

DIFFERENTIATION

1. Less able children may just list some of the things they saw. More able children could make some suggestions for improving the area (providing extra litter bins, emptying them more frequently, and so on).
2. Less able children could work together to make a group set of rules, but all the children should be able to make a poster.

ASSESSMENT

Use the children's written work to assess their knowledge and understanding.

PLENARY

Talk to the children about what they saw on their visit. Ask one or two to read their reports. Discuss with the children ways in which they can help to care for the environment. Do they all obey the rules they have listed?

OUTCOMES

- Can identify ways in which a habitat is damaged.
- Can explain how habitat damage affects things living there.
- Can suggest ways to care for the environment.

LINKS

Literacy: writing for a purpose (report).

LESSON 13

OBJECTIVE

- To know about caring for living things indoors.

RESOURCES

Main teaching activity: A small collection of plants to make a display in the classroom (try to include a rubber plant or something similar that needs dusting), a small watering can, a soft cloth for cleaning the leaves of larger plants, plant nutrient, paper and pencil.
Group activities: 1. Copies of commercial 'How to care for' booklets for pets; writing and drawing materials. **2.** Coleus seeds, compost, plant pots, newspaper, water, labels, plant nutrient, trays to stand pots in.

BACKGROUND

Even young children should learn that if we choose to own or keep another living thing then we must accept responsibility for it and take care of it. It is important that children realise that caring for a living thing is an ongoing responsibility and should not be taken lightly. Keeping animals in school requires a great deal of commitment and may not be possible for a number of

Vocabulary
care, depend, responsible, needs, injection, grooming, exercising, worming, vet, nutrient

reasons. Unless you are really committed, and have a good back-up system for weekends and holidays, it is best just to borrow a pet for short periods, as needed. If a pet cannot be cared for correctly then this will give all the wrong messages; you need to make clear that children should find out as much as possible about the needs of a particular animal or plant before they take on the responsibility of caring for it.

INTRODUCTION

Ask which children have pets at home and what they do to help look after them.

MAIN TEACHING ACTIVITY

Talk about how the children care for their pets at home. Do they help with feeding, grooming or exercising, or is it left to Mum or Dad? If you have a school pet, how is that cared for? Do they take turns to clean out the rabbit or the fish tank, or is it always left to one person? Talk about how important it is to take your turn with duties like these. If animals are in a cage they have no way of finding their own food and water and rely on their owners for their food, drink and well-being.

Look at the display of plants and ask the children how they would care for them. *What do they need?* (Water, light, warmth, but not too much of any.) *What about the plants with big broad leaves? What happens if they get dusty?* Explain that if they were outside in their normal habitat, the rain would clean the leaves. The leaves need to be clean to absorb the sunlight that the plants need to make their food and grow. Explain that when we are keeping plants indoors we need to help them keep clean by wiping the leaves with a damp cloth from time to time. They also need a little nutrient occasionally (be careful not to call it food). Talk about how the children can help to keep the display of plants looking fresh and healthy. Put the children in pairs and make up a rota so that everyone takes a turn to look after the plants. Make a list of the tasks involved.

GROUP ACTIVITIES

1. As individuals, design and write a simple instruction booklet for someone looking after a particular pet. Look at some commercially produced leaflets to see the sort of information that is important. Don't forget that caring may also include worming, getting the appropriate injections and perhaps even insurance.
2. Working in pairs, sow coleus seeds and care for the plants as they grow. Coleus seeds germinate well and produce plants that vary widely in colour and pattern. They do flower but are grown mostly for the colour of their leaves. The children could grow them to give as presents for some special occasion or to sell at a school fair. Sow one or two seeds in each small pot, or sow a number in a larger pot and separate them into individual small pots when the seedlings are big enough to move. They need careful handling to ensure that the delicate new shoots and roots are not damaged. Choose whichever method you think your children will cope best with. Grow the plants on, perhaps transferring them to even bigger pots as they grow.

DIFFERENTIATION

1. More able children may give more detail in their booklets. Less able children could work in a group to produce a group booklet, with each child doing one page.
2. All the children can take part in this activity.

ASSESSMENT

Use the children's work from Group activity 1 to assess their understanding. Observe children as they care for their coleus plants or the class display. Note those children who remember their tasks and those who need to be reminded.

PLENARY

Ask some children to read each other's instruction booklets and explain how to care for a pet. Look at the display of plants or the growing coleus plants and discuss how they have benefited from the care they have received.

OUTCOME

● Can describe how to look after living things in the classroom and at home.

LINKS

Literacy: writing for a purpose (booklets).

LESSON 13

OBJECTIVES

● To know that living things in a habitat depend on each other.
● To know the names of some of the plants and animals in the local environment.

RESOURCES

Assessment activities: 1. A copy of photocopiable page 92 for each child, writing materials.
2. A copy of photocopiable page 93 for each child, writing and drawing materials.

INTRODUCTION

Remind the children of some of the work they have done in this unit. Revise some of the vocabulary learned.

ASSESSMENT ACTIVITY 1

Give each child a copy of photocopiable page 92 and ask them to complete it. Check they understand what each creature is. Explain that they should write what the living thing in each question depends on in its habitat, and what that dependency is.

Answers
1. Bees – pollen and nectar.
2. Flowers – pollinate.
3. Ladybirds – food.
4. Birds – shelter or food (accept either or both, or an answer such as 'to nest in').
5. Plants – spread their seeds.
6. Snails, slugs and caterpillars – plants.
7. Snails, caterpillars and slugs – birds or animals (accept either or both).
8. Spiders – insects.
9. Owls – food (accept mice, voles, and so on).
10. Plants and animals – habitat.

Looking for levels
Most children will be able to answer questions 2, 3, 4, 6, 7, 8, and 9. More able children should answer all the questions correctly. They may be more specific in their answers, for example, listing such things as mice, voles and shrews in question 9. Less able children may have difficulty with questions 1, 5 and 10. They may answer 'food' to several questions, which may show a lack of understanding.

ASSESSMENT ACTIVITY 2

Give each child a copy of page 93 and ask them to complete it by drawing and naming five plants and five animals they would find in the local environment.

Answers
It is impossible to give a definitive answer list as this will depend on the type of environment you have studied. You need to base your marking on the types of plants and animals you found during the lessons on the environment.

Looking for levels
Most children will be able to correctly name four out of five in each group. More able children will name all five (and some may add more). Less able children will name fewer and may be able to draw things but not name them. They may need to explain their drawings to you.

Name

Flower jigsaw

Cut out the pieces and stick them together to make three different flowers.

Name

Habitat record sheet

Habitat	wet	dry	sunny	shady	windy	shelter	plants	animals
1.								
2.								
3.								
4.								

Picture sentences

Draw pictures in the boxes to complete each sentence.

A  takes pollen from  to

A  eats up the

A in the tree eats the  and scatters the

A eats holes in the

An  gets honeydew from

Name

UNIT 3   THE ENVIRONMENT

Life in habitats

1. Bees need the flowers for _____ and _____.

2. Flowers need bees and other insects to _____ them.

3. Ladybirds need aphids for their _____.

4. Birds need trees and hedgerows for _____.

5. Some plants rely on birds to _____.

6. Snails, slugs and caterpillars need _____ to eat.

7. Snails, caterpillars and slugs may be eaten by _____.

8. Spiders need to catch _____ in their webs for food.

9. Owls hunt for _____ at night.

10. Plants and animals in a _____ rely on each other.

Name

Life in habitats

Draw pictures and write the names of five plants you would find in your local environment.

Draw pictures and write the names of five animals you would find in your local environment.

Materials and change

ORGANISATION (14 LESSONS)

	OBJECTIVES	MAIN ACTIVITY	GROUP ACTIVITIES	PLENARY	OUTCOMES
LESSON 1	● To know that there is a range of materials with different characteristics. ● To know that materials can be put to different uses.	Review Y1/P2 work on materials and their properties. Group materials and give reasons. Give examples of the uses of some materials.	Identify the properties and uses of some common materials. Investigate rigidity and flexibility by weaving with different 'threads'.	Group materials according to properties.	● Can identify the properties of materials. ● Can use the properties to group materials. ● Can distinguish between an object and the material it is made from.
LESSON 2	● To know that fabrics are made from different materials.	Identify the materials that some fabrics are made from and consider some of their simple properties.		Name natural fabrics and link them to their sources.	● Can name a range of materials that fabrics are made from. ● Can link some fabrics to their simple properties. ● Can say that natural fabrics come from a plant or an animal and that synthetic fabrics are manufactured.
LESSON 3	● To know about the everyday uses of some materials.	Identify materials in and around the classroom. Note some of the uses and properties of certain materials.	Prepare to present findings to the rest of the class. Construct a block graph to show the frequency of use of materials.	Present findings.	● Can identify common materials and note the frequency of their use. ● Can explain why a material is used for a particular task.
LESSON 4	● To know that some materials occur naturally.	Look at natural materials and link these to where they occur.	Sort materials from living and non-living sources. Understand what needs to be done to natural materials before we can use them.	Identify materials and relate them to their source.	● Can name some naturally occurring materials. ● Can distinguish between materials that come from living and non-living sources. ● Can describe how some materials are treated before they are used.
LESSON 5	● To know that some materials are not natural but are manufactured.	Look at plastics, metal alloys, paper and glass.	Find out how a material is made. Make a zig-zag book. Make a papier mâché saucer or bowl.	Discuss manufactured materials.	● Can name some manufactured materials. ● Can describe how some manufactured materials are made.
LESSON 6	● To know how the application of forces can change the shape of some materials. ● To be able to carry out a simple investigation with help.	Bending, stretching, squashing and twisting materials. Investigate elastic bands.	Investigate different widths of elastic. Make pipe-cleaner people.	Discuss results.	● Can identify materials that can be altered in shape by the application of forces. ● Can distinguish between materials which are permanently deformed and those that regain their shape.
LESSON 7	● To know that materials often change when they are heated.	Study cooked and uncooked food. Bake cakes.	Make clay thumb pots. Fire these if a kiln is available. Make toast.	Examine the uncooked cake mixture.	● Can describe how some materials change when they are heated. ● Can explain how heating can make a material more useful.
LESSON 8	● To know that materials often change when they are heated.	Make popcorn.		Look at the cooked and uncooked corn.	● Can describe how some materials change when they are heated.
LESSON 9	● To know that water turns to steam when it is heated, but the steam turns back to water when it is cooled.	Boil water in a kettle to show water forming on a cold surface.		Discuss what happens when water is heated and when steam cools.	● Can describe what happens when water is heated. ● Can describe what happens when steam is cooled.

ORGANISATION (14 LESSONS)

	OBJECTIVES	MAIN ACTIVITY	GROUP ACTIVITIES	PLENARY	OUTCOMES
LESSON 10	● To know that many materials change when they are cooled.	Observe the effects of freezing on water.	Make jelly. Make ice-lollies.	Examine and discuss the ice.	● Can describe how some materials change when they are cooled.
LESSON 11	● To know that some materials melt and change when they are heated.	Observe ice as it melts.	Candle observation. Make melted chocolate cereal cakes.	Discuss the ice, the candles and the melted chocolate.	● Can describe how some materials change as they melt. ● Can describe how some materials change when they are heated.
LESSON 12	● To know that ice will melt at different rates in different temperatures. ● To be able to plan and carry out a fair test with help.	Investigate the best place for keeping ice frozen for a long time.	Suck ice to see if it melts more quickly. Find out what ice is used for.	Look at the results and discuss uses for ice.	● Know that the warmer the environment, the quicker ice melts. ● Can plan and carry out a fair test with help.
LESSON 13	● To know that heat is a form of energy and that it may be supplied by several sources.	Look at the uses of heat.	Identify appliances that do and don't use heat. Identify what fuel is used to provide the heat.	Discuss sources of heat energy.	● Know that heat is a form of energy. ● Know about different sources of heat energy. ● Can recognise different applications of heat in everyday life.

	OBJECTIVES	ACTIVITY 1	ACTIVITY 2
ASSESSMENT 14	● To know about the everyday uses of some materials. ● To know that materials often change when they are heated. ● To know that many materials change when they are cooled.	Record the uses of different materials.	Complete sentences about the effects of heating and cooling.

LESSON 1

OBJECTIVES
● To know that there is a range of materials with different characteristics.
● To know that materials can be put to different uses.

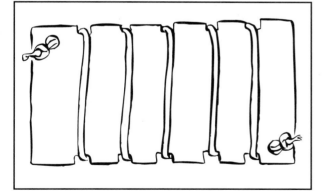

RESOURCES

Main teaching activity: Plasticine, bricks, tiles, stone; a selection of objects made from: wood, rock, metal, elastic, paper, plastic (rigid, sheet and flexible) and glass. Beware of the dangers of broken glass and do not allow the children to handle the glass object you choose. Try to find something that is not easily broken (like a heavy glass bowl).
Group activities: 1. A copy of photocopiable page 115 for each child, writing and drawing materials. **2.** A 'comb' card for each child (see diagram), string, scissors, strips of fabric of different weights, lolly sticks, plastic cutlery, plastic and paper drinking straws, lengths of dowel, twigs, feathers, and other flexible materials.

Vocabulary

materials, properties, fabric, strong, transparent, opaque, flexible, rigid, elastic, waterproof, attributes

BACKGROUND

At this stage, children should be able to identify and name a range of common materials and their properties and link these to the objects that they are made into (see Resources and Vocabulary, above). They should also be developing an understanding that many materials have more than one useful property. Wood is used for its strength, its insulating properties and because it is relatively easy to cut and shape. Metal is strong, it can be shaped and moulded and conducts electricity. This will lead to an understanding that a material may be chosen for a particular object primarily for one property, and for another object because of a different property. Make sure that the children realise that the term 'material' does not just mean fabric. Many modern synthetic materials are very convincing and it may be difficult for children to sort these from the real thing.

INTRODUCTION

Remind all the children of the work they did in Year 1/Primary 2 on materials and their properties. *Can anyone tell me some of the things we learned about materials and the reasons why they are used to make certain things?*

MAIN TEACHING ACTIVITY

Show the children the collection of objects. Lift them up one by one and ask them to say what the object is and what it is made from. Choose one of the objects, such as a metal dinner knife, and show it to the children again. *Why is the knife made from metal? Who can tell me what it is about metal that makes a good knife?* (It is hard and can be shaped and sharpened so that it will cut.) Repeat this with another object, such as the glass bowl. (Glass is good for bowls because it is transparent – if you have made a beautiful fruit salad you can see the lovely colours through the bowl – it is waterproof, it can be shaped when it is heated.) Stress that these are some of the properties of metal and glass that make them suitable to be made into particular objects. *Would a knife made of paper be useful, or a fabric bowl?*

Go through the other objects in the same way, choosing different children to come and hold up an object. Ask them to tell you some of the simple properties of the material from which the object is made. Each time, invite the rest of the class to add to the list if they can. After each object has been discussed it can be grouped with other objects that share one or more of the same properties. For example, wood and metal could be grouped together if the main property chosen for both was 'hard'. When all the objects have been considered, look at them again with the children and ask if they could regroup any of them according to other properties.

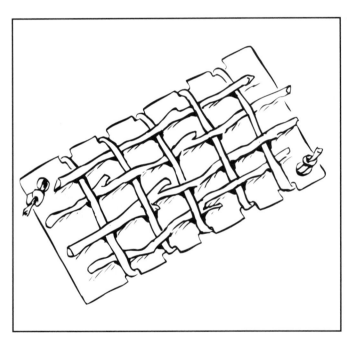

GROUP ACTIVITIES

1. Give each child a copy of photocopiable page 115 and ask them to complete the sheet. Remind the children of some of the properties of materials identified in the Main teaching activity and ask them to think of as many different uses for each material as they can.
2. As individuals, the children can investigate rigidity and flexibility by weaving with different 'threads': fabric, ribbon, dowel, lolly sticks, twigs, plastic cutlery, feathers and so on. Encourage the children to use the appropriate vocabulary as they are working. Point out that, although most of these are flexible, some materials are more flexible than others – thin twigs and ribbon are more flexible than lolly sticks.

Give each child a comb card and a length of string. Ask them to tie a knot in one end of the string and thread it through one of the holes in the card. Wrap the string around the card to form the warp for weaving. Thread the string through the other hole and tie a knot to secure it. Make sure the string is fairly taut so that the things the children use for weaving do not fall out (see diagram, left).

DIFFERENTIATION

1. Some children will need help to link the uses of the materials to the properties identified. You may wish to put a list of possible properties on a flip chart from which the children can choose.
2. All the children can take part in this activity at their own level.

ASSESSMENT

Use the children's work from Group activity 1 to assess the level of their understanding. During the Plenary session, note those children who give correct answers to your questions and contribute well to the discussion.

PLENARY

Shuffle the collections of materials and ask the children to group them again, giving their reasons (properties of the materials) for their choice. Tell the children that the objects may not end up in the same groups as they were in before but, as long as they are grouped according to a common property, this does not matter. Look at some of the children's work and discuss the uses of the materials they have identified. Are the uses sensible, given the properties of the materials involved?

OUTCOMES
- Can identify the properties of materials.
- Can use the properties to group materials.
- Can distinguish between an object and the material it is made from.

LINKS

Art: weaving.
Maths: sorting.

LESSON 2

Objective	● To know that fabrics are made from different materials.
Resources	A range of fabrics such as: wool, cotton, linen, silk, and synthetics such as nylon; a set of labels to attach to the fabrics; if possible, a length of the various threads to go with the fabrics (these can usually be obtained from knitting or craft shops); examples of raw wool, cotton and silk; pictures of sheep being shorn, cotton fields, silkworms and factories making synthetic fabric (optional).
Main activity	Show all the children the fabrics and tell them the materials that they are made from. Match the fabrics to their appropriate threads. Tell the children that some of the fabrics are made from natural materials and some are made from manufactured materials. Introduce the word 'synthetic' and explain to the children that this word is used for fabrics that are not made from natural materials. Ask: *Can anyone think of any animal or plant that we might get natural thread or yarn from?* (Sheep, cotton.) Attach labels to the natural wool and cotton fabrics. Carry on in this way until all the natural fabrics have been labelled, telling the children about each plant or animal that the fabric comes from. Show the children the synthetic fabrics and label these, telling them that these are made from threads or yarn that come from oil, and are manufactured in a factory. Talk to the children about some of the simple properties of the fabrics. Wool keeps us warm, cotton is cool, silk can be made to be warm or cool depending on the thickness of the thread. Natural fabrics are more comfortable, especially in hot weather. Synthetic fabrics are tough, easy to wash and last a long time. It is not necessary for the children to be able to identify specific pieces of fabric but they should know that fabrics can be made from both natural and synthetic materials. As you work through the fabrics, match them to the pictures if you have them.
Differentiation	All the children can take part in this activity.
Assessment	During the Plenary session note those children who are able to answer the questions and who show an understanding of the difference between natural and manufactured fabrics.
Plenary	Ask the children if they can name some of the natural fabrics and link them to the animal or plant that they come from. *Who can explain what a synthetic fabric is? Where do they come from?*
Outcomes	● Can name a range of materials that fabrics are made from. ● Can link some fabrics to their simple properties. ● Can say that natural fabrics come from a plant or an animal and that synthetic fabrics are manufactured.

LESSON 3

OBJECTIVE
- To know about the everyday uses of some materials.

RESOURCES

Main teaching activity: The classroom and indoor environment of the school, clipboards, writing materials.
Group activities: 1. Writing and drawing materials, OHP and transparencies, OHP pens, any other resources requested by the children. **2.** 1cm squared paper for constructing a block graph, writing and colouring materials.

PREPARATION

Head a sheet of paper for each group of four with the name of the material they are to look for (see Vocabulary).

BACKGROUND

The surface finish may confuse some children when they try to identify materials – plastic is used to coat metals, for example, and high-gloss paint may hide wood or metal. The children may need help to distinguish this finish from the material from which an object is made.

Groups looking for uses of plastics should also be made aware that sometimes it is only the surface finish of objects that is made of plastic. Plastics can also be made to mimic many other more traditional materials. Tabletops that look like wood may actually be made of plastic, and pipes, windows and doors are now often made from plastic. Modern buildings are likely to have a very high plastic content.

INTRODUCTION

Remind all the children about the work they did in Year 1/Primary 2 and how they identified some materials inside and outside the school. Ask: *What do we mean by 'materials'?* Tell the children that they are going to go on another walk to look at materials in a different way.

MAIN TEACHING ACTIVITY

Organise the children into groups of four. Give each group a sheet of paper headed with the material they are to look for. Tell them that they are going to look around the classroom and school and focus on a particular material, noting as many different uses as they can. At the end of the lesson they are going to report to the rest of the class not only how many different uses of their material they found, but also say what properties made it the right material for those jobs. They are to count each use only once – don't count every window in the school!

Point out that they need to keep their sheet clean and tidy because other groups will be using it in another activity. (See Group activity 2, below). Choose the materials you allocate to the groups carefully to ensure a range of uses. (Glass, in the school environment, may not yield as many uses as other materials. Stone may be more appropriate in an older school than in a very modern building. If you do choose glass, as it is an important everyday material, you may wish to give that group two materials to survey, such as glass and stone.) Explain that each time they see a different use of their material they must note what it is. Walk around the classroom and school with the children as they list all the uses of their material. Each time they find their material, encourage them to discuss what property or properties made it useful for that particular purpose. (for example, wood for doors because it is strong and can be shaped easily, but is not too heavy to open and close as a metal door might be.) Back in the classroom, gather the children together and discuss some of the uses and properties of the materials.

GROUP ACTIVITIES

1. Give the groups time to prepare their presentations. Remind them that they are not only going to tell the class what uses they found for their material but for which property or properties they think it was chosen. The children could decide for themselves how they are going to present their work. (Pictures, words, OHP presentation, and so on.)
2. Organise the children into the same groups as they were in for the Main teaching activity and give each group a photocopy of all the groups' sheets. Ask the groups to count the number of different ways each material was used, and to construct a block graph to show the frequency of use of each material.

DIFFERENTIATION

1. All the children can contribute according to their ability.
2. Less able children may need help to relate the number of uses of a material to constructing a block graph.

ASSESSMENT

Observe the children as they prepare their presentations and use their work to assess the level of their understanding. During the Plenary session, note those children who report back effectively and are able to link the use of a particular material to its properties.

PLENARY

Ask each group to give their presentation to the whole class. Discuss the block graphs the children have made and identify such things as the most and least commonly used materials.

OUTCOMES

● Can identify common materials and note the frequency of their use.
● Can explain why a material is used for a particular task.

LINKS

Maths: graphs.

LESSON 4

OBJECTIVE

● To know that some materials occur naturally.

RESOURCES

Main teaching activity: Materials such as wood, stone, wool, cotton, linen, silk, sand, water, sponge, clay, shell, cork, rubber, coal, metal (gold, silver, copper, tin); labels of the names of each material; pictures of a woodland, sheep, cotton fields, a quarry, a river, a coral reef with sponges and shells, a gold-, tin-, or coal-mine; two or three artefacts made from some of the materials collected (a woollen jumper, shell jewellery, cork mats and so on).
Group activities: 1. A small collection of materials from living and non-living sources for each group (such as woollen, cotton, or silk yarn, natural sponge, cork, wood, shell, clay, stone, sand, metal); writing and drawing materials. **2.** A copy of photocopiable page 116 for each child, writing materials, reference materials.

Vocabulary

material, natural, manufactured, occurring, source

BACKGROUND

Children, at this stage, should recognise that some materials occur naturally, while others are manufactured. A distinction needs to be made between manufactured materials such as plastics, that are completely new materials made from another raw material (oil), and natural materials that are sometimes shaped in an industrial or craft process.

Most natural materials can be shaped. Wood can be sawn into shapes in a factory and made into doors, window frames or furniture. Wood can also be carved into sculptures, or artefacts for domestic use. Stone can be cut and finished in a factory into uniform blocks for building or paving, but it can also be sculpted, carved and polished by an individual craftsman. In neither case has the material been through the profound manufacturing process necessary to make plastic out of oil, or glass out of silica. All materials originate from substances occurring naturally on the planet, although children do not need to know this at this stage. Their concept of the difference between natural and manufactured needs to be well-established first.

INTRODUCTION

Gather all the children around you and remind them that they talked about natural and manufactured materials, in terms of fabrics, in Lesson 2. Tell them that you are now going to think about some other materials that occur naturally.

MAIN TEACHING ACTIVITY

Show the children the collection of natural materials one by one, asking the children to identify them if they can. Help them with any names they don't know or materials they don't recognise. Label each material as it is identified.

Tell the children that each of these materials is natural, rather than manufactured. *Can anyone tell us what those words mean, and the difference between a natural material and one that has been manufactured?*

Now show the children the pictures of where the materials occur and ask them to link the two. Start with some fairly easy ones (sheep to link with the wool and woodland to link with the

wood). Go through all the location pictures, asking the children to link them to the appropriate material. Help them if they have difficulty.

Talk about where the materials come from. Some children may not be familiar with metal or coal mines. They may not know that cork comes from the bark of cork oaks, or that natural sponges are the skeletons of sea creatures. Discuss the uses of the materials and talk about the fact that, although they are sometimes shaped in a factory or by a craftsperson, they don't have to be 'made' in the same way as materials such as plastic. Wool can be knitted into jumpers or warm hats, shell is sometimes used in jewellery, and wood can be shaped to make spoons or bowls. Show the children the artefacts and put them together with the sample of material from which they are made. Say: *Can anyone see any material that we can use straight away in its natural state without having to do anything to it?* (The sponge, coal and sand.)

GROUP ACTIVITIES

1. Remind all the children that they learned about things that are living and not living in Year 1/Primary 2, and ask them what 'living' and 'not living' mean. Tell them that they are going to sort out materials that come from living things from those that come from non-living sources. Put the children into groups of three or four and give each group a collection of materials. (See Resources.) Explain that you want them to sort the materials into two sets: one where the material comes from a living thing and one where it doesn't. Each child can then choose a material from the 'living' set and draw a picture of where it originates (under the sea, a field of sheep, a woodland and so on).
2. Give each child a copy of photocopiable page 116. Ask the children to complete the sheet by saying which material we get from the various sources and writing about what has to be done to the material before we can use it. The first one is filled in to help them. Remind the children that they can use the reference materials if they need to.

DIFFERENTIATION

1. Some children will need help to distinguish materials from living and non-living sources.
2. Less able children may have to tell you what has been done to the materials rather than write about this.

ASSESSMENT

Use the children's work to assess what they have learned. If less able children explain to you verbally rather than in writing, note whether their explanations are correct.

PLENARY

Go through the collection of materials again, asking the children to identify them and relate them to their sources. Show and read out some of the children's work to reinforce the learning.

OUTCOMES

- Can name some naturally occurring materials.
- Can distinguish between materials that come from living and non-living sources.
- Can describe how some materials are treated before they are used.

LESSON 5

OBJECTIVE
- To know that some materials are not natural but are manufactured.

RESOURCES

Main teaching activity: Glass items, including a tumbler (but don't let the children handle glass objects that are likely to break); as wide a range of plastics as possible (including a transparent plastic tumbler and a plastic sponge); different papers, concrete, metal alloys such as steel or brass; the natural sponge from the last lesson; the fabrics from Lesson 2; pictures of factories, steel works, oil refineries and so on; labels for the sets of materials (plastic, glass, metal alloys, paper, concrete, and so on).

Group activities: 1. Reference materials and CD-ROMs (access to the Internet could also prove useful – searching for terms such as 'paper manufacturing' provides a wealth of useful material), writing materials; A5 card for the zig-zag books. **2.** Newspaper and cellulose paste (not wallpaper paste which contains fungicide) for papier mâché, stirrers (wooden spoons or lengths of dowel, for example), 'formers', such as saucers or small bowls, cling film, paint, adhesive.

> ### Vocabulary
> plastics, paper, pulp, glass, concrete, manufactured, made, raw material, alloy

BACKGROUND

It could be argued that every material on Earth is natural because even materials that we consider to be manufactured come originally from rock or fossil fuel (oil). The distinction we make between made or manufactured and natural relates to the fact that some materials, such as plastics, metal alloys and glass, have to go through a profound manufacturing process, where chemicals are often mixed together in order to create the materials that we use.

Natural materials are sometimes shaped into artefacts and the line between the two is sometimes difficult to draw. Raw clay can be used and shaped straight from the ground, but needs the firing process to make permanent clay artefacts. Glass on the other hand, except for the naturally occurring volcanic glass called obsidian, goes through a profound manufacturing process. Sands (silica) are mixed with differing amounts of other chemicals such as lead, potassium and barium to achieve the desired result in making a range of different types of glass that we use every day.

Unlike alloys, which are a carefully controlled mixture of different metals combined for their various properties, natural metals have usually only to be extracted from the ore and shaped by heat into the desired object. Plastics are manufactured from crude oil (a fossil fuel). Paper (the type that is made from wood) is made by boiling wood chips with chemicals to extract the pulp fibre. The pulp is rinsed to remove impurities and bleached. The pulp is then extracted from the water, more chemicals are added to it and it is pounded to make the paper strong. If you know of any parents who work in a manufacturing industry it might be a good idea to invite them in to talk to the children about what they do.

INTRODUCTION

With all the children around you, look again at the collection of materials used in the Main teaching activity Lesson 4. Ask: *What is it about all these materials that is the same?* (They are all natural and have not been manufactured from other raw materials. Many have been shaped so that we can use them but some, like the natural sponge, can be used just as they are.)

MAIN TEACHING ACTIVITY

Look at the new collection of materials. *Can anyone think why these materials are different from the ones we looked at in the last lesson?* Hold up the objects one by one and ask the children to identify the material that each one is made from. Discuss, in simple terms, what the material originates from and how it is made. (See Background.)

Show the children the pictures of factories, chemical and steel works and link them to the materials in the collection. This would be a good opportunity for a parent in industry (if you have one) to talk to the children. Tell the children that many materials we use every day, both natural and manufactured, are particularly useful because they can be made into so many things. Show the children the collection of plastic artefacts and ask them to think about the very wide range of objects that can be made from plastic. Match the plastic sponge to the natural sponge, the glass tumbler to the plastic tumbler, and tell the children that plastic is often particularly useful because it can be made to look like, and do, the same job as artefacts made from other materials.

GROUP ACTIVITIES

1. Put the children into groups of four. Ask them to choose one of the materials discussed in the Main teaching activity and use the available reference materials to research how it is made. Make sure that they do not all choose the same material. Each group could then design one or two pages for a class zig-zag book containing information about materials. (If you have a large class you may wish to make two books.)

2. Remind the children about the paper manufacturing process (see Background). Then ask the children, as individuals, to make a saucer or bowl from paper pulp combined with cellulose glue (papier mâché). Put some glue into a mixing bowl or other large container for each group. Ask the children to tear newspaper into small pieces (roughly 2cm square) and stir these thoroughly into the glue to form a pulp. Cover one side of the saucers or bowls with cling film and press the pulp evenly over the surface to about 0.5cm thick. Leave to dry completely, peel off the cling film and decorate the final artefacts by painting, and then varnishing with diluted school adhesive.

DIFFERENTIATION

1. Some children will need help with using the research materials and extracting relevant information. Some children may be able to add some of the properties of their material to the information on the manufacturing process.

2. All the children should be able to take part in this activity.

ASSESSMENT

Use the work from Group activity 1 to assess the children's understanding. During the Plenary session note those children who are able to answer your questions.

PLENARY

Show the children the collection of manufactured materials again. Ask them to tell you what they are, and why they are in a collection together. (They are all made or manufactured.) Ask the children to refer to the work they did in Group activity 1 and to tell you some of the things that they have found out about their material. *How is it made? Can you tell me something about the manufacturing process?*

OUTCOMES

- Can name some manufactured materials.
- Can describe how some manufactured materials are made.

LINKS

Literacy: using non-fiction texts.
Art: making a 3D artefact.

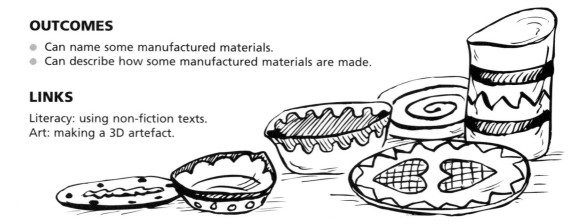

LESSON 6

OBJECTIVES

● To know how the application of forces can change the shape of some materials.
● To be able to carry out a simple investigation with help.

RESOURCES

Main teaching activity: Elastic bands of various widths (but no really narrow ones that could be easily broken), a sponge, a sheet of A4 paper, a piece of balsa wood, a small saw, a vice, a lump of play dough.
Group activities: 1. Force meters (one per group), rulers, writing materials; uniform lengths of three different widths of elastic (perhaps 0.5cm, 1cm and 1.5–2cm wide) – these should be approximately 50cm in length, knotted to make a loop of about 40cm (one loop of each thickness per group). A copy of photocopiable page 67 from Unit 2 for each group would be useful if you wish the children to record their investigation. **2.** Pipe-cleaners (three for each child), large beads, fabric, wool, scissors, adhesive.

BACKGROUND

> ### Vocabulary
> stretch, stretchy, push, pull, twist, shape, altered, force, elastic

Most forces are basically a push or a pull. Children will have learned in Year 1/Primary 2 that they can change the shape of materials or objects by using various types of push (banging, pressing, squashing and rolling). They should also know that pulling, and stretching (a type of pull), will cause materials to change their shape. They need to be made aware that all of the above are types of forces and that use of a force is necessary to effect a change in shape. A twist is a combination of a push and a pull.

The children now need to be made aware that sometimes the force used (cutting or tearing paper, sawing wood) will change the shape of a material permanently, and that sometimes a material can be brought back to its original shape by using another force (rolling the play dough back into a ball, unfolding or untwisting the paper). Children also need to know that some materials (elastic bands, sponges) go back to their original shape of their own accord, and that this is a very useful property. Rehearse the correct vocabulary with the children as often as possible, complete with a definition. (*Use a little more force to stretch the elastic, pull it a little harder.*) Be careful not to use words such as 'pressure' and 'power' in a forces context – they have their own, precise, scientific meaning that the children will learn about later. The children simply need to know that they are using a force to change the shape of things.

INTRODUCTION

Talking to the whole class, remind the children of the work they did on materials in Year 1/Primary 2. *Can anyone remember some of the materials that could be changed in shape by forces?* (Play dough, paper, pastry, wood.) *What were those forces called?* (Pushes and pulls.)

MAIN TEACHING ACTIVITY

Tell the children that there is another type of force, called a twist, which can be used to change the shape of some materials. A twist is a mixture of a push and a pull. Take the A4 sheet of paper and twist it into a spill showing the children the movement of your hands as you do so and how the shape of the paper has changed. *Can we get that paper back to its original shape?* (Yes, if we use a twisting force the other way and then flatten it out, though it will still be a bit creased.)

Do you remember that in Year 1/Primary 2 when you changed the shape of some materials by using forces you could get some of them back to their original shape but some were changed forever, like if you were sandpapering wood, for example? Show the children the wood and the play dough. *When we changed the shape of the play dough by pushing and pulling it, could we get it back to its original shape?* (Yes.) Demonstrate this by changing the shape of the play dough ball and then rolling it back into a ball again. *What about the wood? Could we get the wood back to its original shape after we had cut it with a saw?* (No.) Cut a piece off the wood to demonstrate this. *What did we need to use to change the shape of those materials?* (A force.) *What did we need to use to get the paper and the play*

dough back to their original shape? (Another force.) Show the children the sponge. *What do you think will happen if I use a force to squash this sponge so that it is as small as possible and then let go?* (It will go back to its original shape on its own without having to use another force.)

Give each child an elastic band. Warn them that they must only stretch them very gently, because if they are stretched too hard they might fly off and hit someone or break, and this can be very painful. Ask the children to use a force to gently stretch their band. *What can you feel as you stretch the band? Can you feel it pulling on your fingers? What happens when you let go?* Ask them to swap bands with someone who has a different width of band. *Does it take more or less force to stretch (pull) it?* Tell the children that elastic bands (and other sorts of elastic) are materials that are used specially for their elastic (stretchy) properties – they go back to their original shape when they are no longer stretched.

GROUP ACTIVITIES

1. Put the children into groups of four to investigate the force needed to stretch different widths of elastic to a given length. One child holds one end of the elastic loop by the knot, one pulls gently on the other end of the loop with the force meter and reads the results, one measures the elastic loops to ensure that they are all stretched equally. The fourth member of the group records the force meter reading.

The investigation can also be carried out by holding the knotted end of the loop firmly and placing the other end of the loop, hooked on to a force meter, against the end of the ruler. Pulling gently, but firmly, on the force meter, stretch the loop 10cm along the ruler. Record the force needed to stretch each loop the same distance. (When children are carrying out an investigation it is useful for each child to have a specific 'job', so organise the groups accordingly.) Before they start the investigation ask the children to predict which elastic they think will need more force to stretch it, and why. Help the children to organise a fair test. (It may be useful to give the children photocopiable page 67 from Unit 2 to help with this.)
2. Ask the children, as individuals, to make a pipe-cleaner person, dress it, and give it hair. As the children are doing this ask them to think about the forces they are using to twist the pipe-cleaners into shape (a twist, which is both a push and a pull); to force the head on (push); to cut the fabric and hair (push and pull). As they are working, ask: *Could you get the pipe-cleaners back to their original shape if you wanted to? What about the fabric and wool that you have cut?*

DIFFERENTIATION

1. Less able children may need help with measuring accurately and with their recording. More able children may be able to go on to organise, and carry out, a similar investigation using elastic bands of various widths. (Remind them not to stretch too hard.) You may wish to organise the children into mixed-ability groups so that they can help each other.
2. All the children should be able to take part in this activity according to their ability.

ASSESSMENT

Observe the groups as they are doing their investigation and note those that have some understanding of the need for a fair test. Also note those children who need relatively little help to organise and carry out their test. Use the children's written work and recording to assess their level of understanding and ability to measure accurately.

PLENARY

Choose some children to report back on their investigation. *How did you make it fair? What were your results? Were the results as you predicted?* Ask some other children to show the class their pipe-cleaner person. *How did you make it? What forces did you use to change the shape of the materials that you were working with?*

OUTCOMES

● Can identify materials that can be altered in shape by the application of forces.
● Can distinguish between materials that are permanently deformed and those that regain their shape.

LINKS

Unit 2, Lesson 10: fair test sheet, photocopiable page 67.

OBJECTIVE
● To know that materials often change when they are heated.

RESOURCES
Main teaching activity: Sufficient small tins (such as small baked beans or tuna tins) to cook one cake per child, plus one extra to pull apart and look at after cooking; enough cake ingredients to fill each tin (see recipe on page 117); mixing bowls, spoons, greaseproof paper, kitchen scales, a cooker; an enlarged copy of the recipe on page 117. To decorate (if required) marzipan, fondant icing in two colours, boards, rolling pins, small cutters.
Group activities: 1. Clay, boards, aprons, a kiln (ask your local secondary school to fire your pots if they have a kiln and you do not). **2.** Sufficient loaves of sliced bread for each child to have one slice of toast, a toaster, butter or margarine, jam, knives, paper plates.

PREPARATION
Remove one end of each tin completely. Ensure that they are carefully washed and that the rims are free of sharp edges. Line the tins with greaseproof paper.

BACKGROUND
Some of the most effective methods of teaching young children about the ways in which materials can be changed when heated are through cooking and firing clay. The changes are very noticeable, especially when the cooked or fired materials are compared with a sample kept from before cooking or firing. The children need to understand that, as well as producing a profound change that cannot be reversed, heating (as in the case of making pots) often makes the material more useful. Clay is also a good material for demonstrating to children that some changes are reversible and others are not. An air-dried clay pot looks and feels very different from the damp, shiny, plastic clay that they started with, but the addition of water will soon enable them to return the clay to its original plastic state. When the clay is fired in a kiln the change is irreversible and, no matter how much water is added, the fired clay will not return to the original plastic state. Cooked food, especially when several ingredients have been mixed together, is very different in look, smell, taste and texture from the raw foods. Cooking is another irreversible change.

Vocabulary

ingredients, heat, heated, cool, cooled, change, irreversible, hygiene

INTRODUCTION
Gather the children around you and ask: *Who likes cake?* Tell them that you are going to bake cakes today, but before you do so you are going to look very carefully at the materials (ingredients) that the cake is made from.

MAIN TEACHING ACTIVITY
This activity can be done as a whole class, but would work better in groups of about six, if you have sufficient adult help. Pin up the enlarged copy of the recipe and read through the ingredients and quantities required with the children. Make sure that the children have washed their hands and understand the need to work hygienically. Show them the various ingredients and identify them. Say: *We are going to mix these ingredients together and cook them to make cakes. Who can tell me whether or not they think the ingredients will be changed during the cooking process? Will we be able to get the raw ingredients back again after they have been cooked, or will they be changed forever?* Choose children to come out in turns to weigh out the ingredients, put them into the mixing bowl and stir. Show the children the resulting mixture. *Has it changed at all yet? Will it change more when we cook it? How?* Allow each child to fill a tin with the mixture

ready to go into the oven, but keep some raw mixture aside to compare with the cooked cakes. Fill the extra tin for use in the Plenary session.

When the cakes are cooled, the children could each ice their own cake with marzipan and fondant icing. They could cut a decoration from fondant icing to give a pretty finish, and take the cakes home as presents.

GROUP ACTIVITIES

1. Give each child a ball of clay and a board to work on. Ask the children to have a good look at and feel their clay. *What does it look like?* (Damp and shiny.) *Can you change its shape with your fingers?* Show the children how to push their thumb into the centre of their ball of clay and gently pinch it round and round to turn it into a small thumb pot. Make several extra pots yourself to compare with the children's pots at every stage of the process from raw clay to a finished, fired pot. When the pots are made set them aside to dry. When air-dried, look at them again. *How have they changed? Do they still feel and look the same? Are they useful as pots yet? Could we get the clay back to how it was before we made the pots?* (Yes, because the clay has not yet been changed forever by the heat in the kiln, which is just like a big, hot oven.)

Take one of the pots that you have made and pour water into it. Show the children how the water soaks into the clay until you can eventually roll it up into a ball again.

Fire the pots, keeping at least one unfired for comparison. When the pots are fired, show them to the children and ask the same questions as before. Demonstrate that the fired pot is now more useful because it will hold water (although it may still be porous) so, if it were a bigger pot, you could keep a plant in it. The unfired one still goes soggy and lets the water straight through. Reinforce the fact that heating the clay by firing it in a kiln has changed it forever and made it more useful.

2. Show the children the untoasted bread and ask them how heating it in a toaster (toasting it) will change it. *Has it been changed forever when it is toasted, or can we get it back to the same as it was before we toasted it?* Toast sufficient slices for the entire group to have a piece (but only allow the children to use the toaster under close one-to-one supervision). Ask the group to look closely at their toast when it is done and compare it with a slice of untoasted bread. *How has it changed?* (It has been cooked (toasted) on the outside by the heat of the toaster. It can't be returned to its untoasted state.) Butter the toast and put jam on it for a feast!

DIFFERENTIATION

All the children should be able to take part in these activities at their own level. You may wish some children to go on to write about how their clay or toast was changed by the application of heat, and why the clay was then more useful. Some children may be able to tell you this verbally.

ASSESSMENT

As you work with and question the groups, note those children who can describe how some materials are changed when they are heated, and that this can make some materials more useful. Look at the children's writing (see Differentiation) to help you make your judgements.

PLENARY

Look at the spare cooked cake, pull it apart on a plate and pass it around together with the reserved raw mixture for the children to compare the two. Say: *Look carefully at both mixtures. How has the cooked one changed? Do you think that we could get the cooked one back to what it was before it was cooked, or into the separate ingredients again?* Make sure that the children understand that it is the cooking process, the application of heat, that has changed the ingredients forever.

OUTCOMES

● Can describe how some materials change when they are heated.
● Can explain how heating can make a material more useful.

LINKS

Art: making clay pots.
Technology: food safety and hygiene.

LESSON 8

Objective	● To know that materials often change when they are heated.
Resources	Uncooked popcorn, a cooker, cooking oil, a large saucepan with a lid, paper plates or bowls, paper, writing materials.
Main activity	With the class around you, show the children the unpopped corn, giving them each a grain to handle. Ask them to tell you how it feels. *Does it smell? Is it hard or soft?* Place some popcorn in the pan, together with a little oil and place it on the cooker. Make sure the lid is firmly on the saucepan. Shake the pan gently now and then as the popcorn cooks to prevent it sticking. Ask the children to listen very carefully. *What can you hear?* (The popcorn can be heard popping as it cooks.) When it stops popping, put a little on a plate for each child and ask them to look carefully at and smell the popped corn, comparing it with how it was before cooking. *How has it changed? Does it smell the same? Does it feel very different? Do you think we could change the corn back to the way it was before we heated it, or do you think that heating has changed it forever?* Children could save some of the corn, both popped and unpopped, stick it to some paper and write a sentence or two about how heating (cooking) the corn has changed it. Have fun eating the popcorn!
Differentiation	All the children should be able to take part in this activity at their own level. In the writing part of the task, more able children should give several ways in which the corn has been changed by heating. Less able children may only manage one or two changes and may have to tell you their ideas.
Assessment	During the Plenary session, note which children are able to answer your questions and know that the material (popcorn) has been changed by heat. Look at the children's work to assess the level of their understanding.
Plenary	Look at the cooked and uncooked corn again with the children. Ask them to remind you of some of the ways in which the cooking (heating) of the corn has changed it. Ask: *Has it been changed forever?* Look at some of the children's work and discuss it with them.
Outcome	● Can describe how some materials change when they are heated.

LESSON 9

Objective	● To know that water turns to steam when it is heated, but the steam turns back to water when it is cooled.
Resources	An electric kettle; a large, cold plate or metal tray.
Main activity	With the children around you, but at a safe distance, show them that the kettle is filled with water. Set it on the table and ask them to look closely: can they see any steam? Ask: *What is steam?* (It is what water turns into when it is heated.) Boil the water in the kettle. Ask the children to watch very carefully as the water boils. *What can you see?* (Steam.) When the water is boiling, hold the plate or tray over the steam, but be careful not to scald yourself. Say: *As the steam hits the plate, what can you see?* (Droplets of water forming.) Tell the children that as the water boils it turns into steam and that, when it cools again, it turns back into water. (Put the tray in a fridge for a short while before doing this activity to give a better, quicker, result.)
Differentiation	All the children should be able to take part in this activity.
Assessment	During the Plenary session note those children who are able to answer your questions.
Plenary	Ask the children to tell you what happens to water as it is heated and then as the steam is cooled.
Outcomes	● Can describe what happens when water is heated. ● Can describe what happens when steam is cooled.

LESSON 10

OBJECTIVE

● To know that many materials change when they are cooled.

RESOURCES

Main teaching activity: Ice cube trays or ice cube bags, water in clear plastic jugs, access to the freezing compartment of a fridge or a freezer.
Group activities: 1. An unmade jelly for each group (include a range of different colours, if possible. Agar jellies are available for vegetarians), bowls, spoons; hot – not boiling – water; writing and drawing materials. **2.** A well-washed, empty film canister for each child (the transparent kind would be best. You can usually obtain these free from chemists that do their own film processing), a lolly stick for each child, access to a freezer or the freezing compartment of a fridge, water, fruit syrups, empty ice cream containers (to keep the lollies upright while freezing).
Plenary: A tea towel.

PREPARATION

Freeze some water in ice cube trays and bags the day before the lesson in case those prepared during the lesson do not have time to freeze properly before the Plenary session.

BACKGROUND

Eventually, the children will be expected to know the difference between a reversible and an irreversible change and be able to give definitions. They will also need to know the difference between a solid and a liquid. This lesson is a good vehicle for demonstrating reversible change and liquids changing into solids.

It is worthwhile introducing the correct vocabulary and concepts at this stage, but don't expect all the children to understand or retain them. The main objective of the lesson is that the children should know that some materials change when cooled and that they are able to describe the process.

INTRODUCTION

Talk to all the children about what they did in Lessons 7 and 8. Ask them whether they could return the cooked ingredients of their cakes, the popcorn or clay back to their original state.

MAIN TEACHING ACTIVITY

Remind the children that once the food was cooked and the clay fired they could not get them back to the way they were before. *This is called an irreversible change – it can't be changed back.* Ask: *What about the steam that the water changed into when it was heated, did that change back into water? (Yes.) This is called a reversible change – it can be changed back. Now we are going to look at some more changes that happen when materials are cooled.*

Show the children the ice cube trays or bags and the jugs of water. Ask the children what they would need to do to turn the water into ice cubes. (Fill the trays or bags and put them in the freezer to get really cold.) Invite some children to help you do this and put the trays or bags into the freezer or freezing compartment of the fridge. Ask the children to tell you what they think is happening to the water when it is put in the freezer. *Why is it called a freezer?* If possible, take the ice cube trays or bags out of the freezer during the freezing process so that the children can look at them and see what is happening. Ask: *How is the water changing? What is happening to it?* (It is getting colder and colder and the water is beginning to freeze: it is changing from a liquid to a solid.)

GROUP ACTIVITIES

1. Tell the children that there are some materials that change when they are cooled but that don't actually have to be frozen. Jelly is one of these materials. It needs to be dissolved by adding warm water to it and should then be put somewhere cool to set. (You may need access to a fridge for this.) The children can make jelly in groups of three or four, then write about what they did and what they think will happen as the jelly cools. Encourage them to use as much of the appropriate vocabulary in their writing as they can. You may wish to put a list of words on the board to help them, such as 'warm', 'dissolve', 'cool', 'set', 'liquid', 'solid'.
2. Let the children mix a fruit syrup of their choice with enough water to fill their film canister, put a lolly stick into the canister, then put the canister carefully into an empty ice cream container to go into the freezer. Talk to them as they are doing this and ask them what is going

Vocabulary

cool, cooled, cold, change, set, freeze, reversible, irreversible, liquid, solid, dissolve

to happen when they put the lollies into the freezer. Encourage them to use the appropriate vocabulary to say what that means.

DIFFERENTIATION

1. More able children will be able to use more of the appropriate vocabulary words in their writing and give a more detailed explanation of the process. Some children may draw pictures of the process and explain their pictures to you.
2. All the children should be able to take part in this activity at their own level.

ASSESSMENT

Look at the children's work to give you an idea of the level of their understanding. During the Plenary session, note those children who are able to answer your questions and those who contribute sensibly to the discussion.

PLENARY

Bring the ice cubes out of the freezer and pass them around for the children to look at. (Put a tea towel under the trays or bags to prevent them sticking to the children's hands and to mop up any drips.) *How has the water changed? What would happen if we set these trays and bags aside in the warm classroom? What would happen if we put them into the freezer again once they have melted and changed from a solid to a liquid?* Tell them that this is what they are going to do. They will then see what happens in the next lesson.

Rehearse the appropriate vocabulary with the children, adding, or asking them to add, a definition every time. *What happened to the water as it froze?* (It got very cold and changed from a liquid into a solid.) *Did the same thing happen with the ice lollies?* Look at the jellies, and ask: *What was different when the jellies set and changed from liquid to solid?* (They did not have to go into the freezer.) Look at some of the children's work and read and discuss it with them. Finish the lesson by enjoying the jelly and lollies!

OUTCOME

● Can describe how some materials change when they are cooled.

LESSON 11

OBJECTIVE

● To know that some materials melt and change when they are heated.

RESOURCES

Main teaching activity: Access to a freezer; a bowl or tank of ice cubes for each group of six, containing at least one ice cube per child; paper, writing and drawing materials.
Group activities: For both these Group activities you will need extra adult help to supervise the groups. **1.** A candle and holder in a metal tray filled with sand for each group of four or six, matches (to be retained by the adult working with the group), paper and pencil (for the adult to note the children's comments and vocabulary – see Group activity 1), writing and drawing materials. **2.** Cornflakes or a puffed rice cereal, chocolate, small cake cases, spoons, a double saucepan or a bowl that fits into a saucepan, access to a cooker.

PREPARATION

Freeze sufficient ice cubes for every child in the class to have at least one.

Vocabulary

heat, heated, burn, melt, flame, wax, change, reversible, irreversible, solid, liquid

BACKGROUND

At this stage the children are learning that materials can be changed in a variety of ways. Water can be changed into ice and back again over and over again. Wax melts and then burns in the heat of a candle flame. Chocolate can be melted and hardened again to make chocolate cakes or shaped in to Easter eggs.

Some materials, such as dough or clay, change profoundly when heated or cooked. This leads eventually to an understanding that changes can be reversible or irreversible, and that changes are brought about in different ways such as heating, cooling, burning, using a force, and so on.

INTRODUCTION

Remind all the children about what they did in Lesson 10. Ask: *What happened when we put the water in the ice trays or bags and then into the freezer? Who can remember some of the scientific words that we used?* (Freeze, change, solid, liquid and so on.)

MAIN TEACHING ACTIVITY

Tell the children that in this lesson they are going to find out what happens to ice when it is taken out of the freezer and kept in a warm room. Ask: *Can anyone predict what they think will happen?* Divide the children into groups of about six and sit them around a table with a bowl or tank of ice cubes. Ask them to look closely at the ice cubes to see what is happening to them. Can they write down some words to describe what is happening? (As they melt, the ice cubes are turning back to water. They are going from a solid to a liquid.) Perhaps they can draw some pictures of the process. Encourage the children to pick up an ice cube from time to time and hold it for a short while. *What does it feel like? What is happening as you hold it in your warm hand? Is your hand warmer than the room? Is the ice cube melting more quickly in your hand than it did in the bowl? Does it feel wet? What is it turning into?* (Water, a liquid.) As you work with the groups, ask: *What would happen if we put the ice that has melted back into the freezer? Would it turn back into solid ice? Would we be able to do the same activity over and over again? Is the change when water is frozen into ice a reversible or irreversible one?* Finish the activity by putting some of the water from the melted ice back into the freezer to look at with the children during the Plenary session (or the next day if it has not frozen in time).

GROUP ACTIVITIES

1. Organise the children into groups of four or six, each with an adult. (If you are working with the children yourself you may be happy to work with at least six children and manage the activity safely. If a classroom helper is in charge, he or she may feel more comfortable taking responsibility for only four children. Consult any other adults in advance.) Put the candle in the centre of the table and tell the children that they are going to watch it very carefully, and make as many observations as they can before, during and after it burns.

Ensure that the table is clear of papers and any other clutter, that long hair is tied back and that the children are seated at a safe distance from the candle. Give adult helpers a piece of paper with the initials of the group members written at intervals down the side so that they can note any appropriate vocabulary or comments that the children make during their observation. Remind helpers that the activity is about changes to the materials as they are heated and ask them to draw the children's attention to the change in the colour of the wick, the state of the wax near the flame, and so on.

2. Before starting this activity, make sure that the children have washed their hands and observe the rules of hygiene as they work. Children, again working in groups with an adult, should melt the chocolate and then add sufficient cereal, stirring gently until the chocolate has coated the cereal. Spoon the mixture into cake cases and leave to set. Encourage the adult working with the children to ask questions that will lead the children to observe the process closely and use the appropriate vocabulary. (See Group activity 1, above.)

DIFFERENTIATION

During the Main teaching activity some children will write detailed observations, showing a clear understanding of the process and using the appropriate vocabulary. Some children may need to tell you about their observations and rehearse the vocabulary verbally. All the children should be able to join in the Group activities at their own level.

ASSESSMENT

Look at the children's work from the Main teaching activity to help you with your judgements. During the Plenary session, note those children who use the new vocabulary correctly and are able to answer your questions.

PLENARY

Talk to the children about what they have observed and learned during the three activities in this lesson. *What happened when the ice cubes were brought out of the freezer? Did they melt faster when you held them in your hand? What did the ice change into?* Bring some of the refrozen ice from the freezer to look at with the children and reinforce the idea that water can be melted and refrozen over and over again. This is a reversible change. Is the same true of the wax that has melted and then burned as the candle was burning? (Some of the wax that melted will have gone solid again and could be melted once more, but much of the wax will have vaporised and burned away.) *Could we get that back again? Is the wax gone forever? Is that an irreversible change? What about the chocolate? What happened when it was heated? What happened when it was cooled? Could we melt it again?* Look at, and read, some of the children's work with them and discuss what they have learned.

OUTCOMES
- Can describe how some materials change as they melt.
- Can describe how some materials change when they are heated.

LINKS
Technology: following safe procedures for food safety and hygiene.

LESSON 12

OBJECTIVES
- To know that ice will melt at different rates in different temperatures.
- To be able to plan and carry out a fair test with help.

RESOURCES
Main teaching activity: Four ice cubes in small foil dishes and a copy of photocopiable page 67 per group of four; writing materials, timer or alarm.
Group activities: 1. Two flavoured ice cubes per child (see Preparation, below). **2.** A copy of photocopiable page 118 for each pair of children, reference materials, drawing and writing materials.

PREPARATION
Make two flavoured ice cubes for each child by pouring a mixture of fruit syrup or fruit squash and water into ice cube bags (these can be bought at any supermarket) and freezing them so they are ready for the lesson.

Vocabulary

temperature, investigate, investigation, fair, melt, warm, cool, cold

BACKGROUND
The ability to plan and carry out a fair test by understanding how to control and manipulate variables is not expected of children of this age; it comes at the end of Key Stage 2. However, even at this young age children need to have experience of whole investigations in order to help develop that understanding. They need to practise planning, managing and carrying out investigations, with your help, as often as they can.

Talking to the whole class initially to take them through the planning stage together is a good way to begin. It ensures that all the children understand what the investigation is about, what is expected of them and how to carry out their test fairly. If you go through this process in a questioning way, asking for ideas from the class, it gives those children who have the beginnings of an understanding a chance to verbalise and reinforce their ideas. At this stage, give the children as much help as they need – investigating should be a fun, rather than a frustrating, experience!

INTRODUCTION
Remind the whole class about what they learned in Lesson 11 when they looked at ice cubes melting. *What happened when you held them in your hands? Did they melt faster? Why?* (Because their hands were warmer than the bowl.) Tell the children that they are going to do an investigation to see how quickly ice cubes melt in different places that are at different temperatures.

MAIN TEACHING ACTIVITY
Put the children into groups of four and sit them all around you. Show them four ice cubes in separate foil dishes. Tell them that each group is going to have four ice cubes and they will put them in different places to find out which is the best place for keeping ice frozen for as long as possible. Ask them to think about, and predict, which would be the best place and the worst place in the classroom or around the school. (In the fridge, in the shade, on the window sill, in the Sun and so on.) Discuss how often it would be sensible to check each ice cube. (Every ten

minutes?) Ask: *How can we keep the test fair, so that each ice cube has the same chance?* (Make sure that the ice cubes are the same size, put them in place and check them at the same time.) *How can you check them all at the same time?* (Each member of the group could have responsibility for one of the ice cubes.)

Give each group a copy of photocopiable page 67 ,and ask them to plan their investigation, deciding where to put their four ice cubes. Ask: *Do you need to record anything as you go along?* (The check times, and whether each ice cube is still there or has melted completely.) Before they start, and as they are doing the activity, ask the children to complete the appropriate sections of the record sheet. Check that what they are recording is appropriate and will give them the data to tell which place was best for keeping an ice cube.

GROUP ACTIVITIES

1. Give each child two flavoured ice cubes on a plate. Ask them to predict which will melt first if one is left on the plate and they put the other one in their mouth and suck it. Ask: *Where does ice melt more quickly, in a warm or cold place? Is your mouth warmer than the classroom?* (Try to ignore the slurping noises!)
2. Put the children into pairs and give each pair a copy of photocopiable page 118. Ask them to think of as many uses as they can for ice and write these on their sheet in the correct section. Remind them that they can use the reference materials to help them.

DIFFERENTIATION

Main teaching activity: Some children will need more help than others in planning, recording and carrying out their test. They may need to be reminded about how to keep it fair.
Group activities: 1. All the children should be able to take part in this activity. **2.** More able children will know and be able to find more uses for ice than the less able. They will use the reference materials more effectively. You may wish to put the children into mixed-ability pairs so that they can help each other.

ASSESSMENT

Use the children's work from the Main teaching activity and from Group activity 2 to help you assess their level of understanding.

PLENARY

Look at the record sheets from the Main teaching activity with the children and discuss what they found out. *Does ice take longer to melt in a cold or warm place? How did you keep your test fair? What did you record as you went along? Did your recording help you to remember what happened and which ice cube melted first?* Talk about some of the ways in which ice is used. *Can anyone think of any more?*

OUTCOMES

● Know that the warmer the environment, the quicker ice melts.
● Can plan and carry out a fair test with help.

LINKS

Unit 2, Lesson 10: fair testing.

LESSON 13

OBJECTIVE
● To know that heat is a form of energy and that it may be supplied by several sources.

RESOURCES

Group activities: 1. A copy of photocopiable page 119 for each child, writing and colouring materials. **2.** A copy of photocopiable page 120 for each child, writing materials.

BACKGROUND

Energy is needed to make things work and we all need energy to make our bodies work. Energy comes in many forms and can be changed or transferred from one form to another, most of

which are too complicated or abstract for children of this age. They should, however, be able to understand that energy is needed to make things work and give us heat.

Heat is just one form of energy. Others include light and sound. Some of our energy is provided by waves, water and wind or by nuclear power. These are all used to generate electricity. There is also increasing use of heat energy which is taken directly from the Sun: energy that is collected by solar panels. Houses can be heated and machinery run on electricity generated from solar energy so, in countries where a mains electricity supply is less certain and many daily hours of sunshine can be relied on, more appliances are solar-powered (water pumps, for example). Most of our heat energy comes from gas, electricity or solid fuel in various forms. This lesson concentrates on the everyday sources of heat energy and its uses.

INTRODUCTION

The counting rhyme 'Six Fat Sausages Sizzling in the Pan' would be a good introduction to this lesson.

MAIN TEACHING ACTIVITY

Ask the children when, where and why we use heat. (When we are cold, when we need hot water for a bath, when we want a cup of tea, for the hairdryer or the iron, to cook with or make the toast for breakfast and so on.) Ask the children to close their eyes and try to imagine what it would be like if there were no heat. (Cold baths all the time, raw food, cold houses, crumpled clothes.) *It wouldn't be much fun would it?*

Tell the children that heat is a form of energy and that we get it from different sources. Ask: *Can anyone tell me what supplies the heat energy for cooking?* (Usually gas or electricity, although some children may have solid fuel or oil ranges in their houses.) *What about things like the iron, the hairdryer and perhaps the kettle?* (Electricity.) Ask the children if any of them have solar panels on their houses and get their heat energy directly from the Sun.

Help the children to understand that heat energy plays an important part in our lives. It helps to make our lives much more comfortable than they would otherwise be. Heat has been used in this way since very early people discovered fire. However, heat can also be very dangerous. Ask: *What would happen if you touched something that was very hot, like a hot iron, a kettle full of boiling water or an electric fire?* Tell the children that they need to be very careful with anything that uses heat energy and gets hot.

GROUP ACTIVITIES

1. Give each child a copy of photocopiable page 119. Look at the pictures with them and make sure that they can identify them all. Ask them to colour only those that use heat and to write under each one what it is used for.

2. Give each child a copy of page 120. Ask them to identify and tell you what the pictures are. They should then write what fuel source or sources could provide the heat for each one. (For example, a barbecue might use charcoal or gas.) You may wish to put a list of fuel sources on the board or flip chart such as coal, gas, electricity, charcoal, wood, oil or rubbish.

DIFFERENTIATION

1. Less able children may need help with their writing. Some children may need to tell you their ideas.
2. More able children may be able to write the names of one or two other appliances that use the same fuel source in each box. Less able children may need help to match the appliances to a fuel source that is unfamiliar to them.

ASSESSMENT

Use the children's work to assess the level of their understanding. During the Plenary session note those children who know that heat is a form of energy.

PLENARY

Ask the children: *What is heat? What would we have to do without if we did not have sources of heat energy?* Look at the work that the children have done and discuss it with them. *How many sources of heat energy have we found out about? What appliances give us heat?*

OUTCOMES

- Know that heat is a form of energy.
- Know about different sources of heat energy.
- Can recognise different applications of heat in everyday life.

LINKS

Unit 7, Lessons 5 and 13: light and sound as forms of energy.

ASSESSMENT

LESSON 14

OBJECTIVES

- To know about the everyday uses of some materials.
- To know that materials often change when they are heated.
- To know that many materials change when they are cooled.

RESOURCES

Assessment activities: 1. Photocopiable page 121, pencils. **2.** Photocopiable page 122, pencils.

INTRODUCTION

Ask the children to tell you about some of the things they have learned in this unit. You may want to revise some of the vocabulary that has been introduced to the children.

ASSESSMENT ACTIVITY 1

Give each child a copy of photocopiable page 121 and ask them to complete it by writing as many uses as they can think of for each material.

Answers

Accept any reasonable answers for each material. You may wish to question children about any unusual use they have suggested.

Looking for levels

Most children will be able to suggest at least two uses for each material, with more able children giving more than two for each. Less able children may only manage to suggest one use for each material.

Some children may have difficulty suggesting uses for rock.

ASSESSMENT ACTIVITY 2

Give each child a copy of photocopiable page 122. Read it through with them and make sure that they understand each sentence. Ask them to complete the sheet by answering the questions.

Answers

Accept any answer that indicates an understanding of the following:
1. It gets very cold and goes solid.
2. It melts and goes runny or changes to a liquid.
3. It melts and changes to a liquid.
4. It changes back to water.
5. It cooks and becomes solid. It changes forever.
6. The seeds pop. They get big and fluffy. They are permanently changed.

Looking for levels

Most children will manage an answer to each question that indicates some understanding. More able children may indicate whether the change is temporary or permanent (reversible or irreversible).

Less able children may have difficulty expressing their answers to some of the questions, especially 3, 4 and 6. They may need to tell you their ideas.

Name

How is it used?

Material	Properties	Uses
wood		
metal		
glass		
plastic		

Where do materials come from?

Source	What do we get from the source?	What needs to be done before we use the material?
sheep	Wool	sheep sheared, wool spun, wool knitted or woven, clothes made.
tree		
sponges		
silk worms		
cotton field		
quarry		

Cake recipe

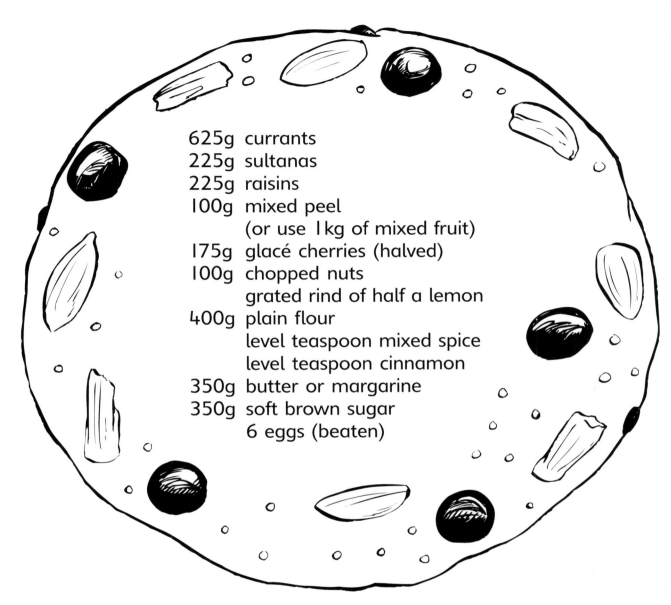

625g currants
225g sultanas
225g raisins
100g mixed peel
(or use 1kg of mixed fruit)
175g glacé cherries (halved)
100g chopped nuts
grated rind of half a lemon
400g plain flour
level teaspoon mixed spice
level teaspoon cinnamon
350g butter or margarine
350g soft brown sugar
6 eggs (beaten)

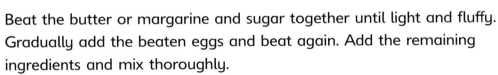

Beat the butter or margarine and sugar together until light and fluffy.
Gradually add the beaten eggs and beat again. Add the remaining
ingredients and mix thoroughly.

This mixture is sufficient for approximately 20–25 small cakes
(depending on the size of your tins).

Bake at 150°C. The time needed will depend on the size of your tins
and type of oven. Check after 45 minutes and test with a skewer: if
the skewer is clean after pushing into a cake, the cakes are cooked.

Name

The uses of ice

Ice is used in the home for:	
Ice is used in shops and supermarkets for:	
Ice is used when we are having fun for:	

What uses heat?

Colour the things that use heat.
Write underneath what each one does.

What fuel does it use?

Write which fuel or fuels each of these things uses for its heat energy.

UNIT 5

Making circuits

ORGANISATION (8 LESSONS)

	OBJECTIVES	MAIN ACTIVITY	GROUP ACTIVITIES	PLENARY	OUTCOMES
LESSON 1	● To know that electricity is used in many different ways. ● To know that mains electricity can be very dangerous and must be treated with extreme care.	Revise safety rules from Y1/P2. Look for devices, plugs and sockets around the school.	Make a plan of the classroom, marking on sockets and appliances. Suggest improvements. Write about the dangers of electricity and how to keep safe.	Discuss electrical safety.	● Can identify electrical devices around the school. ● Can explain why electricity should be treated with extreme care.
LESSON 2	● To know that mains electricity can be very dangerous and must be treated with extreme care.	Consider safety outside – pylons, sub-stations, railway lines, lawnmowers – and the dangers of electricity and water.		Reinforce electrical safety.	● Can explain why electricity should be treated with extreme care.
LESSON 3	● To know that electricity can be supplied by batteries (cells).	Look at devices with and without batteries.	Complete a sheet matching batteries to devices. Practise putting batteries into devices to make them work.	Discuss how to insert batteries.	● Know that a range of devices use batteries for their electricity supply. ● Can put a battery into a device and make it work.
LESSON 4	● To know that a complete circuit is needed for a device to work. ● To know the names of the components needed for a circuit to make a bulb light.	Make a circuit with a bulb.	Identify circuits that will not work and give reasons why. Make a circuit with two bulbs.	Talk about when a circuit works and name the components.	● Can make a simple circuit with one or more bulbs. ● Can draw a circuit that works. ● Can recognise why a simple circuit does not work. ● Can name and label the components used to make a simple circuit.
LESSON 5	● To make a circuit using buzzers and motors.	Make a circuit with a buzzer. Make a circuit with a motor.		Discuss and demonstrate the circuits that have been made.	● Can make a circuit including a buzzer or a motor.
LESSON 6	● To know that the flow of electricity in a circuit is controlled by a switch.	Use switches in a circuit.	Make a labelled drawing of a circuit with a switch. List electrical appliances that use a switch. Make a simple pressure switch.	Discuss the use of switches.	● Can make a switch and use it in a circuit. ● Can make a drawing of a circuit with a switch.
LESSON 7	● To know how to make a simple electrical device or model.	Discuss and plan how models could be made.	Apply knowledge to making models.	Demonstrate the finished models.	● Can make a simple electrical device or model.

	OBJECTIVES		ACTIVITY 1	ACTIVITY 2
ASSESSMENT 8	● To know that a complete circuit is needed for a device to work. ● To know that mains electricity can be very dangerous and must be treated with extreme care.		Understand and draw a complete circuit.	Recognise the dangers of electricity.

LESSON 1

OBJECTIVES

● To know that electricity is used in many different ways.
● To know that mains electricity can be very dangerous and must be treated with extreme care.

RESOURCES

Main teaching activity: The inside environment of the school, a copy of the electricity safety rules generated in Year 1/Primary 2 (see *100 Science Lessons: Year 1*, Unit 5, Lesson 3).
Group activities: 1. An outline plan of the classroom for each child, writing and drawing materials. **2.** Writing and drawing materials.

PREPARATION

Prepare and photocopy an outline plan of the classroom for each child.

BACKGROUND

Children need to understand that electricity is very useful, even essential, but they also need to understand that it can be very dangerous. Make it clear that children should never play with mains appliances or touch electrical sockets. Electricity pylons carry up to 30 000 volts and electricity sub-stations may carry even higher voltages. Both are very dangerous, and should be avoided. If you contact your local electricity company they often have materials, including videos, about the dangers of misusing electricity, and the dangers of playing near pylons and sub-stations.

> **Vocabulary**
>
> danger, dangerous, safe, safety, appliance, plug, socket, pylon, sub-station, electrified

INTRODUCTION

Ask the children if they can remember anything that they learned in Year 1/Primary 2 about electricity. This will tell you what they have retained and if they have any misconceptions.

MAIN TEACHING ACTIVITY

Read out the safety rules devised in Year 1/Primary 2 to the whole class. Explain that in this lesson they will be learning more about electricity and then, at the end of the lesson, they will have a chance to improve or add to the safety rules, if they think they need to.

Tell the children that they are going to walk around the school looking for all the different ways in which the school uses electricity. Explain that they are also going to look for where and how the electricity is delivered. Tell them that wiring circuits are buried in the walls and can't be seen – all we can see of them are the switches to turn the lights on and off and the sockets into which electrical appliances can be plugged.

Walk around the school and look for computers, sound systems, tape recorders, radios, televisions, ceiling lights, vacuum cleaners, floor polishers, fridges, microwaves, electric kettles and so on. Find out if the school has any extension leads and why they are needed. (Multiple plugs in a single socket can cause a dangerous overload.) Perhaps they are needed to operate an appliance some distance from a socket (perhaps a sound system outside on sports day), or the sockets may be in the wrong place. Are the extension leads covered safely or tucked away under furniture so that no one can trip over them? If possible, take the children to look at the electricity meter that measures the electricity that the school uses.

GROUP ACTIVITIES

1. Give each child an outline plan of the classroom and explain that they are going to make an electrical plan of the classroom. Look at the plan with them to make sure that they understand, for example, where the doors and windows are. Ask them to look around and mark on the plan all the electrical sockets and appliances in the room. Then ask them to discuss, in groups of four or six, whether they think the sockets are in the best places. *Could you improve the positioning of the sockets? Are there any long flexes because an appliance, like a computer, is some distance from where it is plugged in? Are the light switches in the most convenient place?* Ask them to use a different colour to mark where they think the sockets would be better placed.

2. Write about the dangers of electricity and how to keep safe. Allow the children, in groups of four or six, to discuss the dangers of electricity and what they need to do or think about to keep themselves safe. Ask them to do a piece of writing about this. They could illustrate their writing if they wish.

DIFFERENTIATION

1. Some children may have difficulty relating a 2D outline plan to the classroom and will need more support. You may wish to put some children into pairs to help each other.
2. More able children should produce a fairly extensive piece of writing full of sensible safety ideas. Less able children may manage only one or two ideas in writing and may need to tell you any other ideas verbally.

ASSESSMENT

Use the children's work to help you make judgements about the level of their understanding. During the Plenary session, note which children have sensible ideas and a good understanding of the dangers of electricity and how to keep safe.

PLENARY

Ask the children to tell you what they saw as they walked around the school. *How many different appliances did you see? Were there any extension leads and what were they used for?* Look at some of the plans of the classroom. *Are there enough sockets? Are they in the best places? Has anyone thought of a better place for them? If they were changed would it make the classroom more convenient? Why?*

Read some of the children's writing about electrical safety and discuss their ideas. Make sure that they understand that too many plugs in one socket can be dangerous and could cause a fire. Remind them of the dangers of trailing flexes. Go through the rules from Year 1/Primary 2 again and ask the children if they would like to amend, add to or improve them.

OUTCOMES
- Can identify electrical devices around the school.
- Can explain why electricity should be treated with extreme care.

LESSON 2

Objective	To know that mains electricity can be very dangerous and must be treated with extreme care.
Resources	'Understanding electricity' videos (these can sometimes be obtained from electricity suppliers); pictures of an electric lawnmower, pylons, sub-stations, railway lines.
Main activity	Gather the children around you and ask them to tell you about some of the things they learned in the last lesson. Remind them that they looked for electricity inside, and tell them that now they are going to think about the dangers of electricity outside. Show them the pictures of the pylons and the sub-stations and tell them that both these things carry electricity. They are very dangerous and no one should ever go near them. If they ever see children playing near a sub-station or pylons they should tell a grown-up immediately. Show them the picture of the railway line and ask if anybody knows why this is a very dangerous place to be even when there are no trains coming. (One of the lines may be electrified and touching it could kill you.) Railway lines are very dangerous because of the trains, and because of the electrified rail. Show the picture of the electric lawnmower and explain its dangers. Tell them also that they should never use electrical appliances near water because water is a very good conductor of electricity; if the appliance falls into the water and anyone has contact with the water, the electricity could kill them.
Differentiation	All the children should be able to take part in this activity.
Assessment	During the Main activity and the Plenary session, note those children who volunteer sensible ideas and show a good understanding of the dangers of electricity.
Plenary	Show the video, if you have one, and discuss and reinforce all the aspects of electrical safety covered in the lesson.
Outcome	Can explain why electricity should be treated with extreme care.

LESSON 3

OBJECTIVE
● To know that electricity can be supplied by batteries (cells).

RESOURCES

Main teaching activity: A collection of devices that run on batteries (radios, torches, cameras, toys, tape recorders, clocks) and their batteries. The items you choose should use a variety of battery types.
Group activities: 1. A copy of photocopiable page 133 for each child, writing materials. **2.** The collection of devices from the Main teaching activity and their batteries.

PREPARATION

Check that everything works, then remove the batteries from all the devices you are going to use, but keep them to hand.

Vocabulary

battery, device, appliance, mains, supply, supplied, volts, recharge, transformer

BACKGROUND

Many electrical appliances work using batteries, and some can be used with batteries or mains. These appliances only require a low voltage and can therefore be operated by batteries that provide a low voltage supply. Any appliances that require a higher voltage must be plugged into the mains supply. Some, such as portable radios, have been designed so that they can work on either batteries or mains, but use a transformer when they are plugged into the mains. In some cases the batteries are an integral part of the equipment and can be recharged using mains electricity via a transformer.

The Volt is a way of measuring electricity. A transformer converts mains electricity (which is usually 230–240V in this country) to the lower voltage required by an appliance. Batteries in devices like torches are usually no more than 6 or 9V. Technically, the small batteries that we use should be called cells; a battery consists of several cells connected together.

Rechargeable batteries can sometimes discharge all their energy at once, creating a great deal of heat, and children could receive a nasty burn if this happens. They should not be used in situations where the children have direct access to them. Batteries contain caustic substances and should never be taken apart. At this stage children do not need to know most of the above, but interested able children can ask difficult questions!

INTRODUCTION

With the children around you, ask them to tell you some of the things that they have learned about electricity so far in this unit of work. Show the children one of the things from the collection of devices and tell them that this also works by electricity, but it does not have to be plugged into the mains supply.

MAIN TEACHING ACTIVITY

With the children, look at the collection of devices without their batteries in. Try to switch one on: *Why won't it work?* Choose one or two devices and decide which battery goes in which device. Fit the batteries into them and switch them on. Tell the children that the battery supplies the electricity that the device needs to make it work. Look at the collection and the separate batteries again. How can they find out which battery is needed for each appliance? Look for information on the appliance and match it to the correct battery. (Look for voltage labels too.)

Invite the children to try fitting the batteries into the devices to make them work. *Which way do they go in?* Repeat this until all the children have had a go at putting a battery or batteries into one appliance and have successfully made it work.

GROUP ACTIVITIES

1. Give each child a copy of photocopiable page 133. Go through the sheet with them and make sure that they understand what they have to do. Tell them to choose devices from the collection and draw them, together with the batteries they need to make them work.

2. Practise putting batteries into devices and making them work. Put the children into groups of four and give each group (if possible) two devices and their batteries. Allow the children to explore and practise putting the batteries into the devices and making them work. If you have a range of appliances, groups could swap when they have succeeded with their first two. Observe the groups as they are working, and ask questions about whether there is a right way and a wrong way to put the batteries in, how the children knew which battery to choose, and so on.

DIFFERENTIATION

All the children should be able to do these activities.

ASSESSMENT

Look at the work the children have done in Group activity 1. Note their answers to your questions in Group activity 2 and during the Plenary session.

PLENARY

Ask the children to tell you what they have learned about how to put batteries into the devices in order to make them work. *How can you find out which battery a particular appliance needs?* (Read the label or instructions.) *Is there a right way and a wrong way to put them in?* (There is usually a guide on the appliance to say which way the battery or batteries should be fitted.) Look at some of the work from Group activity 1 and discuss it with the children.

OUTCOMES

- Know that a range of devices use batteries for their electricity supply.
- Can put a battery into a device and make it work.

LINKS

Technology: assembling components.

LESSON 4

OBJECTIVES

- To know that a complete circuit is needed for a device to work.
- To know the names of the components needed for a circuit to make a bulb light.

RESOURCES

Main teaching activity: For each pair: writing and drawing materials; a battery (the 6V lantern batteries are best. Do not use rechargeable batteries – see Background to Lesson 3, above); two wires with crocodile clips; a bulb in a bulb holder mounted on a board (see diagram). Components mounted in this way are easier for the children to use since they can make a more positive connection with crocodile clips. **Group activities: 1.** A copy of photocopiable page 134 for each child, writing materials. **2.** As for the Main teaching activity, but with the addition of a second bulb in a bulb holder and two more wires with crocodile clips.

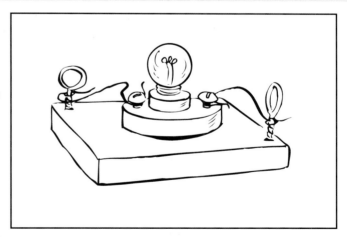

Vocabulary

battery, bulb, bulb holder, wires, crocodile clips, circuit, complete, break, simple, components

BACKGROUND

At this stage, children are required to be able to make circuits and to understand that a complete circuit is needed to make an electrical device, such as a bulb, motor or buzzer operate. Ensure that any batteries are the same voltage as the bulbs, buzzers and motors that you are using. For example, if you use a 6V battery with a 1.5V bulb, the bulb will blow as soon as the circuit is complete. Do not use rechargeable batteries for making circuits as in certain circumstances, such as a short circuit, the battery may discharge all its power in one surge and become dangerously hot.

INTRODUCTION

Talking to the whole class, ask the children to tell you what they remember about the electricity work they did in Year 1/Primary 2. This will give you an idea of the level of their understanding and alert you to any misconceptions.

MAIN TEACHING ACTIVITY

Divide the children into pairs and give each pair the components to make a simple circuit. Go through the equipment they have been given, asking the children to name each component, or naming it for them if they can't. Ask the children to use the equipment they have been given to make the bulb light.

Allow the children to investigate the equipment for themselves, intervening eventually, but only to help those who are struggling and becoming frustrated. *What did you need to do to make the bulb light?* (Connect the battery and bulb together using the wires to make a complete circuit.) Ask the children to take their circuit apart. *Can you make it again?* Ask the children to detach one end of one of the wires and break the circuit. *Does the circuit work now?* Tell the children to reattach that wire and break the circuit somewhere else. *What happens? Will the circuit work if there is a break in it anywhere?* Finish the session by asking the children to draw a complete circuit and label the component parts. You may wish to put a word list on the board or flip chart to help them.

GROUP ACTIVITIES

1. Give each child a copy of photocopiable page 134. Read the words with them, then ask them to identify why the circuits will not work and to complete the sentences.
2. In their pairs, ask the children to make a circuit, but this time lighting two bulbs. Allow them to explore initially, but check that they do not make both bulbs light by putting two wires on each battery terminal and making two separate circuits. Explain this and say that only one wire is allowed on each terminal (see diagram, below), then ask them to try again.

DIFFERENTIATION

1. Less able children may need help to recognise the difference between a complete circuit and one with a break in it. They may need help with writing their sentences. More able children could go on to draw some complete and broken circuits of their own.
2. All the children should be able to take part in this activity, although you may need to intervene and help the less able if they are unable to make both bulbs light without putting two wires into each battery terminal. You may wish to put the children in mixed-ability pairs to help each other.

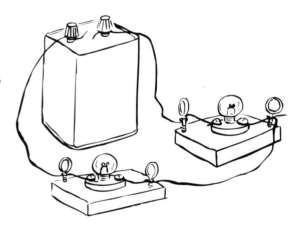

ASSESSMENT

Use the photocopiable sheet from Group activity 1 to help assess the children. Observe them as they are working to judge the level of their understanding.

PLENARY

Ask the children to tell you when a circuit will and will not work. Use some of their drawings and worksheets from Group activity 1 to illustrate this. Ask them to name the various components that they have been using.

OUTCOMES

- Can make a simple circuit with one or more bulbs.
- Can draw a circuit that works.
- Can recognise why a simple circuit does not work.
- Can name and label the components used to make a simple circuit.

LINKS

Technology: assembling components.

LESSON 5

Objective	● To make a circuit using buzzers and motors.
Resources	As for Lesson 4, Group activity 1, with the addition of a buzzer mounted on a board and a motor mounted on a board; writing and drawing materials. If a buzzer fails to work try connecting it the other way round. A buzzer needs to be connected positive (+) to positive (+), and negative (–) to negative (–).
Main activity	Working in pairs, ask the children to make circuits that include a buzzer, and then a motor. *What do you need to make a buzzer and a motor work?* (A complete circuit.) *What happens if you break the circuit?* Children could draw and label their buzzer and motor circuits.
Differentiation	All the children should be able to do this activity.
Assessment	Observe the children as they are working and ask them to tell you what they need to do to make the buzzer and motor work. (Make complete circuits.)
Plenary	Ask the children to tell you what they have done (you may wish some children to demonstrate their circuits) and what is needed to make a buzzer and a motor work.
Outcome	● Can make a circuit including a buzzer or a motor.

LESSON 6

OBJECTIVE
● To know that the flow of electricity in a circuit is controlled by a switch.

RESOURCES
Main teaching activity: One or two electrical appliances (such as a table lamp or a kettle) that are turned on and off by the use of a switch; soft wood or fibreboard blocks, drawing pins, paper clips, circuit equipment as in Lesson 4.
Group activities: 1. Writing and drawing materials. **2.** Folded cards (old Christmas or birthday cards will do), cooking foil, adhesive tape, scissors, circuit equipment as in Lesson 4.

Vocabulary

switch, open, close, break, circuit, pressure switch, flow, controlled

BACKGROUND
A switch in a circuit is a convenient way of completing and breaking circuits in order to turn lights and other electrical appliances on and off. The circuit is broken, and the flow of electricity interrupted, when the switch is open; the circuit is completed, and the electricity is able to flow, when the switch is closed. Children in Year 2/Primary 3 need to experience the completing and breaking of a circuit with a simple switch and to understand that the switch is being used for this purpose. Learning about more sophisticated switches such as dimmer, and perhaps tilt, switches will come towards the end of Key Stage 2. Although commercial switches can be bought to put into circuits, they are enclosed and it is not possible to see how they operate. It is best if the children have the experience of making their own switch (see diagram) and putting it into a circuit.

In Group activity 2 the children will enjoy making and operating a simple pressure switch (see diagram, below). This will show them that there is more than one type of switch. The principle is the same as the switch that they will make in Group activity 1, or as in Lesson 4 when they completed and broke their circuits just by attaching or removing a wire.

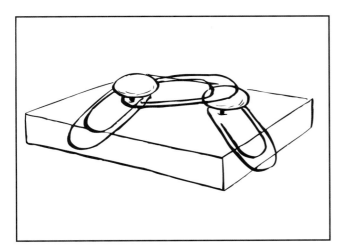

INTRODUCTION
Talking to the whole class, ask the children to remind you about what they learned in Lesson 4 when they were making circuits. Talk about how a complete circuit was needed to make their bulb light and that when the circuit was broken the bulb did not work. Tell them that they are now going to make switches to turn their bulb on and off.

MAIN TEACHING ACTIVITY
Turn the electrical appliances that you have on and off so that the children can see that when switched on the appliance works and when switched off it does not. Explain that opening the switch interrupts the flow of electricity around the circuit and the circuit is broken.

Turn the classroom lights on and off and explain to the children that wherever there is a switch it works to complete or break a circuit. Put the children into pairs and give each pair a set of components. Demonstrate how to make a switch. Ask the children to make a switch and put it into a circuit so that they can turn their bulb on and off by completing or breaking the circuit.

GROUP ACTIVITIES

1. As individuals, ask the children to draw the circuit with the switch in it that they have made and then to label their drawing. (You may want to put a list of words on the flip chart or board to help them.) Underneath their drawing they can make a list of some electrical appliances that use a switch to turn them on and off.

2. Again in pairs, use the materials provided to make a simple pressure switch and include it in a circuit (see diagram, below). A fun extension of this activity is for one pair's pressure switch to be included in a circuit containing a buzzer. Place the pressure switch under a thin mat just inside the door so that anyone entering the classroom closes the switch and makes the buzzer buzz.

DIFFERENTIATION

1. More able children will give a fairly extensive list of electrical appliances. Less able children may manage only two or three and may need help with drawing and labelling their circuit.

2. All the children should be able to take part in this activity.

ASSESSMENT

Observe and question the children during the Main teaching activity and note their level of understanding. Use their drawing of a circuit to help you make judgements.

PLENARY

Ask the children to tell you what a switch in a circuit is used for. *How does it work?* Look at some of the pressure switches that the children have made and ask them to demonstrate them. Ask: *Do these pressure switches work in the same way as the other switches? What is happening to the circuit as the switch is opened and closed?*

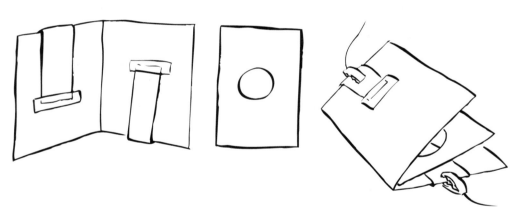

OUTCOMES

● Can make a switch and use it in a circuit.
● Can make a drawing of a circuit with a switch.

LINKS

Technology: making a switch.

LESSON 7

OBJECTIVE

● To know how to make a simple electrical device or model.

RESOURCES

Main teaching activity: Battery, wire, bulb, switch.
Group activity: Batteries, wire, wire cutters, screwdrivers, card, paper, boxes, insulating tape, scissors, a flashing light circuit (optional), bulbs, buzzers, adhesive, found materials as required, paint for decorating.

PREPARATION

Prepare a selection of bulb holders, buzzers, switches or motors (according to the models being made) ready-wired with about 15cm of wire from each terminal. Some children may be able to do this for themselves but it is quite a tricky job. The majority of children of this age will find it easier to attach an extra length of wire to a prepared component by twisting the bare wires together and covering the join with insulating tape. The objective of this lesson is to make a simple model including an electrical circuit, not to spend the lesson chasing missing screws around the classroom!

Vocabulary

model, circuit, battery, wire, bulb, switch, wire cutters, buzzers, component, device

BACKGROUND

Keep the models simple and with simple circuits. Leads with crocodile clips attached can be used but they are rather cumbersome and it may be better to attach wires directly to the component being used (see Preparation). Circuits in models may be difficult for children to manage if the routing of the wires becomes complex. A very simple model can be made by using a shoebox to make a room and pushing a bulb through a hole in the top to make a ceiling light. The wires can be taped to the outside of the box leading to a battery and switch at the back.

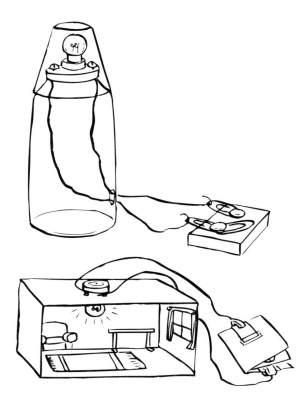

A soft drinks bottle can be used as the basis for a lighthouse. Make a hole in the side of the bottle near the base and thread the wires through and up to the top where the bulb holder will rest on the neck of the bottle. A flashing bulb can give a more realistic effect. Put a clear plastic cup over the bulb, and finish off by sticking paper around the bottle and painting it to look like a lighthouse.

Some children may have made a pressure switch in Lesson 6. This idea could be adapted to make an alarm to inform when a marble has completed its journey down a marble run or a newspaper has landed on a doormat. Children may want more than one light, for the eyes on a robot, for example. They may unwittingly slip into making parallel circuits, and this could become too complicated. At this stage it may be better to make two separate circuits – one for each eye. A series circuit (putting two bulbs in the same circuit) could be used, but the eyes might be rather dim.

Each group could make a shoebox room and then add a house front made from card, with cut-out windows, to make a street of houses lit up at night. Add a bulb to a Christmas display to make the star above the stable or Rudolf's nose really shine.

INTRODUCTION

Remind all the children that a complete circuit is needed if a device is to work. Ask a child to come out and make a simple circuit to make a bulb light.

MAIN TEACHING ACTIVITY

Talk about how a simple circuit can be incorporated into a model to make it more interesting. Ask the children for ideas about what they could make and discuss the feasibility of their suggestions. You may wish to give more or less guidance on the models the children make according to your resources. Do not take too long over these discussions as the children will need lots of time to get on with their models.

GROUP ACTIVITY

Divide the children into pairs or threes. Friendship groups work well in this type of activity and more than one pair of hands may help when trying to stick things together. Encourage the children to talk about what they are going to make and to think carefully about what they need before raiding the materials box! You may need more than one lesson to complete the models.

DIFFERENTIATION

The children will make models according to their abilities. Less able children may get on better if they adapt a pressure switch that they have already had experience of.

ASSESSMENT

Observe the children while they are making their models and note those who have particular difficulties. During the Plenary session ask the children to explain how their model works.

PLENARY

Look at the finished models. Ask the children to demonstrate how they work.

OUTCOME

● Can make a simple electrical device or model.

LINKS

Technology: making models.

ASSESSMENT

LESSON 8

OBJECTIVES

● To know that a complete circuit is needed for a device to work.
● To know that mains electricity can be very dangerous and must be treated with extreme care.

RESOURCES

Assessment activities: 1. A copy of photocopiable page 135 for each child, pencils. **2.** A copy of photocopiable page 136 for each child, pencils.

INTRODUCTION

Ask the children to remind you of some of the things that they have learned about electricity and the benefits and dangers associated with it.

ASSESSMENT ACTIVITY 1

Give each child a copy of photocopiable page 135. Go through it with them and make sure that they understand what is required. Ask them to complete the sheet by writing what is needed to make a device work and then drawing a complete circuit, labelling its parts.

Answers
1. A complete circuit.
2. A drawing of a circuit which includes a battery, two wires and a bulb, all connected together correctly to form a complete circuit.

Looking for levels
1. Most children should understand that a complete circuit is needed to make a bulb light. More able children may also list the equipment needed for the circuit.
2. Most children should be able to draw a complete circuit. More able children will label the components of the circuit without help. Less able children may need a list of words.

ASSESSMENT ACTIVITY 2

Give each child a copy of photocopiable page 136. Ask them to look carefully at the pictures and write why each one is dangerous.

Answers
Accept any answer that conveys an understanding of the following:
1. The flex is trailing and could cause someone to trip.
2. The socket is overloaded and could cause a fire.
3. Pylons carry a high voltage of electricity so you should never play near them.
4. Electrical appliances should never be used near water; if the hairdryer fell into the bath the electricity could kill you.

Looking for levels
Most children should be able to answer these questions correctly. More able children will answer all the questions correctly and in detail. Less able children may manage a correct, if undetailed, answer to questions 1 and 3. Accept correct verbal answers and note them on the children's sheets. Remember that you are assessing their scientific understanding, not their ability to write.

Name

Match the battery

Draw a picture of each device that you choose and the type of battery it needs to make it work.

Write the voltage (V) of each battery on your picture.

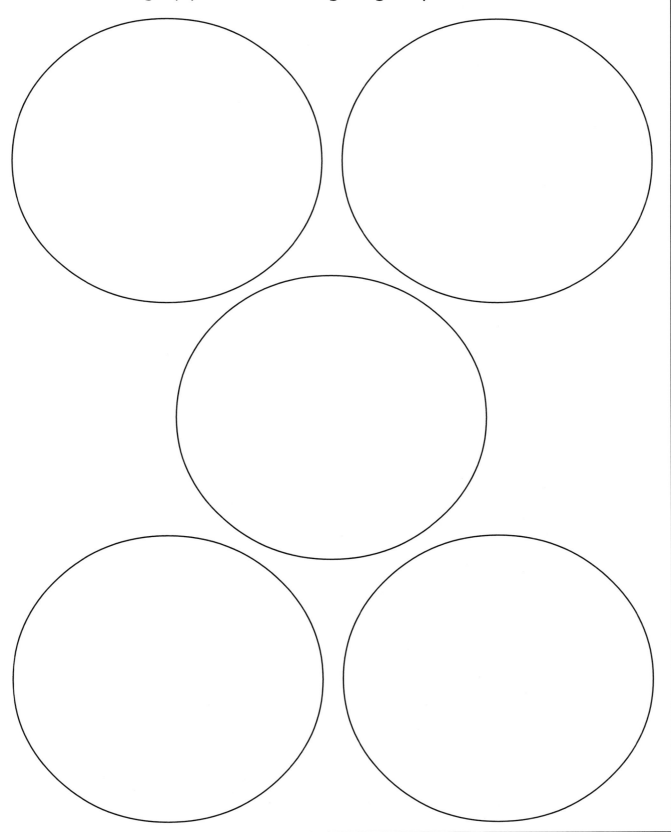

Circuits that will not work

Look at each of these circuits and write underneath why they will not work.

This circuit does not work because _____

_____

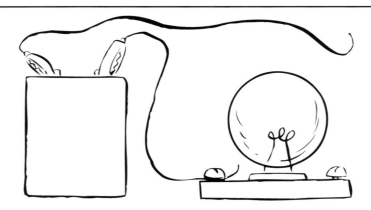

This circuit does not work because _____

_____

This circuit does not work because _____

_____

Making circuits

1. To make a bulb light up I need to _____

_____

2. Draw a circuit that will make a bulb light up in the space below. Label the equipment you have used.

Name

Making circuits

What is happening in the pictures below? Why is it dangerous?

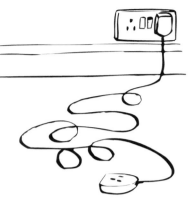

1. This is dangerous because

_____

_____

_____

_____

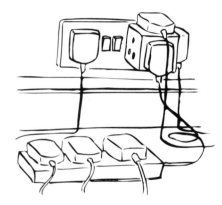

2. This is dangerous because

_____

_____

_____

_____

3. This is dangerous because

_____

_____

_____

_____

4. This is dangerous because

_____

_____

_____

_____

Making things move

ORGANISATION (11 LESSONS)

	OBJECTIVES	MAIN ACTIVITY	GROUP ACTIVITIES	PLENARY	OUTCOMES
LESSON 1	● To know that forces make things move.	Review Y1/P2 work on forces. Move objects and discuss the forces involved.	Identify forces. Play a game of 'Forces Snakes and Ladders'.	Talk about forces.	● Know that forces make things move.
LESSON 2	● To know that actions such as stretching, squeezing, squashing, twisting and turning can be explained as forces (pushes and pulls). ● To plan and carry out a simple fair test with help.	Analyse stretching, twisting, squeezing and other actions into pushes and pulls.	Plan a test to find out which fabric sample will stretch most. Make a list of examples of twists at school and at home.	Discuss forces and report findings.	● Can describe a range of actions such as stretching, squeezing, squashing, twisting and turning in terms of forces (pushes and pulls). ● Can plan and carry out a simple fair test with help.
LESSON 3	● To know that there is a force of friction between two surfaces. ● To know that friction is stronger between rough surfaces than smooth surfaces. ● To plan and carry out a simple fair test with help.	Investigate friction, and how brakes work. Pull a brick over different surfaces.	Make a graph from the data collected. Play 'Shove 2p'	Rub hands together to experience friction. Look at and interpret the graphs.	● Know that there is a force called friction acting between two surfaces. ● Know that the rougher the surface, the stronger the friction. ● Can plan and carry out a simple fair test with help.
LESSON 4	● To know that friction is stronger between rough surfaces than smooth surfaces.	Race vehicles down ramps onto different surfaces.		Talk about the test.	● Know that the rougher the surface, the stronger the friction. ● Can plan and carry out a fair test with help.
LESSON 5	● To know that the rougher the surface, the stronger the friction.	Slide smooth and rough blocks down a slope. Write about what happened.		Discuss the children's writing about friction.	● Know that rougher surfaces slide less easily because the friction is stronger.
LESSON 6	● To know that forces can make moving objects go faster, change direction, slow down or stop.	Roll balls on the ground and hit them with a bat to examine forces.	Roll a painted ball on black paper, against a wall. Investigate pushing and pedalling toys with wheels.	Talk about the effects of forces.	● Know that forces make objects speed up, slow down, change direction or stop.
LESSON 7	● To develop further an understanding of how to make a test fair. ● To know how to compare distances travelled by vehicles.	Push vehicles to compare how far they go. Make sure the test is fair.	Compare the distances vehicles travel down ramps. Write about how the test was made fair.	Discuss how the test was made fair. Interpret the graphs and compare results.	● Gain a better understanding of how to make a test fair. ● Can compare the distances travelled by vehicles.
LESSON 8	● To investigate the effect of weight on distance travelled.	Organise a fair test to see the effect of increased weight on distance travelled.		Report findings.	● Can carry out a fair test with help. ● Know that the weight of a vehicle affects the distance it travels.

ORGANISATION (11 LESSONS)

	OBJECTIVES	MAIN ACTIVITY	GROUP ACTIVITIES	PLENARY	OUTCOMES
LESSON 9	● To carry out a fair test with help. ● To investigate the effect of ramp heights on distance travelled.	Organise a fair test to see the effect of ramp height on the distance a vehicle travels.		Discuss the findings.	● Can carry out a fair test with help. ● Know that ramp height affects the distance a vehicle travels.
LESSON 10	● To know that some objects float because water pushes up on them.	Load margarine tub boats to see how much they will hold before they sink.	Predict, then investigate, what will float. Make plastic bottles sink and float.	Discuss the findings and compare these with the predictions.	● Can recognise that an object floats due to the upward push of the liquid being greater than the downward pull of gravity.

	OBJECTIVES	ACTIVITY 1	ACTIVITY 2
ASSESSMENT 11	● To know that forces can make moving objects go faster, change direction or slow down. ● To know that there is a force of friction between two surfaces. ● To know that friction is stronger between rough surfaces than smooth surfaces. ● To know that actions such as stretching, squeezing, twisting and turning can be explained as pushes and pulls.	Complete sentences about friction.	Identify pictures of pushes and pulls.

LESSON 1

OBJECTIVE

● To know that forces make things move.

RESOURCES

Main teaching activity: A collection of wheeled objects such as toy cars, toy shopping trolleys, pull-along toys, toy wheelbarrows, bikes and tricycles; a range of balls; the hall or playground (if you wish the children to have more room to move about); a day when there is enough wind to move the bushes and trees.

Group activities: 1. A copy of photocopiable page 151 for each child, writing materials.
2. Sufficient game boards made from photocopiable page 152 (see Preparation, below), counters and dice for each group.

PREPARATION

Enlarge to A3 sufficient copies of photocopiable page 152 to give one to each group of four children. Colour and laminate these before use.

BACKGROUND

Forces are difficult for young children to understand because they are so abstract. At this stage children should understand that forces make things move and be able to identify them in simple terms. They should know that when someone is pushing a shopping trolley, or pulling a wheeled toy, that the forces they are using are making the objects move and that those forces are called a push or a pull.

Vocabulary

force, push, pull, gravity

Forces are often described in terms of the effect they have. When children jump, they move themselves by pushing against the floor and the force of gravity moves them back down again; they do not go on moving upwards. The concept of gravity is particularly difficult and abstract but is, perhaps, the force that has the most effect on our lives. Young children are not expected to understand gravity or to explain it, but they do need to experience the effect of gravity, understand that the force of gravity moves all objects downwards, not upwards, and that gravity is a pull force: it pulls things towards the centre of the Earth.

INTRODUCTION

Remind all the children about the work on forces moving things that they did in Year 1/Primary 2. Ask them to tell you what they remember and see if they can name any of the forces (pushes and pulls).

MAIN TEACHING ACTIVITY

If you wish, you could do this activity in the hall or out on the playground so that the children have more room to move about. Show the children the collection of wheeled objects. Select a vehicle and ask: *Will this move on its own?* (No, we need to use a force to start it moving.) Push the vehicle along the ground. *What force am I using to make this move?* (A push.)

Put the children into pairs and give each pair a wheeled object. Ask them to take turns to move their object. *What force are you using to make your object move?* (A push or a pull.) When each child has had a turn they could swap their object with another pair and repeat the activity. Try to make sure that each pair has a chance to work with something that needs to be pushed and then with something that has to be pulled. Gather the children together to discuss what they did and the forces that they were using to move the things they were working with.

Now give each pair a ball, and ask them to take turns to throw the ball up in the air. *What force are you using to throw the ball up?* (A push.) Allow the children to do this several times, then gather them together again. Throw a ball up into the air yourself. Remind them that they were using a push force as they threw the ball. Now ask them to watch what happens to the ball. *Does it carry on going upwards?* Explain to the children that a force called 'gravity' pulls (moves) things downwards. Ask the children to jump as high as they can. *What are you doing?* (Using a push force to move up off the ground.) *What happens next?* (Gravity pulls you back to land on the ground again.) If you are outside, ask the children to look around at the bushes and trees. *What is happening to them?* (The wind is pushing them and making them move.)

GROUP ACTIVITIES

1. Give each child a copy of photocopiable page 151. Ask them to look carefully at the pictures and at the arrows showing which way the object in each picture is moving. Ask them to write under each picture the name of the force that is moving the object.
2. Put the children into groups of four with a 'Forces Snakes and Ladders' game board made from photocopiable page 152, counters and dice. Explain to the children how to play the game (like snakes and ladders). Ask them to notice the forces. It is always helpful if an adult can play the game with the children the first time.

DIFFERENTIATION

All the children should be able to take part in these activities at their own level, although you may wish to put a list of the forces involved on the flip chart or board for Group activity 1 to help less able children with their writing.

ASSESSMENT

During the Main teaching activity discussion and the Plenary session, note those children who show an understanding that forces move things and who can name the forces involved (push, pull, gravity).

PLENARY

Talk about what the children did in the Main teaching activity. *Would the objects or your bodies have moved by themselves?* (No, a force was needed to make them move.) *What were the forces involved?* (Pushes, pulls and gravity pulling things downwards.) Look at some of the work from Group activity 1 and discuss it with the children.

OUTCOME

● Know that forces make things move.

LESSON 2

OBJECTIVES

● To know that actions such as stretching, squeezing, squashing, twisting and turning can be explained as forces (pushes and pulls).
● To plan and carry out a simple fair test with help.

RESOURCES

Main teaching activity: A collection of objects and materials that can be stretched, squashed, squeezed and twisted such as: a range of strips of fabric and elastic, sponges, a jar or bottle with a screw top, play dough, a shoe with laces, a corkscrew (with cork to demonstrate), a cloth such as a tea cloth in a bowl of water that can be wrung out (twisted) before drying.
Group activities: 1. Writing and drawing materials, rulers; a range of strips of fabric of the same width and length (10cm × 1.5 cm) cut from fabrics of different 'stretchiness' such as nylon tights, wool, cotton, acrylic and so on. **2.** Writing and drawing materials.

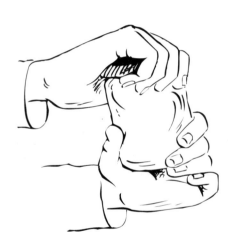

Vocabulary
push, pull, twist, stretch, squash, squeeze, turn

BACKGROUND

The concept of forces is very abstract and is therefore one of the most difficult areas of the science curriculum to teach, and for young children to grasp. We cannot see a force, only the effect of one – the resulting movement when something is pushed, pulled or twisted. Forces can start something moving (a push, pull or gravity), make it stop (a train hitting buffers), make it slow down (friction, travelling over a very rough surface or putting on a brake), make it go faster (an increased push or pull) or make it change direction (hitting a ball with a bat).

Eventually, in Key Stages 2 and 3, children will be expected to know that forces are acting all the time, even when there is no movement. They will also be expected to identify and name other forces and be able to say in which direction the main forces are acting. At Year 2/Primary 3 the children only need to be given experience of forces and to be able to identify them in simple terms.

INTRODUCTION

Remind the children that they learned something about forces in Year 1/Primary 2, and again in Lesson 1 of this unit. Ask: *Who can remember what we learned? What do forces do?* (Make things move, slow down, speed up, change direction and stop.) *What are the names of some of the forces we learned about?* (Pushes and pulls.) *Can you remember that we talked about twists when we were investigating elastic during our work about materials?*

MAIN TEACHING ACTIVITY

Show the children the collection of objects and materials and go through them one by one, asking the children to predict what force you are going to use and to identify the force each time. Help them if necessary. (Stretching the fabrics and elastics are pulls, squashing or squeezing the play dough, springs and sponges are pushes; opening and closing the jar or bottle, wringing out the cloth and using a corkscrew are twists – a push and a pull combined). Tying a shoelace into a bow is quite complicated, as it is a mixture of twists and pulls! When you have finished, go through the collection again, this time asking some children to come up and squeeze, squash, stretch or twist as appropriate, saying what they are doing and naming the force or forces involved.

GROUP ACTIVITIES

1. Put the children into groups of three. Give each group about three different strips of fabric (see Resources) that will stretch to different lengths. Ask them to look closely at and feel the fabric before they begin, and to predict which one they think will stretch the most and why. Allow them to plan a test to find out. As they are working ask questions such as: *How are you going to organise yourselves to find out which is the fabric that will stretch the furthest? Do you need to record anything as you go along?* (The length to which each fabric stretched.) Only intervene to tell the children how to organise the test if their method is clearly not going to give them a proper result. The children could hold one end of the fabric tightly against the edge of the table, measure its length, then stretch the fabric and measure again. Ask them what force they are using as they stretch their fabrics. (A pull.)
2. As individuals, ask the children to make a list, with pictures, of examples of twists at home and at school. (Door knobs, jam jars, corkscrews, taps, radio volume knobs, pepper and salt mills, wood screws, using a screwdriver, wind-up toys and so on.)

DIFFERENTIATION

1. More able children will have had enough practice in organising simple tests in previous units to manage to carry out the one in this lesson. You should only have to give minimal help with their organisation and recording. Less able children may need to be told how to organise their test and what to record, especially those that cannot read a ruler. You may wish to put the children into mixed-ability groups so that they can help each other.

2. You may wish to revise some examples of twists and turns with less able children.

ASSESSMENT

Observe the children as they are stretching their fabrics and note their level of understanding of what they are doing. Do they know that a stretch is a pull force? Use their work from Group activity 2 to help you make your judgements. Also note those children who respond with understanding to your questions during the Plenary session.

PLENARY

Look together at the collection of objects and materials again, very briefly, and ask the children to tell you what squeezing, squashing, twisting and turning are examples of. (Forces, pushes and pulls.) Ask some children to report the findings from their test. *Which fabric stretched the most? Was it the one you expected?* Go through some of the work from Group activity 2 and look at the twists (pushes and pulls) that the children have listed. *Can anyone think of any more?*

OUTCOMES

● Can describe a range of actions such as stretching, squeezing, squashing, twisting and turning in terms of forces (pushes and pulls).
● Can plan and carry out a simple fair test with help.

LESSON 3

OBJECTIVES

● To know that there is a force of friction between two surfaces.
● To know that friction is stronger between rough surfaces than smooth surfaces.
● To plan and carry out a simple fair test with help.

RESOURCES

Main teaching activity: A large empty matchbox, a few matches, a bicycle. For each group of four: a force meter; a house brick with string tied around it and a loop at one end (see diagram, below); a range of surfaces of different degrees of roughness (tiled floor, rough carpet, plastic, linoleum and so on). Photocopiable page 67 could be used if you wish.

Group activities: 1. The results obtained from pulling a brick across different surfaces in the Main teaching activity, squared paper or graph paper for each child, writing and colouring materials. **2.** 2p pieces; a range of surfaces of different roughness for each group, rulers.

PREPARATION

Tie the string around each brick and put a loop in it so that a force meter can be hooked into the loop (see diagram, below).

Vocabulary

friction, force, surface, rough, smooth, rub, rubbing

BACKGROUND

Whenever two surfaces slide over each other there is a force called friction acting between them which tries to oppose one surface moving over the other. This slows them down and even stops them if the force of friction is big enough. The smoother the surfaces are, the less friction there is between them. Most people have experienced this when walking on ice!

When working on friction and investigating surfaces using wheeled vehicles and slopes, always put the surface to be investigated on the floor at the bottom of the slope. This allows the slope to give each vehicle the same (fair) gravitational pull before it hits the surface.

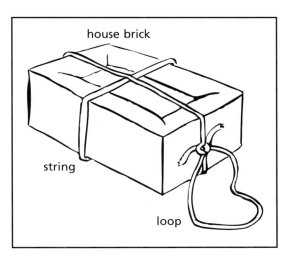

house brick

string

loop

The vehicle slows and stops partly because of the friction between the wheels and the surface. There is also a certain amount of friction between the axle and the surface that it is rubbing on, and some air resistance (another form of friction). In some cases (rubbing a match across the rough surface of a matchbox) the force of friction is converted into heat energy. Children can easily observe this by rubbing their hands together.

INTRODUCTION

Gather the children around you and ask them to rub their hands together vigorously. *What is happening? What can you feel?* (Their hands get warmer and warmer.) Tell the children that this is the result of a force called friction that acts whenever two surfaces rub together.

MAIN TEACHING ACTIVITY

Strike a match. Explain to the children that there is a force called friction between the surface of a match and the rough surface on the side of the matchbox. That friction can also produce heat, just as when they were rubbing their hands together. Pass the empty matchbox around so that the children can feel the rough surface. Remind them that matches are dangerous and that they should never play with them.

Turn the bicycle upside down on a table. Point out the brakes to the children and tell them that brakes work by friction. When you put the brakes on, one surface rubs against the other and the friction between the two surfaces slows the bike down and stops it. Spin the wheel and operate the brakes so that they can see this happening. Do this several times, asking them to watch closely.

Divide the children into groups of four or six (four would be better if you have enough equipment) and give each group a brick, a force meter, a range of surfaces to investigate and a copy of photocopiable page 67 if required. Make sure the children know how to read a force meter. Ask them to look at, and feel, the surfaces. *Which one do you think it will be harder to pull the brick over? Do you think that the smoother or the rougher surfaces will cause more friction?* Tell them to hook their force meter into the loop of string at the end of the brick, then pull the brick over the various surfaces. They should measure the force needed with the force meter and record the results. Tell the children not to record anything until the brick is moving because the force of friction is not acting until one surface is rubbing against another. Discuss the results with the children. *Was it easier to pull the brick across the rougher or smoother surfaces? Which surface caused the most friction? Which caused least?*

GROUP ACTIVITIES

1. As individuals, ask the children to use the results from their brick-pulling activity to construct a block graph or bar chart showing how much force was needed to pull the brick over surfaces.
2. Put the children into groups of four and give them a range of surfaces of different roughness. Tell them that they are going to play 'Shove 2p'. Place each surface, in turn, on the table so that the edge of the surface is at the edge of the table. Place the 2p piece on the surface so that half of it is sticking over the edge of the table. Now shove the 2p with the flat of the hand to send it across the surface. Ask the children to predict the surface on which they think the 2p will travel farthest. *Over the rough surface or the smooth surface?* They can use a ruler to measure the distance the 2p has travelled and record their findings. Remind them that, in order to make the investigation as fair as possible, they need to try to use the same force for each 'shove'!

DIFFERENTIATION

1. Less able children may have difficulty in transferring the information from the recorded results onto their graph. You may wish to put some children into pairs to help each other.
2. All the children should be able to take part in this activity.

ASSESSMENT

During the Main teaching activity note the children who are predicting that the rough surface will produce more friction than the smooth. During the Plenary session note those children who show an understanding that the force that is acting between two surfaces is friction and that the rougher the surface, the greater the friction.

PLENARY

Ask the children to rub their hands together again. Can they tell you the name of the force that is acting when two surfaces are rubbing together? *When is the force of friction stronger?* (Between rougher surfaces.) Look at a few of the graphs with the children and ask some of them to come and interpret their graph, telling the class about their findings.

OUTCOMES
● Know that there is a force called friction acting between two surfaces.
● Know that the rougher the surface, the stronger the friction.
● Can plan and carry out a simple fair test with help.

LINKS
Maths: making graphs.

LESSON 4

Objective	● To know that friction is stronger between rough surfaces than smooth surfaces.
Resources	For each group: a wheeled vehicle, a ramp and stand (a shelf or plank on a pile of books will do), several surfaces (rough and smooth) to put on the floor at the bottom of the ramp, metre sticks, writing materials, a copy of photocopiable page 67.
Main activity	Give each group their equipment (see Resources, above) and a copy of photocopiable page 67. Ask them to devise a test to find out which surface produces most friction. (The vehicle will travel the shortest distance on the surface with most friction.) Ask them to complete the first part of the sheet before doing the test, and then record their findings on it. To keep their test fair they will need to use the same vehicle for each surface, keep the slope at the same height and start the vehicle in a fair way (without pushing), from the same place on the slope every time. Tell them that some groups will be asked to report to the whole class on how they organised their investigation and what they found out. Move around the groups as they are preparing to carry out their test, helping them where necessary.
Differentiation	Some groups may need more help with organising their test. You may wish to put the children into mixed-ability groups so that they can help each other.
Assessment	As you move around the groups note the level of the children's understanding and their ability to organise the test. Use the group recording sheets to inform your judgements. Note those children who are able to contribute sensibly during the Plenary session and who understand that the rougher the surface, the stronger the friction and its effect on the distance travelled by the vehicle.
Plenary	Ask some of the groups to talk about how they managed their test and what they found out. Ask for the name of the force that is acting between the two surfaces. *When is friction stronger?*
Outcomes	● Know that the rougher the surface, the stronger the friction. ● Can plan and carry out a fair test with help.

LESSON 5

Objective	● To know that the rougher the surface, the stronger the friction.
Resources	A smooth slope and stand, a block of wood with coarse sandpaper stuck to one surface, a block of ice (freeze water in an empty tub or margarine pot roughly the same size as the block of wood), newspaper or paper towels for mopping up, writing and drawing materials.
Main activity	Show the children the blocks of wood and ice. Ask them to point out which is rougher and which is smoother. *Which one do you think will slide down the slope more easily and quickly?* Try them out. *What happened? Did the smoother one slide more easily? Why?* (Because the rougher the surface, the stronger the friction, and that slows things down.) Ask the children to write about what happened, and why, and to draw pictures of the equipment.
Differentiation	More able children will write what happened and why clearly and in detail. Some children may need help, and a list of words on a flip chart or board might be helpful. Less able children may need to tell you their ideas. All the children should be able to draw the equipment. Some will be able to label it.
Assessment	Note the children's level of understanding from the way they answer your questions during the Main teaching activity and the Plenary session. Use their writing to help you make judgements.
Plenary	Ask some of the children to use their writing to tell everybody what was happening during the Main teaching activity and why. *Why do rougher surfaces slide less easily? What is the force between two surfaces called?*
Outcome	● Know that rougher surfaces slide less easily because the friction is stronger.

LESSON 6

OBJECTIVE

● To know that forces can make moving objects go faster, change direction or slow down.

RESOURCES

Main teaching activity: A range of balls, bats and hockey sticks (enough for one between two); space on the playground or playing field.
Group activities: 1. Large sheets of black paper, small sponge or tennis balls, shallow trays of different coloured paint, newspaper, aprons or other covering for the children. **2.** A collection of wheeled toys such as bicycles, tricycles and scooters. If you do not have enough you could borrow from younger classes or ask the children to bring in their own for this lesson.

Vocabulary
force, speed up, slow down, change direction

BACKGROUND

Forces start something moving (a push, pull or gravity), make it stop (a train hitting buffers), make it slow down (friction, travelling over a rough surface or putting on a brake), make it go faster (an increased push or pull) or make it change direction (hitting a ball with a bat).

　　The children should be encouraged to develop the appropriate language of moving things and to realise that a throw is a type of push. Hitting a ball with a bat is a push force that can change the direction of the object that is hit. They should begin to appreciate that the amount of force (push or pull) that they apply will affect the way in which the object moves; that a harder throw, hit or roll (push force) will make a ball go faster and further.

INTRODUCTION

Singing the nursery rhyme 'Row, row, row your boat' would be a good introduction to this lesson. Ask the children to sit around you and mime the rowing action as they sing. *What happens to a boat when you row?* (It moves along.) *What are the oars doing?* (Pushing against the water and pulling the boat along.) *If you use a greater force on the oars what will happen?* (The boat will go faster.)

MAIN TEACHING ACTIVITY

Talking to the whole class, tell the children that in this lesson they are going to find out more about push and pull forces and what they can do. Put the children into pairs, each with a ball and a bat or hockey stick, and take them out onto the field or playground. Ask the pairs to stand about two metres apart and to roll the ball very gently backwards and forwards. *What is happening?* (The ball is going slowly.) *What force are you using?* (A push.) Now ask them to roll the ball harder and harder to each other. *What is happening?* (The ball has picked up speed and it is going faster.) *What is the difference between the push force that you are using now and the one you used at first?* (It is bigger.) *Can you use a force to stop the ball?* (Put your hand out so that the ball hits it and stops.)

　　Now put the children into groups of three with a bat or a hockey stick and a ball between them. Ask each group to stand in a triangle. The child with the ball should throw or roll it to the child with the bat or stick, who should hit the ball so that the third child in the group can catch it. Ask the children to notice what is happening. *When the ball has been hit is it travelling in the same direction?* (No, the push force of the bat hitting the ball has made it change direction.)

　　If you have designs painted on the playground, the children could finish the activity by trying to use a bat or hockey stick to change the direction of the balls so that they follow the playground patterns.

GROUP ACTIVITIES

1. Ask the children to roll a painted ball on black paper. This is a potentially messy exercise so make sure the children are well-covered! Place some large sheets of black paper

on the floor against a wall or other solid obstacle (make sure this is covered with newspaper). Put the children into groups of three or four, each with a ball and a shallow tray of paint. Explain that the children should take turns to dip the ball into the paint and roll it across the black paper to hit the wall and roll back. *Can you see the track the ball has left? Has it changed direction? If so when? What made it change direction?* Try rolling the ball gently, and then harder, to see what difference it makes to the track. You could use different colours for hard and soft rolls.
2. Put the children into groups of three or four and give each group a bike, tricycle or scooter. Ask them to take turns to push gently on the pedals or, for a scooter, push gently with their feet. *How fast do you go?* Push harder. *How does that change your speed? If you stop using your feet what happens?* (You slow down and eventually stop.) *How else could you stop?* (Put on the brakes or use their feet on the ground.) *What is the force slowing you down?* (Friction.)

DIFFERENTIATION

All the children should be able to take part in these activities.

ASSESSMENT

Throughout the lesson, note which children are able to answer your questions with understanding and can tell you that forces make things speed up, slow down, change direction or stop.

PLENARY

Ask the children to tell you how they made things speed up, slow down, change direction or stop. Look at some of the tracks made by the painted balls. Ask the children to explain what happened when the balls hit the wall.

OUTCOME

● Know that forces make objects speed up, slow down, change direction or stop.

LESSON 7

OBJECTIVES

● To develop further an understanding of how to make a test fair.
● To know how to compare distances travelled by vehicles.

RESOURCES

Main teaching activity: *Mr Gumpy's Motor Car* by John Burningham (Picture Puffin); two different toy vehicles, a metre stick, a hall or corridor where there is sufficient room for the children to stand around you and watch what is happening; a slope and stand (see diagram, below – a shelf or piece of stiff card and a pile of books will do if you have no slope and stand). A sheet of paper or card to record the distances travelled, pencils, a felt-tipped marker pen.
Group activities: 1. A ramp and stand and a selection of three or four vehicles for each group of four (vehicles could be made from construction kits or bought toy vehicles), metre sticks, coloured adhesive tape, scissors or chalk, writing materials, large squared graph paper, colouring materials. **2.** Writing and drawing materials.

Vocabulary
ramp, slope, measure, test, vehicle, fair, unfair

BACKGROUND

Children at this stage are not expected to be able to identify, control and manipulate variables in order to understand and devise a fair test on their own. This comes towards the end of Key Stage 2. Even so, Year 2/ Primary 3 children need to be given help to organise and carry out fair tests as often as possible. Children, from a very young age, have a well-developed notion of social

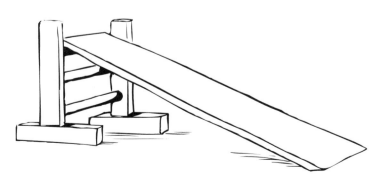

fairness and of things having the same chance, so developing their understanding of fair testing in this way can be very helpful.

Fair testing is important in scientific terms. Without fair testing any data collected is unreliable and cannot be used to draw valid conclusions. Children can be asked: *Have the vehicles had the same chance, have we treated them fairly?* Children need to be given the chance to interpret and compare results as often as possible – this is part of the expected Sc1 capability at the end of KS2 and is an area that is often neglected.

INTRODUCTION

Singing 'The wheels on the bus go round and round' or reading a story such as *Mr Gumpy's Motor Car* would be a good introduction to this lesson.

MAIN TEACHING ACTIVITY

Gather the children around you and show them the two different vehicles. Ask them which one they think will go the farthest if it is pushed along. Put a mark (with coloured adhesive tape or

chalk) on the floor to indicate where the vehicles are going to start. Push one vehicle, then ask a child to come and use the metre stick to measure how far the vehicle has travelled. Use the felt-tipped marker to make a note on the sheet of paper: 'Vehicle 1 …cm'. Push the second vehicle from the same starting point and ask another child to come and measure the distance travelled. Make a note: 'Vehicle 2 …cm'. *Which vehicle went further? Was it the one you predicted?* Ask the children whether they thought the test was fair. *Did both vehicles have the same chance? They started from the same place, so that was fair, but what about the push that they were given, was that fair? Can we be sure that I gave the same push to each vehicle? Is there any way of measuring that? If I gave one a harder push and one a more gentle push by mistake would that have been fair?*

Set up the slope and stand, marking on the slope where the starting point is. Repeat the test, this time running each vehicle down the slope from the same starting point. Be sure to place the vehicle and then let go without pushing it. Again, ask some children to measure the distances travelled and make a note on the sheet. *Did the same vehicle win?* Ask the children if they think that using the ramp made the test fairer. *How?* (They both ran down the ramp, from the same starting point, with the ramp at the same height, and without pushing, so they both had the same 'chance'.)

GROUP ACTIVITIES

1. Put the children into groups of four or six and give each group a ramp and stand, a selection of three or four vehicles and a metre stick. Ask the children to test the distance each vehicle travels, making the test fair in the same way as was done in the Main teaching activity. They should record the distance travelled by each vehicle, turn their recording into a block graph and compare the distances to find which vehicle travelled the furthest, which came next, and so on. Two or three groups could then join together to compare their graphs and find out which vehicle was the overall winner and which travelled the shortest distance. They could construct a master graph to show this.

2. As individuals, ask the children to write about how you made the test fair in the Main teaching activity. They could draw the equipment used. *What did you need to do to give each vehicle a 'fair chance'?*

DIFFERENTIATION

1. Putting the children into mixed-ability groups so that they can help each other should enable all the children to take part in this activity.

2. Expect a fairly detailed piece of writing with a good level of understanding from the more able children. Some children, although they may write less, will show some understanding of making the test fair. Less able children may need to tell you their ideas.

ASSESSMENT

Use the children's work from both Group activities to help you make judgements about the level of their understanding. During the Plenary session, note those children who are able to answer your questions.

PLENARY

Discuss what was done in the Main teaching activity and ask some of the children to read their piece of writing or tell you about the test and how you made it as fair as possible. Use the children's graphs from Group activity 1 to compare the distances travelled by all the vehicles. *Was there an overall class winner? Was there an overall class loser?* Ask some children to come to the front and interpret their graphs, comparing the distances their vehicles travelled.

OUTCOMES

● Gain a better understanding of how to make a test fair.
● Can compare the distances travelled by vehicles.

LINKS

Maths: graphs and measuring.

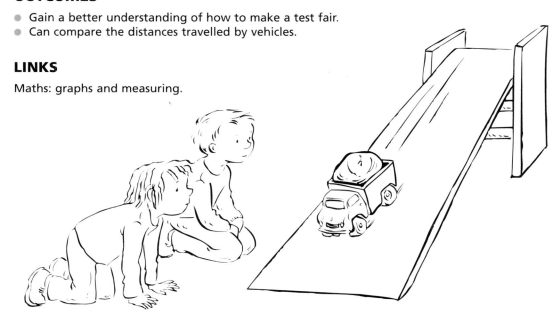

LESSON 8

Objective	● To investigate the effect of weight on distance travelled.
Resources	For each group: a ramp and stand (shelves and a pile of books will do), a wheeled vehicle (one that can be loaded with play dough to increase the weight), metre sticks, play dough, writing materials, a copy of photocopiable page 67 for each group (if required).
Main activity	Divide the children into groups of four or six (four is better if you have enough ramps because each child in the group will then have a job to do – rolling the vehicle, increasing the load, measuring, recording). Tell the children that they are going to find out if increasing the weight of a vehicle makes any difference to the distance it travels. Help them to organise their test to make it fair (same height of ramp each time, same car, same surface at the bottom of the ramp, release the vehicle from the same place each time, don't push the vehicle). Use photocopiable page 67 if you wish. The children should increase the weight by roughly the same amount each time. Remind them that they need to measure the distances and record them as they are working. They could go on to make a graph of their findings.
Differentiation	You may wish to put the children into mixed-ability groups to provide support for any who find it difficult to organise and carry out a fair test.
Assessment	As the children are working, note those who show some understanding of how to organise and carry out a fair test. Note those children who are, themselves, beginning to identify the things that should be kept the same (variables). Which children are able to read the metre stick and record accurately?
Plenary	Ask some of the children to report what they did and what they found out to you and the class. *Did the weight of the vehicle make a difference to the distance it travelled? How did you keep your test fair?* They could refer to their recording sheet to help them.
Outcomes	● Can carry out a fair test with help. ● Know that the weight of a vehicle affects the distance it travels.

LESSON 9

Objectives	● To carry out a fair test with help. ● To investigate the effect of ramp heights on distance travelled.
Resources	For each group: a wheeled vehicle, a slope and stand (if shelves and books are used, the books must all be of the same thickness to make the test fair), photocopiable page 67, metre sticks, writing materials.
Main activity	Divide the children into groups of four or six (four is better if you have enough ramps because each child in the group will then have a job to do – rolling the vehicle, increasing the load, measuring, recording). Tell the children that they are going to find out if increasing the height of the ramp makes any difference to the distance their vehicle travels. Help them to organise their test to make it fair (increase the height of the ramp by the same amount each time, use the same car, same surface at the bottom of the ramp, release the vehicle from the same place each time, don't push the vehicle). Use photocopiable page 67 if you wish. Remind the children that they need to measure the distances and record them as they are working. They could go on to make a graph of their findings.
Differentiation	Some children will find it more difficult to carry out a fair test. Put the children into mixed-ability groups so that they can help each other or if you have extra adult help in the classroom less able groups could work with an adult.
Assessment	Note those children who show an understanding of how to organise and carry out a fair test and those who are making accurate recordings.
Plenary	Talk to the children about their test. *What have you found out? How did you organise the test to keep it fair? Did the height of the ramp make a difference? Did the vehicle travel furthest when the ramp was as high as possible or was there a 'best height' somewhere in the middle?* Go through some of the recording sheets with the children and discuss how they have recorded their findings.
Outcomes	● Can carry out a fair test with help. ● Know that ramp height affects the distance a vehicle travels.

LESSON 10

OBJECTIVE

● To know that some objects float because water pushes up on them

RESOURCES

Main teaching activity: One plastic tank or washing-up bowl per group (of four or six) filled with water; one small, empty margarine tub per group (or two per group of six); a selection of small heavy objects such as marbles, pebbles or washed gravel; paper towels for mopping-up!
Group activities: 1. A copy of photocopiable page 153 for each child, a flip chart or board, a tank or bowl for each group (as above) with a collection of objects, some of which will float and some of which will sink (stone, piece of wood, paper clip, cork, marble, lolly stick, coin and so on. Try to include some relatively light things that sink, like a paper clip, so that the misconception that light things always float is not reinforced). **2.** A tank of water and two small empty plastic bottles with lids for each group.

PREPARATION

Write a list of the names of the objects to be used in Group activity 1 on the flip chart or board.

BACKGROUND

Vocabulary
float, sink, push, pull, gravity, upthrust

At this stage, children do not need to know about why things float or sink in any greater detail than in the outcome for this lesson. It is useful for you to have a bit more information in order to avoid reinforcing misconceptions and to help you answer the more difficult questions that able children sometimes ask!

When an object is greater in density than water it sinks. It displaces the water molecules easily and sinks through the water because of the force of gravity. Water also exerts a force called upthrust. When the upthrust of the water equals the weight of an object, that object floats. Plasticine is denser than water, so a ball of Plasticine occupying a volume of 50ml will displace 50ml of water, but will weigh more and therefore sink. If you then make the same piece of Plasticine into the shape of a boat it will have a greater volume and displace a larger amount of water than when it was rolled in to a ball. This amount of water weighs more than the boat itself does and so will float.

INTRODUCTION

The story of Noah's Ark, or any story about boats and floating would be a good stimulus for this lesson. Some of the passages about Ratty and Mole going boating from *The Wind in the Willows* by Kenneth Grahame would also be suitable.

MAIN TEACHING ACTIVITY

Remind the children about the work that they did in Year 1/Primary 2 when they pushed down on a ball that was floating and felt the water trying to push the ball up. They were feeling the upthrust of the water against the ball and when they let go of the ball it bobbed to the surface and floated again. Ask: *Do you remember that we talked about gravity in an earlier lesson? What does gravity do?* (Pull things down towards the centre of the Earth.)

Put the children into groups of four or six and give each group one or two empty margarine tubs (see Resources) plus a supply of small, heavy objects to load their tubs with until they sink. Groups of four would be preferable, but this may depend on how many tanks or bowls you can muster. Ask them to predict whether they think that their tub will float or sink if they put it on the water, then let them have a go.

Explain to them that their tubs float because the upward push of the water (upthrust) is greater than the force of gravity that is trying to pull them down and make them sink. Ask: *What do you think will happen if you load the margarine tub boats*? (They will sink.) Remind them that gravity is pulling down on everything, including the objects that they are going to load into their boats. Allow them to load their boats until they sink. Ask: *What do you think has happened? Why have the boats sunk?* (Because when the boats are loaded the force of gravity pulling down on the boat, plus the things in it, is greater than the force (upthrust) of the water pushing the boat up.)

GROUP ACTIVITIES

1. Put the children into groups of four or six and give each group a tank of water and a collection of objects. Give each child a copy of photocopiable page 153. Ask the children to look carefully at the objects and predict whether they will float or sink, writing the name of the object (using the list on the flip chart to help them if necessary) and their prediction on the sheet. Set the sheets aside so that they don't get wet! The children should now place each object onto the water and make sets of things that float and things that sink. Mop up before checking the sets against the sheets!

Did you predict correctly? Explain again that things float when the upthrust of the water is greater than the force of gravity pulling the object down, and sink when the force of gravity pulling down is greater than the upthrust of the water.

2. Put the children into groups of four or six. Give each group a tank of water and one or two small, empty plastic bottles with lids. Ask the children to put the bottles in the water. *Do they float or sink?* Now ask them to fill each bottle, carefully replace the lid, and put them back in the water. *What happens now?* Ask the children if they can find a way to make the bottles float just below the surface of the water. (They need to partially fill the bottle and replace the top.) Remind them that when the bottles are floating the upthrust is greater than the pull of gravity. When they sink the reverse is true. When the bottles float just below the surface the increased weight of the bottle is not quite enough to overcome the upthrust of the water.

DIFFERENTIATION

All the children should be able to take part in both these activities, but some may understand this difficult concept better than others.

ASSESSMENT

During all the activities and the Plenary session note which children can answer your questions and show an understanding that an object floats due to the upward push of the liquid being greater than the downward pull of gravity.

PLENARY

Review what the children have done. *Why do things float? Why do they sink?* Look at some of the recording sheets from Group activity 1 and discuss them with the children. How accurate were their predictions?

OUTCOME

● Can recognise that an object floats due to the upward push of the liquid being greater than the downward pull of gravity.

LESSON 11

OBJECTIVES

● To know that forces can make moving objects go faster, change direction or slow down.
● To know that there is a force of friction between two surfaces.
● To know that friction is stronger between rough surfaces than smooth surfaces.
● To know that actions such as stretching, squeezing, twisting and turning can be explained as pushes and pulls.

RESOURCES

Assessment activities: 1. A copy of photocopiable page 154 for each child, pencils. **2.** A copy of photocopiable page 155 for each child, pencils, a flip chart or board.

INTRODUCTION

Ask the children to remind you of some of the things they have learned in this unit. *What are forces? What do they do?*

ASSESSMENT ACTIVITY 1

Give each child a copy of photocopiable page 154. Go through it with them to make sure that they understand it and can read the words at the bottom of the page. Ask them to choose the correct words to complete the sentences.

Answers

1. stop, 2. change direction, 3. faster, 4. higher, 5. friction, 6. more slowly, 7. rough, smooth.
8. Accept any answer that indicates understanding that ice is slippery because it is so smooth that there is little friction between it and shoes or skates.

Looking for levels

Most children should be able to answer questions 1–7 and should show some understanding of question 8. More able children will answer questions 1–7 correctly and give a detailed and accurate answer to question 8. Less able children should be able to answer questions 1, 3, 4 and 6, but may have trouble with 2, 5 and 7. They may not be able to answer question 8. As scientific understanding is being assessed, rather than the ability to write, accept a verbal explanation and annotate the child's sheet.

ASSESSMENT ACTIVITY 2

Give each child a copy of photocopiable page 155. Read the instructions at the top of the sheet with them, making sure that they understand what they have to do. Write 'push', 'pull' and 'push and pull' on the flip chart or board and remind the children that these are the forces they need to think about. Ask them to complete the sheet by writing the correct name of the force or forces being used underneath each of the pictures.

Answers

1. pull, 2. push and pull, 3. push, 4. push and pull, 5. pull, 6. push. 7 and 8. For the drawings of pushes and pulls accept answers that show that the child understands the difference between a push and a pull.

Looking for levels

Most children should complete questions 1–6 correctly. They may be able to draw two examples of other pushes or pulls. More able children will complete questions 1–6 correctly and draw three examples of both pushes and pulls. Less able children should be able to complete questions 1, 3, 5 and 6, but may write 'twist' rather than 'push and pull' for 2 and 4. They may have difficulty in thinking of any other examples of pushes and pulls. Some children may need to explain their pictures to you. If the explanations show understanding, accept this and annotate the sheet.

Which force?

Write 'push' or 'pull' in the box under each picture.

Forces snakes and ladders

33	34	35 Gravity pulls you down the slide.	36	37	38	39 You fall out of a tree. Gravity pulls you down.	40
32 Pull the light switch.	31	30	29	28	27	26	25
17	18	19	20	21 Push and pull to climb the ladder.	22	23	24 Push the ball down to make it bounce.
16	15	14	13	12 Pull your duck along to 14.	11	10	9
1	2 Pull yourself up a rope.	3	4	5	6	7 Push yourself off the floor and jump up.	8

Will it float or sink?

Name of object	Prediction		Was your prediction correct? ✓ or ✗
	Will float ✓	Will sink ✓	

UNIT 6 FORCES & MOTION

Making things move

Complete these sentences with the correct words from the list below.

1. If I put the brakes on, my bike will _____

2. When I hit the ball I am using a force to _____

3. If I push the car harder it will go _____

4. If I push the ball harder it will bounce _____

5. If I push the car on the carpet it will go slower
than on the playground because of the force of _____

6. If I push the car less hard it will go _____

7. There is more friction between _____ surfaces than

_____ surfaces.

change direction   faster   smooth   rough
        more slowly   stop   higher   friction

Now write an answer to question 8.

8. Why do we slide about on ice? _____

_____

_____

_____

Making things move

Write the names of the forces being used in these pictures.

1.  _____	2. 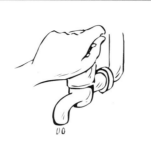 _____	3.  _____
4.  _____	5.  _____	6.  _____

7. Draw three more pictures of a push force being used.

8. Draw three more pictures of a pull force being used.

Properties and uses

ORGANISATION (14 LESSONS)

	OBJECTIVES	MAIN ACTIVITY	GROUP ACTIVITIES	PLENARY	OUTCOMES
LESSON 1	● To know that light sources are used in different ways.	Revise Y1/P2 work on light sources. Discuss the use of light sources.	Consider and record how many lights there are at home. Write a story or poem about what it would be like without any light.	Discuss the uses of light and share the children's writing.	● Can recognise different uses of light sources.
LESSON 2	● To know that light cannot pass through some materials and that is how shadows are created.	Investigate and have fun with shadows.	Investigate which materials make shadows. Draw silhouettes.	Discuss findings. Identify the silhouettes.	● Can explain that a shadow forms due to light being blocked.
LESSON 3	● To know that light cannot pass through some materials and that is how shadows are created.	Make simple shadow puppets. Create plays. Act them out with the puppets.		Watch the plays or stories.	● Can explain that a shadow forms due to light being blocked.
LESSON 4	● To know that light can pass through some materials, but not others.	Test different materials with a lamp. Distinguish between transparent, translucent and opaque materials.	Choose materials for stained glass windows. Make a peg doll.	Look at the children's work.	● Can recognise transparent, translucent and opaque materials.
LESSON 5	● To know that light is a form of energy.	Discuss different forms of energy, including solar energy.	Investigate the effect of light on a solar cell. Leave trays of water in Sun and shade to find out what happens. Find out some uses of solar energy.	Report findings.	● Know that light is a form of energy.
LESSON 6	● To know that we make use of sounds in a variety of ways.	Discuss everyday uses of sound.	Complete a sheet about different types of sound. Create musical sounds to reflect different moods.	Talk about the uses of sound. Listen to the children's musical sounds.	● Can describe different ways in which we use sound.
LESSON 7	● To know that sounds can act as warnings.	Think about sounds that give us a warning.		Discuss important sounds.	● Know that some sounds give us warnings.
LESSON 8	● To know how to make a range of sounds using a collection of materials and objects.	Make musical instruments.	Make up a simple tune using instruments. Record this or play it to the rest of the class. Investigate sounds around the classroom.	Listen to the children's instruments, tunes and sounds.	● Can make a simple instrument to make sounds.
LESSON 9	● To be able to relate home-made instruments to real instruments.	Match home-made instruments to real ones.		Play the home-made instruments.	● Can relate home-made instruments to real instruments.

ORGANISATION (14 LESSONS)

	OBJECTIVES	MAIN ACTIVITY	GROUP ACTIVITIES	PLENARY	OUTCOMES
LESSON 10	● To know that devices can be made to improve our hearing. ● To plan and carry out a simple investigation with help.	Revise Y1/P2 work on ear defenders. Discuss methods of improving hearing, including ear trumpets and stethoscopes.	Use a stethoscope to listen to each other's bodies. Make a yoghurt pot telephone.	Discuss ways to enhance hearing.	● Know that hearing can be enhanced. ● Can plan and carry out a simple investigation with help.
LESSON 11	● To know that sounds get fainter as they travel away from a source and that loud sounds travel further than quiet sounds. ● To carry out a simple investigation.	Revise Y1/P2 work on sound. Repeat this work, but take measurements and produce a table.	Use the results to create a bar chart. Make ripples on a bowl of water to understand how sound waves travel.	Discuss findings.	● Know that sounds get fainter as they travel away from a source. ● Can carry out a simple investigation.
LESSON 12	● To know that loud sounds travel further than quiet sounds. ● To carry out a simple investigation.	Compare loud and quiet sounds.		Consider why loud sounds travel further than quiet sounds.	● Know that loud sounds also get fainter as they travel away from a source but travel further than quiet sounds. ● Can carry out a simple investigation.
LESSON 13	● To know that sound is a form of energy. ● To make and test a simple prediction.	Watch moving energy change to sound energy, and vice versa. Use a tuning fork to see sound and movement energy.	Investigate if more movement makes more sound. Make a prediction on the sound made by beads in a pot. Watch rice on a drum to show that sound can move things.	Report findings.	● Can recognise that sound is a form of energy. ● Can make and test a simple prediction.

	OBJECTIVES	ACTIVITY 1	ACTIVITY 2
ASSESSMENT 14	● To know that light cannot pass through some materials and that shadows are created. ● To know that sounds get fainter as they travel away from a source. ● To know that loud sounds travel further than quiet sounds.	Understand why, and where, a shadow is formed.	Show understanding that sounds become fainter as they travel away from the source.

LESSON 1

OBJECTIVE

● To know that light sources are used in different ways.

RESOURCES

Main teaching activity: Flip chart or board.
Group activities: 1. A copy of photocopiable page 176 for each child, writing materials.
2. Writing and drawing materials.

Vocabulary

navigate, sunset, streetlight, floodlight, fuel, reliable, gas, electric, oil, candle, illuminated

BACKGROUND

The Sun is there for everyone during daylight hours, as the light from the Sun is so strong that it can even penetrate through cloud. It gives us light to get on with all our work. Plants need sunlight to make food so that they can grow. The Moon sometimes gives light at night (it is not a true light source: it reflects the Sun's light), and this is very important in rural areas where there are no streetlights. However, moonlight can be obscured by cloud and because of the phases of the Moon it is not always visible! The stars don't give a great deal of light, but they can sometimes be important for sailors who use them to navigate. These natural sources of light are also very important for people who don't have access to artificial lighting.

Artificial lighting comes in many forms. Fire is probably the most basic but we have learned to use other fuels to produce light – mostly oil, gas or electricity. Nowadays light is used in different ways, and for different purposes: decorative as well as purely utilitarian.

INTRODUCTION

Working with the whole class, remind the children of the work that they did in Year 1/Primary 2 about different light sources.

MAIN TEACHING ACTIVITY

Ask the children to name some light sources and, as they do, note them on the flip chart. Make sure that the list includes the Sun and stars. Group other sources according to the fuel they use, for example gas (camping gas lamps, gas lights), wax (candles of various sorts), oil (oil lamps, Divali lamps, Aladdin's lamp), electricity (ceiling lights, desk or table lamps, torches, floodlights,

advertising and so on). The Moon reflects light from the Sun, but is not a light source.

How do we use the different lights? (We use sunlight as much as we can. We have windows to let the sunlight into our buildings. Sometimes there are extra windows or skylights in the roof to give us even more light. We can't always see the stars so we can't rely on them.) Sailors used to navigate by the stars but now most of them have more reliable instruments to tell them where they are. We can't rely on the stars and so we need other, more sophisticated, sources of light when it is dark.

But do we only use light sources when it is dark? Point to the group on the board that includes candles. Ask: *How, and when, do we use candles?* (They have to be lit with a match. They are used on birthday cakes, in church or for other religious celebrations, in the garden, at barbecues or around the house to smell nice). Tell the children that before we had gas or electricity, people often only had candles to light their homes and they often had to do their work by candlelight. Nowadays we use them for fun and celebrations. Remind the children of the dangers of playing with matches or lighted candles.

Now look at the oil lamp group. *Where might these be used?* (Historically, some rich people may have had oil lamps instead of candles. They are still used in some remote places where there is no electricity supply. Some farmers may still use oil lanterns, but these have mostly been replaced by electric torches.) Next, look at the light sources using gas as a fuel. Tell the children that before electricity was discovered, people used to have gaslights in their houses and the first streetlights were also gas. A man, called a lamplighter, would go along every evening to light the lamps and then again in the morning to put them out. Ask: *Where do we use gas lights today*? (Sometimes when we go on a camping or caravanning holiday we use lights that run off a small cylinder of a special gas.)

Now look at the biggest group, light sources that use electricity. This will be the type of lighting that the children are most familiar with but try to help them appreciate how much, and in how many different ways, we use it.

Ceiling lights give a general light for everyone in the room, but a desk or table lamp gives a concentrated light over a smaller area. *When might that be useful?* (For someone reading or sewing or doing other delicate work.) *Some people have a light just outside their front door. Why is that useful? Why do we have streetlights?* (So that people can see who is there or where they are going, to prevent accidents, to keep people safe.) Ask the children, next time they go on a journey, to check if all streetlights are the same. Those on side roads are often a different design from those on main roads or motorways, and some roundabouts have very tall posts with a cluster of lights at the top. *Why do you think this is? Where else might you see clusters of lights on a tall frame or post?* (Some children may have been to a football match or other sports meeting and seen the floodlights.)

These are all 'useful' lights, but sometimes lights are used just for decoration. Can the children think of any examples? (Christmas decorations, coloured lights on shops or theatres.) Some of these lights are also there to tell us something important or to warn us of possible danger. They might be advertising food or drink, or what is happening inside the building. Ask the children if they can think of anywhere lights are used to warn us. (Illuminated road signs, traffic lights, road crossings, flashing lights on railway crossings, flashing blue lights on emergency vehicles or yellow ones on other road hazards.) *Why are flashing lights used?* (These are more likely to attract attention than a continuous light.)

GROUP ACTIVITIES

1. Give each child a copy of photocopiable page 176 and ask them to think very carefully about all the lights they have in their house; not just those hanging from the ceiling or on desks, but all the little warning lights on the television, video, washing machine, cooker and so on. Ask them to make a list of the lights found in each room.

2. Ask the children to use their imaginations to think and write about what it would be like if there were no light at all. *Would it be hot or cold without the Sun? What would happen to plants and animals? How would we find our way about?* The children could present their thoughts as prose or poetry.

DIFFERENTIATION

1. Less able children might present their lists in a pictorial format. Some children might like to take their lists home to check them against the real thing. They could add any lights they have forgotten and report back the next day.
2. All the children can do this activity, according to their ability.

ASSESSMENT

Use the children's work from the Group activities to assess their understanding.

PLENARY

Ask some of the children to share the lists of lights they have in their homes. Do any of them have special lights anywhere, such as a bright light for Mum's sewing, or a night light? Ask other children to read their stories or poems and share what they think it would be like without light.

OUTCOME

● Can recognise different uses of light sources.

LINKS

Unit 8, Lessons 1 and 2: the Sun as a source of light.

LESSON 2

OBJECTIVE

● To know that light cannot pass through some materials and that is how shadows are created.

RESOURCES

Main teaching activity: The poem 'My Shadow' by Robert Louis Stevenson from *A Child's Garden of Verse* (Puffin); a sunny day, the playground.
Group activities: 1. For each group of three or four: white card to make a screen, a torch or small lamp; a collection of materials such as card, clear plastic, net, coloured acetates, greaseproof paper, plastic sheet, fabric and so on, to be used as filters. **2.** Large sheets of black and pale paper, chalk, OHP, scissors, adhesive.

Vocabulary

shadow, shade, transparent, opaque

BACKGROUND

Children often find shadows fascinating, but have difficulty understanding them. Some may have a problem getting the light source, object and shadow in the right order. If asked to draw themselves and their shadow many children will draw them side by side or one under the other but without them actually touching.

Shadows are formed when light is blocked by an opaque material.

The area of the shadow where no light gets through, and which is darkest, is called the umbra. At the edges of this there may be an area of lighter shadow

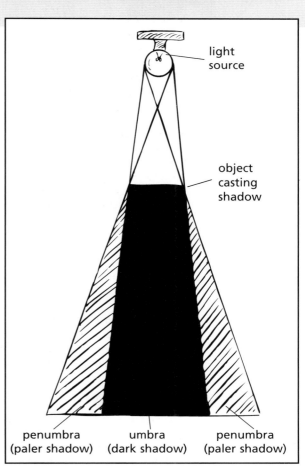

light source

object casting shadow

penumbra (paler shadow)   umbra (dark shadow)   penumbra (paler shadow)

called the penumbra. Children do not need to know these terms at this stage, but they should be aware that shadows are not always of the same density. Learning why this is so will come later.

INTRODUCTION

Read 'My Shadow' by Robert Louis Stevenson.

MAIN TEACHING ACTIVITY

Choose a nice sunny day and take the children out on to the playground. *Can you all see your shadow? Is it always in front of you or behind you? Can you jump on your shadow or run away from it?* Put the children in pairs and let them play at trying to jump on each other's shadows.

Gather the children together and, if possible, sit them down while they get their breath back. Ask them if they can remember where their shadow was, in relation to the Sun. *If you had your backs to the Sun where would the shadow be?* (In front of them.) *If you were facing the Sun, where would it be then?* (Behind them.)

Ask the children to stand up with a partner so that their shadows are in front of them. *Where do your shadows begin?* (At their feet.) *Is there a gap between you and your shadow?* (No.) *What happens if one partner stands in front of the other?* (There is only one shadow.) *Can you make your shadow have four arms? Four legs? Stand a little way apart and make your shadows shake hands without touching each other.* Ask: *Why do we have a shadow?* (Because the Sun's light cannot go through us.) *Does everything stop light passing through?* Look around the playground to find some more shadows. Ask the children to point them out to you and say what is causing them.

GROUP ACTIVITIES

1. Ask the children, working in groups of three or four, to investigate which materials make shadows. They should shine a torch or a lamp on each piece of material, placed in front of a white screen, and should then sort them into two sets: those that make shadows and those that do not. Some children may decide that they need a third group for things that are in-between.

2. Ask the children to work in pairs to draw silhouettes. One of the pair should sit sideways in a strong light so that a clear shadow of his or her profile is thrown on to a piece of black paper pinned up behind. (Several children may be able to sit in the beam of an OHP. Make sure that the beam is not shining in their eyes or that they sit with their eyes closed. Pin sheets of black paper to the wall or painting easels.) The other partner draws carefully around the shadow with chalk. The children then change places and repeat the process. Cut the silhouettes out and mount them on a pale background. Reverse the silhouette before mounting to hide any stray chalk marks – the child will just be looking the other way! As the children are working ask them what is happening and why a shadow is being formed.

DIFFERENTIATION

1. If the children work in mixed-ability groups they should all be able to take part, otherwise less able children may need help to set up their investigation.
2. All the children should be able to take part in this activity. Some may need help with cutting out the silhouettes.

ASSESSMENT

Observe how the children carry out their investigation. Note those children who can arrange the screen, light and object in the correct order, or those who can tell you, in the Plenary session, how they did it. Note those children who, in Group activity 2, can tell you how the shadow is being formed.

PLENARY

Discuss what the children found out in their investigation. Tell them that materials that block the light are called opaque and those that let light through are transparent. Look at the silhouettes and ask the children to tell you the order in which the screen, object and light have to be in order to get a shadow. Can the children recognise the silhouettes of each other?

OUTCOME

● Can explain that a shadow forms due to light being blocked.

LINKS

Unit 8, Lesson 2: shadows.

LESSON 3

Objective	● To know that light cannot pass through some materials and that is how shadows are created.
Resources	Card, scissors, coloured acetates, pipe-cleaners, adhesive, paper sticks or thin dowel, a light source (OHP), an old sheet for a screen.
Main activity	In groups of six, make shadow puppets and act out a simple well-known story, or one devised by the children. Draw characters on card and cut them out. Pipe-cleaners can be used to make arms or legs on small figures or whiskers on animals. Coloured acetate can be used to cover 'cut-outs' to make the figures or objects more interesting. The play is best viewed with the audience on the other side of the screen from the puppeteers.
Differentiation	All the children should be able to participate in this activity. More able children can create their own story and characters. Less able children may make less-complicated puppets and choose simple stories.
Assessment	Observe the children making their puppets and performing their plays. Note those who show an understanding of how shadows are formed.
Plenary	Enjoy watching the plays or stories from each group.
Outcome	● Can explain that a shadow forms due to light being blocked.

LESSON 4

OBJECTIVE

● To know that light can pass through some materials, but not others.

RESOURCES

Main teaching activity: A collection of materials that are transparent, translucent or opaque (such as clear and opaque plastic, glass, pottery, wood, metal, fabrics such as wool and voile); a lamp or torch; small pieces (5cm × 5cm) of tracing paper, dark sugar paper and clear cellophane or plastic, adhesive tape or adhesive; a copy of photocopiable page 177 for each child.
Group activities: 1. Black paper; small pieces of coloured tissue, acetate, cellophane (sweet wrappers) and other coloured papers; scissors, adhesive, reference books containing pictures of stained glass windows **2.** A wooden dolly peg for each child; small pieces (8cm × 20cm) of transparent, translucent and opaque plastic (many supermarket carrier bags are translucent, food bags are transparent and the more up-market carrier bags are opaque); scissors, small elastic bands, felt-tipped pens, scraps of wool or wood shavings, pipe-cleaners, adhesive.

Vocabulary

transparent, translucent, opaque, good, poor

BACKGROUND

Most children will quickly grasp the idea that some things are transparent and others opaque, but some may find it difficult to sort translucent objects from the other two. Transparent materials are those, such as clear glass, where an object can be seen clearly through the material almost as if it weren't there. Some transparent materials are coloured, but it is still possible to see through them quite clearly. Opaque materials do not allow light through at all, so we can see the material, but not what is behind it. Translucent materials do allow some light to pass through but it is sufficiently diffused to prevent us from seeing objects on the other side of the material clearly (frosted glass windows, for example). We may be able to see shadowy shapes, but no detail.

MAIN TEACHING ACTIVITY

Working with the whole class, explain that a transparent material is one that you can see through because it lets all the light through. Explain also that an opaque material is one that doesn't let any light through so you cannot see through it at all. Show the children the collection of materials, beginning with those that are clearly transparent or opaque. Hold them up one by one in front of a lamp and ask the children into which set they would put each material – transparent or opaque.

Now hold up the translucent materials and ask the children if they can describe how they are different from the materials they have already sorted. Would they put them in one of the two groups you have already, or should they be in a different group? Explain that these materials that let some light through are called translucent. Ask the children: *Where might materials like this be useful?* (Windows where some light, but also some privacy, is needed; light fabrics for curtains and dresses; tracing paper.)

Give each child one small piece each of tracing paper, sugar paper and clear cellophane or plastic and a copy of photocopiable page 177. Tell the children to stick one piece of paper on each dotted line so that it covers the smiley face. They should use adhesive or tape just along the top edge of the paper so that it can be lifted like a flap. They should then complete the sentences, choosing words from the bottom of the page.

GROUP ACTIVITIES

1. Give each child a piece of black paper from which to cut a pattern of holes, and a selection of small coloured pieces of transparent, translucent and opaque paper. (The coloured paper could be put in the middle of a table for a group to choose from.) The holes can be random shapes or regular patterns cut from folded paper. Each hole or space must then be covered with coloured transparent material from the selection to give a 'stained glass' effect when the finished pictures are mounted on a window. Make sure that the children leave a reasonable margin between each hole so that there is space to stick the transparent materials to the paper.
2. Give each of the children a wooden dolly peg and tell them to choose materials from a collection to make a three-layered skirt for their peg doll. The first layer should be opaque, the next translucent and the top layer transparent. (They must be in this order.) Fix each layer with an elastic band. The children could then finish their dolls by drawing a face with felt-tipped pens, adding arms made from pipe-cleaners and wool or wood shavings for hair.

DIFFERENTIATION

1. Some children may need help in cutting out their patterns from the black paper. You may wish to give some children a pattern already cut out for them to fill in. More able children might try to replicate the shape of a church window.
2. Some children might find it easier to work with a partner so that one can hold the skirts while the other fixes the elastic band.

ASSESSMENT

Use the children's work from the Main teaching activity to assess their understanding. Observe the children as they sort the materials in Group activity 1 and, in Group activity 2, check that they have the layers in the right order and can name them.

PLENARY

Ask some of the children to show the work they have done. Ask them to name the properties of the three different types of material they have been using, then ask them to think where the different properties would be useful. (Transparent where you need to see through the material in such things as windows, covers for books or work cards and some storage boxes or jars.

Translucent where you want light but don't need to see through, or where privacy is needed – frosted windows, tracing paper. Opaque where light is not needed and you do not need to see what is on the other side – boxes or cases.)

OUTCOME

● Can recognise transparent, translucent and opaque materials.

LINKS

Art: investigating materials.

LESSON 5

OBJECTIVE

● To know that light is a form of energy.

RESOURCES

Main teaching activity: A torch, a battery-powered calculator, a solar-powered calculator.
Group activities: 1. A solar-powered calculator for each group (make sure the calculator is not dual-powered or it will continue to work on batteries even in the dark), small pieces of tissue paper to cover the solar cells on the calculators, writing materials. **2.** For each group: two shallow trays (of the same size and colour), water, two thermometers, a sunny day, writing materials, reference materials about the use of solar power. The Centre for Alternative Technology in Machynlleth, Powys, Wales (tel: 01654 705950; www.cat.org.uk), provides information on all kinds of alternative and sustainable energy sources.

Vocabulary

heat, light, movement, change, energy, electrical energy, solar power

BACKGROUND

Energy is needed to make things, including our bodies, work. We get our energy from the food we eat: that is our fuel. A car gets its energy from petrol or diesel, and many devices use electrical energy. A torch uses electrical energy from a battery, while a ceiling light or table lamp uses electrical energy from the mains supply.

Energy comes in many forms and can be changed or transferred from one form to another, most of which are too complicated or abstract for children of this age. They should, however, be able to understand that energy is needed to make things work and that we can get energy in different ways. Energy can be stored in the form of fuels (energy in the form of light and heat is released from the wax in a candle as it burns; we get light and heat from burning wood or coal). Sometimes this energy is used to create movement (in a steam engine or in a power station to drive turbines and produce electricity). Light is a form of energy that we can get directly from the Sun. It can be used as light, heat or can be changed into electrical energy.

INTRODUCTION

Ask the children what they think the word 'energy' means. Where have they heard it used? They may have heard parents or teachers saying: *You have got a lot of energy today. You must have had an extra egg for breakfast!* or something similar. While this is not strictly a definition of energy, it may help the children to understand that energy is needed for something to work. If we have no energy, we don't feel like doing anything.

MAIN TEACHING ACTIVITY

Electricity is one form of energy and most children can understand that electrical devices need electrical energy to make them work. Ask the children if they can name some things that need electricity. (Lights, food mixer, kettle, fan, heater, torch, radio.) Tell them that electricity is a form of energy and that energy is needed to make things work. All the devices that they have named require energy in the form of electricity.

Show them a torch and switch it on to show that it works. Then take the batteries out and switch it on again. *Why doesn't it work?* (It has no energy supply.) Replace the batteries and ask the children if they think it will work now. (It should do!) Show them a calculator that uses a battery and talk about it needing the electrical energy from the battery to make it work. Now show them a solar-powered calculator. *Does anyone know how this works? It doesn't have any batteries so how does it get its energy?* (From sunlight or artificial light falling on special light-sensitive cells.) Explain that light is another form of energy and some things can use light to make them work. Remind them how plants need light to make their food so that they can grow. Plants use the light to provide the energy they need to do this.

GROUP ACTIVITIES

1. Divide the children into groups of three or four and give each group a solar-powered calculator. Ask them to look carefully to find the solar cells. Explain that these are special things that can change light energy into electrical energy to make the calculator work. Ask them to investigate placing layers of tissue paper over the solar cells to see what effect this has. They should then write about what they find out.

2. Ask the children, working in groups of three or four, to put one small, shallow tray of water in a shady spot and a similar one in full Sun (or use a spotlight). Use a thermometer to measure the temperature of the water every hour or so to find out what happens.

Encourage the children to use the reference materials to find out other uses for solar energy. In some countries banks of mirrors are used to focus the Sun's rays to heat water. Some houses, even in this country, have solar panels on their roofs to help heat the water for the house. There are groups of people experimenting with solar-powered cars. Remind the children that they are going to report back to the rest of the class so they may need to make some notes.

DIFFERENTIATION

1. All the children should be able to do this simple investigation. Explain to more able children that solar cells are properly called 'photosensitive' or 'photovoltaic'. *Can you use a dictionary to find out what 'photo' means when it is put in front of a word?*
2. The children could do research in mixed-ability groups so that able readers can help those who are less confident.

ASSESSMENT

Listen to the children as they report back their findings from the Group activities and note those who make sensible contributions.

PLENARY

Ask the children from each group to report back on what they have discovered. Ask children from Group activity 1 to explain why the calculator does not work when the light-sensitive cells are covered. Then ask children from Group activity 2 to explain what happened to the trays of water. *Can you explain why one got hotter than the other? Have you discovered any other uses for light energy?*

OUTCOME

● Know that light is a form of energy.

LINKS

Unit 4, Lesson 13: heat as a form of energy.
Literacy: taking notes, using reference materials and a dictionary.

LESSON 6

OBJECTIVE

● To know that we make use of sounds in a variety of ways.

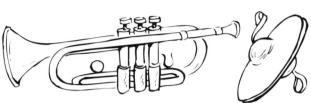

RESOURCES

Main teaching activity: An old or toy telephone.
Group activities: 1. A copy of photocopiable page 178 for each child, writing materials. **2.** 'Mood cards' (see Preparation, below), a collection of musical instruments, a tape recorder (optional).

PREPARATION

Prepare a set of 'mood cards' by writing the names of moods (angry, sad, happy, jolly, peaceful) for the children to interpret through musical sounds.

BACKGROUND

Sound plays an important part in our lives, and for most humans it is the main means of communication. We speak to each other directly, or by telephone, television or radio. We use bells or buzzers, and other sounds, to send messages or warnings. We enjoy music or drama. Retailers use sound to influence our shopping habits and increase their sales.

Unfortunately these days there is often so much sound around that we become accustomed to it and no longer listen to the individual sounds. The hum of the boiler or the motorway drone is no longer registered unless our attention is drawn to it. It is, however, important that we do learn to listen to the sounds around us. We can pick up clues and information about what is happening, some of which could be very important in helping to keep us safe. (Many modern lorries emit a warning sound if they are reversing, and pelican crossings bleep to let you know it is safe to cross the road.)

INTRODUCTION

Remind the children of what they learned in Year 1/Primary 2 about sounds and noise. Ask the children to close their eyes. Can they still guess what is happening around them? *How do you know?* (They can hear sounds.)

MAIN TEACHING ACTIVITY

Tell the children to open their eyes and ask: *What sounds can you hear?* (People talking, chairs and tables scraping on the floor, perhaps music in the distance, footsteps.) *What is happening? Most of us do lots of talking but why do we talk and what do we talk about?* Ask the children for some suggestions. (To greet people and pass on news, to ask for and give information, to communicate when playing games or working together in lessons, we can shout to give

Vocabulary

sound, noise, call, voice, mood, instrument, feeling, pleasure, information, warning

warnings.) *What else can a voice tell you?* (The tone of voice can tell you whether a person is happy, sad or angry.) We can recognise people by their voices even if we can't see them. *These days we can make our voices travel over very long distances. How do we do that?* (Telephone, radio, television.)

Ask if any of the children talk to Grandma, or another distant friend or relative on the phone. Ask the children what sort of things they talk about. Use an old or toy telephone to role-play a telephone conversation. Sometimes the telephone is very important in calling for help. Can the children remember from Year 1/Primary 2 how to make an emergency call? Ask one or two children to demonstrate how they would call the emergency services. Talk about how important it is only to do so when there is a real emergency and the dangers of making false calls. *How do we know that someone wants to speak to us on the telephone?* (It rings or, if it is a mobile, it might play a little tune.) *What other sounds might we hear during the day that tell us something?* (Alarm clock, school bell, road crossing, microwave ping, doorbell.) Talk about each of these sounds and what they tell us.

Point out to the children that these are all useful sounds, but that sometimes we use sound to give us pleasure. *Can you tell me any sounds that you enjoy?* (There could be a wide range of answers to this question but, if no one else mentions it, suggest that music gives pleasure to lots of people). Some people sing, whistle or play a musical instrument. Sometimes we just listen to music but at other times we dance or exercise to it. *Why do soldiers often march to music?* We often use music in celebrations or religious ceremonies. *Where else might you hear music?* (On the radio or television, on CD or tape, in shops, in lifts, at a football match.) *Does music sometimes make you feel happy or sad?*

GROUP ACTIVITIES

1. Give each child a copy of photocopiable page 178 and ask them to complete it.
2. Divide the children into groups of four and give each group a 'mood card' (see Preparation). Encourage the children to choose from the collection of musical instruments to create sounds to express the mood on their card. Give them a short time to work together and then ask each group to play their sounds, while the rest of the children try to guess what the mood is. If there is enough time groups could exchange cards and create a new sound sequence.

DIFFERENTIATION

1. Some children may draw pictures instead of writing when they complete the photocopiable sheet. Expect more able children to give longer and more varied lists.
2. All the children should enjoy participating in this activity.

ASSESSMENT

Use the children's completed sheets from Group activity 1 to assess their understanding. Note those children who contribute to the Plenary session and understand ways in which we use sound and that it plays an important part in keeping us safe.

PLENARY

Talk about how sound helps us to understand what is happening around us and how some sounds help to keep us safe. Ask some groups to play their sounds from Group activity 2 so that the rest of the children can try to guess the mood they are expressing.

OUTCOME

● Can describe different ways in which we use sound.

LINKS

Music: listening, creating and developing musical ideas.

LESSON 7

Objective	● To know that sounds can act as warnings.
Resources	A flip chart or board.
Main activity	Ask the children to think about the sounds they hear during a day. Ask them to think about how many sounds give a warning of some kind. It may just be a gentle reminder or it may be of real danger. Make a list on the flip chart of all these sounds, and talk about the importance of each one. *Are there any that should never be ignored?* (Ambulance, fire engine, police car, road crossing, a lorry reversing. Other sounds might include: alarm clock, microwave ping, doorbell, oven timer, shop bell, car or burglar alarm.) See if you can arrange a fire drill so that the children hear the fire alarm and can practise their response to it.
Differentiation	This activity is accessible to all the children.
Assessment	Note the children's reaction to the fire alarm. Do they understand that it is a warning that must be acted upon? During the Plenary session note those children who understand the importance of warning sounds.
Plenary	Talk about the importance of listening for and heeding warning sounds. How many can the children remember? Return to the list you made on the flip chart and ask the children if they want to identify any sounds as 'important' sounds. Mark these in some way.
Outcome	● Know that some sounds give us warnings.

LESSON 8

OBJECTIVE
● To know how to make a range of sounds using a collection of materials and objects.

RESOURCES

Main teaching activity: Instruments from the music trolley; elastic bands, small pieces of wood and dowel and small empty boxes for guitars; drinking straws for flutes; catering-size tin cans, plastic sheeting and string for drums; long card tubes, beads, rice or dried peas for rain makers; clay plant pots, beads, string and support for xylophones; combs, tissue paper, adhesive tape, string, scissors or other tools as appropriate.

Group activities: 1. Instruments made by the children, tape recorders. **2.** A range of beaters from the music trolley including rubber, wood and soft. Use short lengths (20–30cm) of dowel if you have insufficient beaters.

Vocabulary

percussion, shake, rattle, twang, bang, pluck, blow, stringed

BACKGROUND

The children made shakers or very simple elastic band guitars in Year 1/Primary 2. Make sure that they think of something different this time. A very wide range of instruments can be made by the children, using almost anything you care to name. The list of resources provided above should not be restrictive: allow the children to use their imaginations and use anything you think safe and reasonable. Encourage them to make as wide a range of instruments as possible.

INTRODUCTION

Look at a selection of instruments from the music trolley and rehearse how the different sounds are made (pluck, bang, scrape, blow).

MAIN TEACHING ACTIVITY

Working with the whole class, show the children the collection of materials and ask them to think about what kind of instruments they could make from some of them. Simple guitar-type instruments can be made from a box and elastic bands. Tissue boxes are often used but these tend to collapse if the bands are too tight. Margarine or ice cream tubs work quite well: turn the box upside-down and try putting a small piece of wood (or a pencil) under the elastic bands. This acts like a bridge and by moving this 'bridge' different notes can be produced by plucking the band on either side. A large catering-sized coffee tin can be made into a drum by stretching a piece of plastic sheeting across the top. Claves or rhythm sticks are very simple to make from short lengths of dowel sandpapered until they are smooth.

Clay plant pots can be suspended from a pole to make a xylophone. Retort stands and bar clamps make good supports and you can use a wooden bead to stop the string slipping through the hole in the bottom. Cardboard tubes from kitchen rolls, or better still those from rolls of fabric, can be made into rain makers by adding rice or other seeds which slide up and down as the tube is tipped and sealing each end. Corrugated card stuck to a length of wood or pieces of sandpaper stuck to blocks make simple scrapers. Blowers can be made from plastic drinking straws, or combs and tissue paper.

Give the children time to experiment and make their instruments.

GROUP ACTIVITIES

1. Divide the children into groups of four to six, making sure that there is a good mix of instruments within the group. Ask them to make up a simple tune using their instruments. They could record their tunes on a tape recorder or play them to the rest of the class.
2. Give each child a beater of some kind. Ask them to explore the sounds that can be made by gently hitting the furniture and fittings in the classroom (tables, chair legs, radiators, cupboards, floors and so on). Warn the children not to 'beat' the computer, windows, or any other delicate objects. Encourage the children to exchange beaters and try a different type. *What difference does this make to the sounds produced?*

DIFFERENTIATION

All the children should be able to take part in these activities according to their abilities.

ASSESSMENT

Observe the children as they make their instruments. Ask them to explain how they will work. *Will you need to bang, rattle, scrape, pluck or blow?*

PLENARY

Ask some of the children to show their instruments and say how they made them. Listen to the tunes composed by the groups. Ask some of the children to demonstrate any interesting sounds they discovered around the room.

OUTCOME

● Can make a simple instrument to make sounds.

LINKS

Technology: select tools, techniques and materials for projects.
Music: explore, choose and organise sounds.

LESSON 9

Objective	● To be able to relate home-made instruments to real instruments.
Resources	The instruments made by the children in the previous lesson, pictures of real musical instruments (or real ones, if available).
Main activity	Spread out the pictures or real instruments on a table. Look at the pictures and talk about how each one is played. Ask the children to think about how their own instrument is played and to place it by the picture, or instrument, that best matches it. Discuss any instruments that are missing (either a real instrument that doesn't have a child's instrument to match it or vice versa). After the children have matched their instruments to any available, play a few notes on the real thing to see if their instrument makes a similar sound or not.
Differentiation	Some children may need to be reminded how the real instruments are played in order to match them with their own.
Assessment	Observe those children who can match their instruments to real ones and understand how they are played.
Plenary	Sing 'Oh, we can play on the big bass drum' ('The Music Man'), but use the children's own instruments for the sounds.
Outcome	● Can relate home-made instruments to real instruments.

LESSON 10

OBJECTIVES

● To know that devices can be made to improve our hearing.
● To plan and carry out a simple investigation with help.

RESOURCES

Main teaching activity: A stethoscope, an ear trumpet made from card (see diagram below), earphones; if possible, a picture of a water board official using a listening device to listen for leaks and a picture of an old-fashioned ear trumpet.
Group activities: 1. Stethoscopes, antiseptic wipes or disinfectant; short pieces of dowel (1.5–2cm diameter and 15cm long) or short pieces cut from a broom handle; card ear trumpets. **2.** For each group: two or three different types of string, yoghurt pots, cocoa tins, syrup tins, plastic cups and so on; photocopiable page 67 if required.

PREPARATION

Make several cones from card to act as ear trumpets. Roll the card into a cone shape, fix with adhesive tape and cut off the extreme point.

BACKGROUND

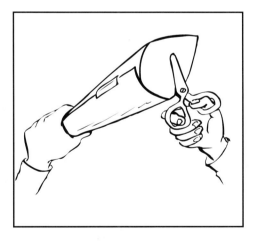

Many children will have experienced temporary hearing impairment due to glue ear or a heavy cold. As we grow older hearing often becomes less acute. The children learned in Year 1/Primary 2 that hearing can be seriously damaged by very loud noises and they need to be reminded of this. Individuals may naturally have different levels of hearing so be sensitive to any children who have difficulty.

Some occupations involve using devices to enhance hearing. A doctor may use a stethoscope to listen to a chest or a small listening trumpet to listen for foetal sounds in the womb. A water board official uses a long listening device to hear the water running through pipes buried in the ground. Bomb disposal experts need a stethoscope to help them hear what is happening inside an explosive device. It may be safer to avoid discussing the use of a stethoscope to help crack a safe!

Vocabulary

listen, stethoscope, hearing, enhance, vibration, ear trumpet, headphones, damage

INTRODUCTION

Remind all the children that they learned about ear defenders in Year 1/Primary 2. These help to protect our ears from the damage that can be done by very loud noises. Tell the children that in this lesson they are going to learn about things that enhance our hearing and help us to hear very quiet sounds.

MAIN TEACHING ACTIVITY

Whisper something to the children and ask: *Who could hear?* Ask them to cup their ears with their hands and whisper again. *Did any of you find it easier to hear then?* Explain or remind the children that some animals can move their ears so that they can collect the sounds and hear better. (Cupping ears is a bit like this.) Humans can't usually move their ears. In the past, people used ear trumpets to collect more sound when they became hard of hearing. Show the children the card trumpet and explain that old-fashioned ear trumpets worked like this to collect more sound. Of course, people can always talk louder so that others can hear, but some sounds are very quiet and we may need help to hear them. Ask: *Who has been to the doctor? Did the doctor listen to your chest? What did he or she use? Who else needs to listen to quiet noises?* Show the children a picture, if you have one, of a water board official listening for leaks. Remind the children that sound is caused by vibrations. The vibrations from the water pipes travel up the rod so that the official can hear if the water is flowing properly.

Sometimes we use devices that help us to concentrate on what we are listening to (headphones to listen to a tape). Show the children the headphones. These also help to cut out other sounds that might be distracting. *Who else might use headphones?* (Metal detectors, sound engineers, telephonists.)

GROUP ACTIVITIES

1. Working in groups of three or four (according to the level of your resources) use a stethoscope to listen to each other's hearts or stomachs. If it is spring, and you have some fairly large trees in the vicinity, the children could go out and use a stethoscope to listen to the sap rising. Make sure that the stethoscope ear pieces are disinfected between users. Some children could use lengths of dowel to listen to water moving in radiators or to listen to someone tapping on the other end of a desk. Some groups could use card ear trumpets to see if whispered messages are more easily heard using it. Groups could exchange their listening devices and try a different one, if there is time.

2. Investigate using plastic cups or tin cans with different strings to find out which is best for hearing messages. A yoghurt pot telephone is simply made by making a small hole in the bottom of two yoghurt pots and threading a long length of string through each hole. Tie a knot to secure the string inside each pot.

Children could investigate the effect of different types of string or change the type of pot (syrup or cocoa tins work well, but beware of tins with sharp edges). Make sure that the children have two pots of the same type on the string at any one time and that they investigate either pots or strings, not both at the same time. If you wish, you could ask them to use photocopiable page 67.

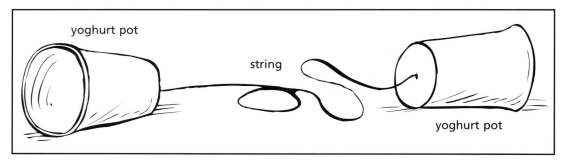

yoghurt pot

string

yoghurt pot

DIFFERENTIATION

1. All the children can take part in this activity.
2. Less able children should compare just two different strings or two different types of pot. More able children could find which they think is the best pot and then go on to investigate strings to make the best telephone they can.

ASSESSMENT

Observe the children using the listening devices in Group activity 1. Who understands that these devices are enhancing their hearing? In Group activity 2 observe the children as they plan and carry out their investigations. Note which children make sensible suggestions. The record sheet could be used to help you make judgements.

PLENARY

Talk about the different ways hearing has been enhanced. *How well did the different devices work?* Discuss people who have real hearing difficulties and the ways in which they can be helped. (Hearing aids, sign language, lip reading and so on.) It may be possible to invite a visitor into the class to demonstrate and talk about sign language or how a hearing aid helps them to hear.

OUTCOMES

● Know that hearing can be enhanced.
● Can plan and carry out a simple investigation with help.

LESSON 11

OBJECTIVES

● To know that sounds get fainter as they travel away from a source and that loud sounds travel further than quiet sounds.
● To carry out a simple investigation.

RESOURCES

Main teaching activity: The hall or playground, beanbags, a buzzer (or a cassette recorder and tape of music), metre sticks, surveyor's tapes (available from many educational catalogues), writing materials. A buzzer is preferable as it gives a more constant sound.
Group activities: 1. Squared paper, writing materials. **2.** A washing-up bowl of water for each small group, plastic pipettes or other droppers.

Vocabulary

investigate, fainter, louder

BACKGROUND

Sound waves travel out in all directions from the source of a sound. They are often likened to the ripples on a pond travelling out from where a stone is dropped into the water. This is a reasonable analogy, but not entirely correct in that sound waves travel in all directions: up and down as well as out, so the model should really be a sphere. As the ripples (waves) travel away from the source they decrease until they can no longer be seen (or heard). A bigger stone (or louder sound) will make bigger ripples that travel further, while a small pebble hardly disturbs the surface.

Some children may be experiencing a temporary loss of hearing for various reasons. Explain that we are all different and may cease to hear the sound at different distances from the source.

INTRODUCTION

Remind the children about the work they did on sound in Year 1/Primary 2. Can they remember the investigation they did with a beanbag to find out about sound getting fainter as it travelled from its source?

MAIN TEACHING ACTIVITY

Tell the children that they are going to repeat the investigation they did last year, but that this time they are going to be much more scientific. They are going to take measurements and record their results so that they can show other people what they have found out. Remind the children how they stood in a circle with a tape recorder or buzzer making a sound in the middle. They then walked away and dropped a beanbag when they could no longer hear the sound. They then repeated the experiment, but this time walked towards the sound, rather than away from it. *Why did we do this?* (When walking away from a sound, some children may 'remember' the sound after they have ceased to hear it.)

This time they must ensure that their results are reliable and that their test is fair. *How will you do that?* (The sound must be at the same volume all the time.)

In a large space such as the hall or playground, stand the children in pairs in a tight circle facing outwards and give one child of each pair a beanbag. Turn on the buzzer (or the tape recorder - medium volume outside or low if you are in the hall.) Tell the children to walk slowly away from the sound and stop when the child with the beanbag can no longer hear any sound.

They should mark the spot with the beanbag. The pair should then work together to measure the distance from the sound source to the beanbag and make a note of it. They then repeat the activity, but with the other child holding the beanbag. Measure again.

After the children have collected their data you could ask them to move to a different place in the circle and repeat their experiment (without measuring) so that they can appreciate that sound travels in all directions from a source.

GROUP ACTIVITIES

1. Put pairs together to make groups of eight or ten so that they have a reasonable amount of data to deal with. Ask them to make individual bar charts using all the measurements from the group. *What information can you get from your charts?*
2. Give each small group a washing-up bowl about half-full of water. Make sure that the children can see the water but understand that they have to be very careful not to disturb the flat surface. Using a plastic pipette, gently drop one drop of water into the middle of the bowl. Watch the ripples as they move outwards. Explain to the children that this is how the sound waves move out from the sound source. Let each child have a turn to use the dropper.

DIFFERENTIATION

1. Some children may manage better in smaller groups so that they have less data to deal with. Challenge able children to make a bar chart using all the data from the class.
2. All the children should be able to take part in this activity.

ASSESSMENT

During the Plenary session, listen to the children's explanations. Note those children who can explain what was happening in the Main teaching activity and Group activity 2, and can understand that sound gets fainter as it travels away from a source. Which children can interpret their bar charts and give you information from these?

PLENARY

Talk to the children about what they found out in their investigation. Do they understand that sound travels away from a source? Look at some of the bar charts and discuss the results. Ask some children to explain what happened when they dropped water on the still surface. Can they relate this to how sound gets fainter as it travels away from a source?

OUTCOMES

- Know that sounds get fainter as they travel away from a source.
- Can carry out a simple investigation.

LINKS

Maths: measuring and bar charts

LESSON 12

Objectives	● To know that loud sounds travel further than quiet sounds. ● To carry out a simple investigation.
Resources	The hall or playground, a tape recorder and music, beanbags of two colours.
Main activity	Repeat the activity from Lesson 11, but without formal measuring. Use a sound that can be increased or decreased in volume. Keep the volume very low at first and ask the children to drop one of their beanbags when they can no longer hear the sound. Repeat this with the volume as high as possible and compare the distances. The children could use beanbags of different colours for each volume.
Differentiation	This activity is accessible to all.
Assessment	During the Plenary session ask the children if they can say why they could hear one sound from a greater distance than the other.
Plenary	Talk to the children about why they could hear the loud sound further away from the source than the quiet sound.
Outcomes	● Know that loud sounds also get fainter as they travel away from a source but travel further than quiet sounds. ● Can carry out a simple investigation.

LESSON 13

OBJECTIVES
● To know that sound is a form of energy.
● To make and test a simple prediction.

RESOURCES

Main teaching activity: Cymbals, beater, a bowl of water, a tuning fork, a table tennis ball on string (see Preparation, below).
Group activities: 1. A copy of photocopiable page 179 for each child, pots with lids, beads.
2. Drum and beater, rice or confetti.

PREPARATION

Use adhesive tape or PVA glue to stick a length of string (about 30cm) to a table tennis ball.

Vocabulary

vibrate, vibration, movement, energy

BACKGROUND

Energy is found in different forms. In Lesson 5 children looked at light as one form of energy and how it can be changed into electrical energy. Sound energy is often transferred into kinetic or movement energy, and vice versa: moving cymbals collide to make sound; sound coming from an aeroplane can make the doors and windows in a house vibrate. We are able to hear because sounds entering our ears make our eardrums vibrate. These vibrations are passed through the inner ear by tiny bones to the cochlea from where they are sent to the brain and interpreted as sounds.

INTRODUCTION

Remind the children that they learned in Lesson 5 that light is a form of energy.

MAIN TEACHING ACTIVITY

Working with the whole class, tell the children that sound is also a form of energy. Show the children a pair of cymbals and ask them what you need to do to make a sound with them. (Bring them together.) Bring the cymbals together, gently at first and then with more force. Explain to the children that you are changing movement energy into sound energy. If you use a lot of movement energy, you get more sound energy (a louder sound) than when you use just a little movement energy.

Hold up just one cymbal and hit it with a beater. *Does it make a difference how much movement energy you use?* Ask a child to gently touch a vibrating cymbal with their fingertip. *What can you feel?* Explain that the sound energy is changing to movement energy and causing the cymbal to vibrate. Show the children a tuning fork and explain how it works. (When struck, the fork vibrates to produce a sound.) Strike it several times so that the children can hear the sound. You may even be able to see the forks vibrate, depending on the note produced. Hold the table tennis ball on its string and gently touch it with the vibrating tuning fork. The ball will bounce away from the tuning fork, magnifying the vibrations. *Why do you think the ball is bouncing like that?* Explain to them that the sound energy is being changed into movement energy which is making the ball move.

Gather the children around a table on which you have a bowl of water. This time gently touch the surface of the water with the vibrating tuning fork. You may get a slight splash, and then ripples moving out from the tuning fork. Again, sound energy is being changed into movement energy.

GROUP ACTIVITIES

1. Divide the children into groups of three or four. Give each group a small pot with a lid and enough beads or dried peas to fill the pot. Give each child a copy of photocopiable page 179 on which to record their prediction and findings. Tell the children that they are going to find out if they get a louder sound from their shaker by putting more beads in the pot, but first they must predict what they think will happen and write it on their sheet. Next they put a few beads in the pot, shake it, and decide whether the sound is loud or quiet. They then add more beads and test again. *Is the sound louder or quieter? What happens when you fill the pot with as many beads as you can?* (There should be very little noise because the beads do not have room to move in order to make a sound.)

2. Divide the children into pairs, or groups of three, and give each group a drum, a beater and a few grains of rice or a little confetti. Tell the children to put a few rice grains or pieces of confetti on the drum and beat it gently. *What happens to the rice or confetti? What happens if the drum is beaten harder?* (The rice or confetti will jump up and down as the drum skin vibrates. A louder sound will cause a bigger vibration, so the rice or confetti will bounce higher.) Ask the children to think about how the sound was made: the beater moved to hit the drum (moving energy), the drum made a sound (sound energy), which then made the drum vibrate (movement energy).

DIFFERENTIATION

1. Less able children may need to try putting different numbers of beads in the pot before they can make a prediction.

2. Less able children could report their findings verbally while more able children could try to explain their findings in writing.

ASSESSMENT

Use the children's work from the Group activities to assess their understanding.

PLENARY

Ask the children to demonstrate and explain what they have discovered. Help them to describe the forms of energy involved at each stage.

OUTCOMES

- Can recognise that sound is a form of energy.
- Can make and test a simple prediction.

LINKS

Unit 4, Lesson 13: heat as a form of energy.
Unit 7, Lesson 5: light as a form of energy.

LESSON 14

OBJECTIVES

● To know that light cannot pass through some materials and that shadows are created.
● To know that sounds get fainter as they travel away from a source.
● To know that loud sounds travel further than quiet sounds.

RESOURCES

Assessment activities: 1. Photocopiable page 180 for each child, pencils. **2.** Photocopiable page 181 for each child, writing and colouring pencils.

INTRODUCTION

Read the poem 'My Shadow' (see Lesson 2) again to the children and ask them if they can remember what they learned about shadows, or give out some musical instruments and let the children practise making loud and soft sounds.

ASSESSMENT ACTIVITY 1

Give each of the children a copy of photocopiable page 180 and ask them to complete it.

Answers

A shadow should be drawn to the right of the tree, coming from the base of the tree and with no gap between the tree and the shadow. Accept any drawing that shows an understanding of this and do not worry about the size of the shadow. (Although the shadow should be tree-shaped.) The explanation should indicate that the tree is blocking the light from the Sun and a shadow is formed. Accept any answer that shows that the child has understood this.

Looking for levels

Most children will draw a shadow on the correct side, but it may not be attached to the base of the tree. They should be able to explain that the tree blocks the light.

Less able children may draw the shadow pointing in the wrong direction or alongside the original tree. The shadow may not join the base of the tree. They may not be able to explain why a shadow is formed.

More able children will draw the shadow in the correct place, attached to the base of the tree and of an appropriate size and shape. Their explanations of how a shadow is formed may be clearer and more detailed.

Accept a verbal explanation if a child's understanding is better than his or her ability to write.

ASSESSMENT ACTIVITY 2

Give each child a copy of photocopiable page 181. Explain to them what they have to do to complete the sheet.

Answers

The figure nearest the sound source should be circled blue, and the one furthest away red. Accept any explanation that indicates an understanding that sounds get fainter as they travel away from a source.

Looking for levels

Most children will colour the figures correctly and be able to explain that sound gets fainter as it travels away from a source. They will know that the figure further away will hear a loud sound better than a fainter one. Less able children may not be able to give explanations.

Name

How many lights are in your house?

Record all the lights in your house in the spaces below.

Name _____

Look through it

Put one of your pieces of paper over each dotted box. Trace the smiley face through each one if you can. Complete each sentence with words from the list below.

This paper was _____ for tracing

because _____

_____

_____

_____

This paper was _____ for tracing

because _____

_____

_____

_____

This paper was _____ for tracing

because _____

_____

_____

_____

| translucent   transparent   opaque   good   not so good   poor |

Different sounds

We hear different kinds of sounds.

These sounds give
us pleasure.

These sounds give
us information.

These sounds give us warnings.

Name

Beads in a pot

Will more beads make a louder sound?

My prediction.
I think...

Put four beads in a pot. What kind of sound did it make?

_____

_____

Put ten beads in the pot. What kind of sound
does it make now?

_____

_____

Fill the pot with beads. What kind of sound does it make?

_____

_____

Explain what happened and why.
Was your prediction right?

_____

_____

_____

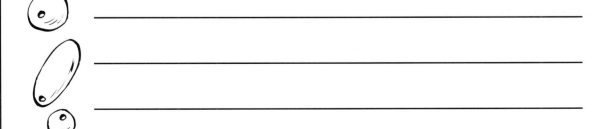
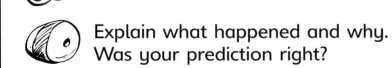

Properties and uses

Name

Draw the shadow of the tree.

Explain why the tree has a shadow.

Properties and uses

Which person will hear the loudest sound? Circle that person in blue.

Who will hear the faintest sound? Circle that person in red.

Why don't they both hear it the same?

If the sound were louder, would the figure furthest away hear it better than a fainter sound? Why?

The Sun and the seasons

ORGANISATION (6 LESSONS)

	OBJECTIVES	MAIN ACTIVITY	GROUP ACTIVITIES	PLENARY	OUTCOMES
LESSON 1	● To know that the Sun appears to move across the sky in a regular way.	Make a class display of the apparent movement of the Sun.	Create and position collage shapes of a cat and a mouse. Order pictures of the Sun.	Discuss the class display and the progress of the Sun.	● Can describe how the Sun appears to move across the sky.
LESSON 2	● To know that the Sun is higher in the sky at midday in summer than in winter.	Compare pictures of the Sun and shadows in different seasons. Examine shadow lengths.	Interpret the results of the investigation. Draw a picture showing midday in either summer or winter.	Report findings.	● Know that the Sun is higher in the sky at midday in summer than in winter.
LESSON 3	● To know that the Sun appears to have a longer path through the sky in summer than in winter.	Create a picture and measure the Sun's track.		Discuss the difference in hours of daylight in summer and winter.	● Know that the Sun appears to stay longer in the sky in summer than in winter.
LESSON 4	● To know that we only see the Moon because it reflects light from the Sun.	Use a ball and an OHP to show reflected light.	Complete a sheet to show how much light we see. Comment on differences between the Sun and the Moon.	Review that we see different amounts of light reflected from the Moon each night.	● Know that the Sun is a light source but that the Moon is not. ● Know that the Moon reflects sunlight. ● Know that we see a different amount of the reflected light each night as the Moon moves around the Earth.
LESSON 5	● To use weather records to see the pattern of the seasons. ● To collect, present and interpret data.	Discuss weather patterns and examine weather recordings.	Use weather data to create a block graph of sunshine, rain, snow, wind and so on. Write about 'birthday weather'.	Interpret the block graphs.	● Can use records to describe how the weather changes from season to season. ● Can transfer data to a graph. ● Can interpret data from a block graph.

	OBJECTIVES			ACTIVITY 1	ACTIVITY 2
ASSESSMENT 6	● To know that the Sun appears to move across the sky in a regular way. ● To know that we see the Moon by the light it reflects from the Sun.			Draw the apparent path of the Sun across the sky.	Complete a sheet to show how a person on Earth sees moonlight.

OBJECTIVE

● To know that the Sun appears to move across the sky in a regular way.

RESOURCES

Main teaching activity: A sunny day, a display board with a silhouette of the local skyline, yellow paper discs to represent the Sun.
Group activities: 1. Drawing, painting or collage materials. **2.** A copy of photocopiable page 192 for each child, scissors, adhesive.

PREPARATION

Main teaching activity: Make a silhouette, on a display board, of the skyline you see from the classroom (if the room is are south-facing), or any other convenient south-facing vantage point.
Group activity 1. Use a little bit of trial and error investigation to work out the correct position for the mouse in a game of 'cat and mouse'. Stick a piece of paper to a south-facing window and, at a convenient time of the day, note where its shadow falls on an opposite or adjacent wall. Place the mouse there. You might prefer to have a car going into a garage, or a rabbit into a hutch.

BACKGROUND

Vocabulary

Sun, orbit, Earth, rotate, axis, sunrise, sunset, east, west, apparent

The fact that the Sun is stationary and the Earth is moving seems to contradict the evidence we see with our eyes. It is important, therefore, to make sure that you always talk about the 'apparent' movement of the Sun, or the Sun 'appearing' to move. Emphasise the fact that it is the Earth moving, not the Sun. The Earth is spinning at almost 2000 miles an hour, and takes a day to complete one full rotation. The Sun appears to rise in the east because of the direction of rotation of the Earth. (Anti-clockwise, looking down on the North Pole.)

INTRODUCTION

Remind the children of what they learned about the Sun in Year 1/Primary 2. *When is the Sun in the sky? Why is the Sun important to us?* (It gives us light and heat.)

MAIN TEACHING ACTIVITY

Ask the children: *Is the Sun in the same part of the sky all day?* (Many children will know that the Sun is in the sky, but may never have noticed that it appears to move.) If no one volunteers this information ask: *Where was the Sun as you came to school this morning? Was it shining in your eyes or was it on your back? Can anyone remember?*

Remind the children that they should never look directly at the Sun as it can damage their eyes, even if they are wearing sunglasses. Draw the children's attention to the silhouette on the display board and point out any particular landmarks. You may have a church tower, a block of flats or a particular tree. Go outside and decide where the Sun is now, in relation to your silhouette. Note what the time is and write it on one of the yellow discs. Go back into the classroom and stick the disk in the appropriate place on the display.

Go out each hour through the day, if possible, and repeat the exercise. Encourage the children to note the height of the Sun, as well as its apparent movement across the sky. You will obviously get a better idea of the apparent movement if you can start this activity as early in the day as possible. The positions may be approximate, as you will not be able to look directly at the Sun but, by the end of the day, you should have several 'Suns' progressing across the display (see diagram, below).

Remind the children that it is the Earth that is moving (rotating) and not the Sun. If you have a south-facing window in your classroom, you could stick the 'Suns' directly onto the window using the actual skyline. Watch how shadows move around the classroom and help the children to relate this to the direction the sunlight is coming from.

GROUP ACTIVITIES

1. Working in small groups of three or four, ask the children to create collage shapes of a pouncing cat and a mouse. Cut out the cat and stick this on a south-facing window, then cut out the mouse and stick this on an opposite or adjacent wall, where the Sun casts shadows (see Preparation). *What time is it when the cat catches the mouse?* Other groups could work on variations of this theme.
2. Give each child a copy of photocopiable page 192. Ask them to cut out the pictures and stick them in the right order in their books or on a separate piece of paper. Remind the children that the Sun rises in the east.

DIFFERENTIATION

1. Most children will be able to take part in this activity. More able children may go on to explain why the cat moves to catch the mouse. (As the Sun appears to move across the sky the direction of the shadows changes.)
2. Some children may find this activity easier once the class display has been completed in the Main teaching activity and they have watched the Sun's apparent progress throughout the day.

ASSESSMENT

Use the children's work from Group activity 2 to assess their understanding.

PLENARY

When you have completed the class display, talk to the children about how it shows that the Sun appears to move across the sky. Ask the children to notice where the Sun is in the morning when they come to school. Tell them that they should watch the Sun again tomorrow just to check that it does the same thing every day.

You could finish by telling the story of Ra (Re), the Ancient Egyptian Sun God. Ra was supposed to travel across the sky each day in his boat only to be swallowed each evening by the sky-goddess Nut. He spent the night battling the monster Apep who, every day, failed to prevent the Sun God emerging again.

OUTCOME

● Can describe how the Sun appears to move across the sky.

LINKS

Unit 7, Lessons 2 and 3: shadows.

LESSON 2

OBJECTIVE

● To know that the Sun is higher in the sky at midday in summer than in winter.

RESOURCES

Main teaching activity: Pictures of winter and summer daytime scenes showing clear shadows, a lump of play dough, a metre rule, a torch (one with a narrow beam will give a clearer shadow), a large sheet of white paper, a model tree, coloured pencils or crayons; a darkish working area where shadows will show up.
Group activities: 1. Paper and writing materials. **2.** Drawing and painting materials.

Vocabulary

Sun, apparent, rotate, rotation, shadow, length, seasons, spring, summer, autumn, winter

BACKGROUND

The Sun appears higher in the sky at midday in summer than in winter because the Earth is tilted on its axis. Throughout the Earth's orbit of the Sun, the angle and direction of the tilt remain more or less the same (apart from a slight wobble). Because of this, in the summer, we see the Sun from a more direct angle and this makes it appear higher in the sky. In the winter the angle is more acute and so the Sun appears lower on the horizon.

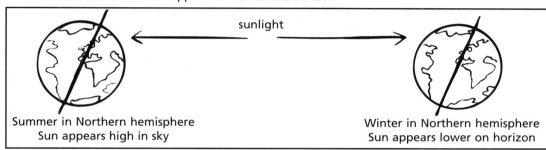

Summer in Northern hemisphere
Sun appears high in sky

sunlight

Winter in Northern hemisphere
Sun appears lower on horizon

INTRODUCTION

Ask the children to name the four seasons. *What is the main difference between summer and winter?* (Summer is usually warmer than winter.)

MAIN TEACHING ACTIVITY

With the class gathered around you, look at pictures of a winter scene and a summer scene which show clear shadows and the (if possible) Sun. Ask: *Which picture do you think is of summer and which one is of winter? How can you tell the difference?* (People are dressed differently, trees have leaves, there may be snow or flowers on the ground, the summer picture may be brighter and so on.) If nobody mentions the shadows say: *Look at the shadows. Can you see that those in the winter are longer than those in the summer?* Explain that this is because the Sun seems to climb higher in the sky in the summer than it does in the winter.

In your darkish working area stand a metre rule in a large lump of play dough (or sandwich it between books) to hold it upright. Similarly, stand a model tree in play dough and place it on the white paper, about a metre away from the rule. Shine the torch onto the model tree, from the metre rule, to make a clear shadow. (You may have to move the tree and paper to find the best place.) Explain to the children that the torch represents the Sun and the model tree something down on Earth.

Now shine the torch down from near the top of the metre rule and ask the children to look at the shadow. Mark the length of it with a coloured crayon. Move the torch about half-way down the metre rule and look at the shadow of the tree again. *Has it changed?* Mark the end of this shadow with a crayon of a different colour. Now move the torch near to the bottom of the metre stick. *What has happened to the shadow now?* Mark its length with another colour. Allow time to repeat the investigation and ask: *Where was the torch when the shadows were shortest? Where was it when the shadows were longest?*

GROUP ACTIVITIES

1. Divide the children into groups of four or five to talk about what they have observed. Pin the winter and summer pictures up so that the children can see them. Tell them that the torch represented the Sun. Ask them to think about where the torch was on the metre rule when the shadows were longest and shortest. *Was it high up or low down?* Ask them, individually, to write, explaining in which season the Sun is highest in the sky and in which the lowest.
2. Working individually, ask the children to draw or paint a picture showing the Sun in the sky in the middle of the day in either the summer or the winter. Ask them to show how long the

shadows would be from any houses, trees or figures that they include. Make sure that there are a mixture of summer and winter pictures. Mount the pictures to make a display and label these: 'In winter the shadows are long because the Sun is low in the sky at midday.' and 'In summer the shadows are short because the Sun is high in the sky at midday.'

DIFFERENTIATION

1. Less able children may produce a group report, which could be written or verbal.
2. More able children could write a sentence about their picture explaining which season it is meant to show and why the shadows are the length they are.

ASSESSMENT

Use the children's writing or pictures to assess their understanding. Some children may struggle to grasp this concept and may have trouble understanding that the torch represents the Sun.

PLENARY

Ask the children to report back from their groups. One or two from each group could read out their sentences or give a verbal report. Look at some of the pictures they have drawn or painted. Ask the artists to explain which seasons they represent, and why the shadows are the length they have drawn them. Help them to understand that when the Sun is higher in the sky the shadows are shorter, when it is low the shadows are longer, and that shadows are shortest in the summer and longest in the winter.

OUTCOME

● Know that the Sun is higher in the sky at midday in summer than in winter.

LINKS

Unit 7, Lessons 2 and 3: shadows.

LESSON 3

Objective	● To know that the Sun appears to have a longer path through the sky in summer than in winter.
Resources	The display of the Sun's track made in Lesson 1, yellow and orange discs to represent the Sun, string, tape measures, sticky labels, sheets of paper stuck together to make a very large sheet (about the size of the window you used previously).
Main activity	Remind the children that they learned in Year 1/Primary 2 about there being more daylight hours in summer than in winter. Look at the display of the Sun's track that you made in Lesson 1 and use extra yellow discs to transfer the shape of this track to the large sheet of paper. Remind the children about the Sun being higher in the sky in summer than in winter. If you are doing this lesson in winter, ask the children what shape they think the track would be in summer (or vice versa). *Will it be higher or lower than the one in Lesson 1?* Place the orange discs on the paper to form this track, either higher or lower than the original. Ask several children to hold a piece of string around the shape of the first track. Cut it off and attach a sticky label so that you know which is which. Repeat for the second track. Measure the length of each string and decide which is longer. *Was it the summer one or the winter one?*
Differentiation	Less able children will need help to relate the length of the string to the path of the Sun in summer and winter.
Assessment	Discuss the fact that the piece of string representing the track of the Sun through the sky in the summer was longer than that for winter. Explain that this means that the Sun is in the sky longer in the summer than in the winter and that therefore there are more hours of daylight.
Plenary	Note during the Main activity and in the Plenary session which children understand that the length of the string relates to the length of time the Sun is in the sky.
Outcome	● Know that the Sun appears to stay longer in the sky in summer than in winter.

LESSON 4

OBJECTIVE

● To know that we only see the Moon because it reflects light from the Sun.

RESOURCES

Main teaching activity: OHP, a 'Moon on a stick' (see Preparation, below), a room that can be blacked out, extra adult help (optional).
Group activities: 1. A copy of photocopiable page 193 for each child, writing and drawing materials. **2.** Writing and colouring materials.
Plenary: Flip chart or board.

PREPARATION

Make a 'Moon on a stick' by pushing a thin piece of dowel into a polystyrene ball. The size of the ball is not very important, but the bigger the better. If you have no curtains with which to black out a room, stick sheets of black paper over the windows. Choose a dull day if possible.

Vocabulary

Moon, Sun, rock, reflect, light, shine, illuminate, phases, light source, crescent Moon, half Moon, full Moon

BACKGROUND

The Moon is a natural satellite of the Earth. It is made of rock covered in a thick layer of dust and orbits the Earth about once every twenty-eight days. A full Moon can appear to be very bright, but the Moon has no light of its own. Moonlight is merely a reflection of the light from the Sun. Because the Earth and the Moon are moving in orbit around the Sun, the light is reflected at different angles during the orbit, and this makes the Moon appear to change shape. Although the Moon orbits the Earth in approximately twenty-eight days the movement of the Earth and Moon around the Sun means that we see a new Moon approximately every thirty days.

Children in Year 2/Primary 3 are not expected to understand this concept. They will need a firm understanding of how shadows are formed and a grasp of the complex movements involved before they can do so. (Many adults still struggle with the concept!) Even so, try to avoid reinforcing the misconception that the Earth's shadow causes the phases of the Moon. The Earth's shadow only crosses the Moon during a lunar eclipse and the different phases are seen purely because of the way light is reflected from a sphere (the Moon). Eclipses occur because the Moon's orbit is not in the same plane as the Earth's and, just occasionally, the Earth comes between the Sun and the Moon, causing a shadow to pass across the Moon.

INTRODUCTION

Working with the whole class, remind the children what they learned about light in Year 1/Primary 2. We can only see things when there is light, and we see things because light is reflected from them.

MAIN TEACHING ACTIVITY

For this lesson you will need a room that can be blacked out (see Preparation), but with room for the children to sit in a circle. It is also helpful, but not essential, to have the assistance of a second adult.

Sit the children in a tight circle facing outwards. You may need to sit them in two circles, one inside the other, to keep the circle as small as possible. Explain that they are sitting in a band right around the Earth and they are going to look up into the sky to look at the 'Moon'. Hold up the 'Moon' (the ball on a stick) and ask if the children can see it. They may be able to see it, but not very well, depending on the level of light in the room.

Turn on the OHP and place a piece of paper over part of the glass so that the light shines upwards, but not into the children's eyes. Stand outside the circle, on the opposite side to the OHP, and hold the 'Moon on a stick' in the beam of the light. *Can you see it now? What shape can you see?* They may describe it as round, or as a circle. Explain that this is the shape we see when we have a full Moon.

Telling the children that they must only look straight in front of them, walk slowly around the circle (anti-clockwise), keeping the 'Moon' in the beam of light and above the children's heads so that there are no shadows on it. (This is where a second pair of eyes and hands can help to adjust the 'Sun' to keep the 'Moon' in full light). Tell the children to look at the illuminated (bright) part of the ball. *Does it change shape as it goes past you?* Stop at regular intervals and ask the children how much of the 'Moon' they can see. (All, not quite all, half, just a bit, and so on.) Point out to the children that the light is travelling from the Sun to the Moon and then is reflected (travels) to the Earth. (See Assessment activity 2, photocopiable page 197.) Explain to the children that it takes a whole month (or 28 days) for the Moon to go around the Earth and that each night we see a slightly different amount of the reflected light. Rearrange the children and repeat the activity so that they get a different view of the 'Moon'.

GROUP ACTIVITIES

1. Give each child a copy of photocopiable page 193 and ask them to complete it. Remind the children that sometimes we only see a small amount of the light that is reflected from the Moon so the Moon appears as a crescent shape, and sometimes we see all the reflected light: we call that a 'full Moon'.
2. Ask the children to draw pictures of the Sun and the Moon and to write a few sentences to explain how they are different. They should comment that the Sun is a light source and the Moon is not, and that we only see the Moon because it reflects light from the Sun.

DIFFERENTIATION

1. Some children may find this difficult and may find a poster of the phases of the Moon a helpful reference.
2. All the children should be able to draw the Sun and the Moon. Less able children may need help to write their sentences or give verbal reasons. More able children may write something about what the Sun and Moon are made of.

ASSESSMENT

During the Plenary session ask the children: *What is it that shines in the day and gives us light?* (The Sun.) *Why do we get light and heat from the Sun?* (Because the Sun is a big ball of burning gas.) *Why do we get light from the Moon?* (Because it reflects the light from the Sun.) Check their understanding from their answers.

   Use the children's completed photocopiable sheets from Group activity 1 to assess their understanding that we sometimes see different amounts of light reflected from the Sun.

PLENARY

Ask the children what it is that gives us light during the day. (The Sun.) *What do we see at night?* (The Moon.) *Why do we see the Moon?* (Because it reflects the light from the Sun.) Draw a diagram on the flip chart or board to show how the light travels from the Sun to the Moon and then to the Earth. Remind the children of when they were sitting in a circle and looking at the 'Moon on a stick'. *Did you see the same amount of light reflected all the time?* Explain that the Earth and the Moon are moving around the Sun, so we see different amounts of light reflected each night.

OUTCOMES

● Know that the Sun is a light source but that the Moon is not.
● Know that the Moon reflects sunlight.
● Know that we see a different amount of the reflected light each night as the Moon moves around the Earth.

LINKS

Unit 7, Lesson 1: light sources.
Unit 7, Lesson 2: shadows.

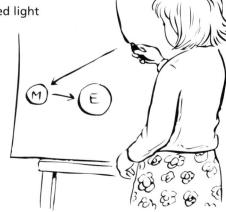

OBJECTIVES

● To use weather records to see the pattern of the seasons.
● To collect, present and interpret data.

RESOURCES

Main teaching activity:
Weather data. If you have no school records from previous years, you can obtain information and data from the Meteorological Office over the Internet (www.met-office.gov.uk). Simple information is supplied free of charge to schools, but more complex data carries a charge. You can ask for fairly specific information over a given period of time for your area, for example the rainfall over the last six months. This can be useful if you have no school records, but apply in plenty of time.

If these alternatives are not available a fictitious set of recordings is supplied on photocopiable page 194. This data is purely fictional but could be used to give children practice in reading a chart and gaining information. The chart represents an aggregate of weather information for the three months of each season in order to simplify the data sufficiently for Year 2/Primary 3 children. These records should help the children to see that there is a pattern in the weather (even though it is rather stereotypical). Use local records if they are available, or adapt this record to suit the conditions in your area.
Group activities: 1. A copy of photocopiable pages 194 and 195 for each child, pencils.
2. Writing materials.

PREPARATION

You may have weather data from previous years, or choose to use data obtained from the Internet (see Resources). Alternatively you could start a system of weather recording with the class early in the year so that you have sufficient data to use by the time you do this lesson. Weather recording need only take a few minutes each day but can build into a very useful school resource if carried out regularly throughout the year. One year's records may then be compared with another year, but they will be records of your own area. Young children may keep a fairly simple 'tick if we have it' record while older children could keep more detailed records on a spreadsheet.

BACKGROUND

Vocabulary
weather, season, record, data, pattern

Even though weather patterns in the British Isles seem to be getting more confused it is still basically warmer in the summer than in the winter. Northern areas often get a significant snowfall in the winter but many southern areas have seen very little snow over the last few years. (If you want to do a lesson on snow take the opportunity as it arises and sort out the planning later!)

This lesson is really about handling and interpreting data, which is just as important in science as it is in maths. It is meant to help the children to see that there is a pattern to the weather, and that we are more likely to get certain types of weather in particular seasons. (It is more likely to be frosty in the winter than the summer; in spring and autumn the weather may be fairly similar but in spring we are moving from colder to warmer weather and in autumn from warmer to colder.) It does not matter too much if you were unable to collect data yourself, but interpreting your own data is always more interesting.

INTRODUCTION

Ask the children if they can name the four seasons. *Can you say how we tell the difference between them?* (Warm in summer, cold in winter, flowers come out in spring, we collect conkers in the autumn, and so on.)

MAIN TEACHING ACTIVITY

Ask the children: *Why is it useful to know the pattern of the weather? Who might need to know?* Point out that weather patterns are very important for some people. A farmer relies on the pattern of the weather to know the best time to sow crops and harvest them. He sows seed in the autumn or spring so that the crop has time to grow and ripen in the warmer summer weather. Holiday-makers also choose the best time for their holiday, depending on whether they want to sunbathe or ski. Fishermen and sailors need to make special preparations for bad weather, as do the people who look after our roads. They need to make sure that they have supplies of salt and grit to put on the icy roads that they expect in the winter.

Some people say that our weather patterns are changing but how do they know? It is because people have kept records of the weather for years and years. It is therefore possible to look back at records to see how the weather changes from season to season and to check if, and how, the pattern is changing.

Divide the children into groups of three and give each group a copy of the weather data you have. If you have no local records you could use those on photocopiable page 194 which have been kept very simple. If you do have local records you may need to edit them to make them accessible for the children.

Help the children to find which season had the most rain, sunshine, or fog. Ask: *Is there a pattern? Is it always the same season that has more rain, frost, and so on?*

GROUP ACTIVITIES

1. Give each child a copy of photocopiable pages 194 and 195 and ask them to use the weather data to create a block graph of sunshine, rain, snow, and other types of weather. The children have to add the number of ticks to create the block graph and from this find out in which season there is most sunshine, rain, fog, and so on.

2. Make a list of whose birthdays fall in spring, summer, autumn and winter respectively. Ask the children, as individuals, to use the weather data to write about the sort of weather that they might expect to have on their birthdays.

DIFFERENTIATION

1. Some children may be able to enter the information into an appropriate computer program and create their graph electronically. If you are using the fictional data, you may wish to give less able children only one or two types of weather data on page 194 for them to graph.

2. All the children should be able to attempt this activity.

ASSESSMENT

During the Plenary session note which children can explain that there is a pattern in the weather.

PLENARY

Look at the block graphs the children have prepared. Ask them to tell you what kinds of weather you are most likely to experience in each season. *When is it most likely to snow? To be foggy?*

OUTCOMES

- Can use records to describe how the weather changes from season to season.
- Can transfer data to a graph.
- Can interpret data from a block graph.

LINKS

Maths: handling data.

ASSESSMENT

LESSON 6

OBJECTIVES
● To know that the Sun appears to move across the sky in a regular way.
● To know that we see the Moon by the light it reflects from the Sun.

RESOURCES
Assessment activities: 1. Copies of photocopiable page 196, drawing materials. **2.** Copies of photocopiable page 197, pencils.

INTRODUCTION
Remind the children about what they have learned in this unit. They have been thinking about how we get light from the Sun and how the Moon reflects this light, how the Sun appears to move across the sky, and how the Moon seems to change its shape.

ASSESSMENT ACTIVITY 1
Give each child a copy of photocopiable page 196. Explain that they are to draw circles to represent the path of the Sun across the sky.

Answers
The Suns should describe a shallow arc across the picture. (See diagram in Lesson 1, page 184.) The Sun is higher in the sky during the summer.

Looking for levels
Most children will draw the Suns in a line across the sky showing a slight curve. They should be able to complete the sentence. Less able children may draw the Suns in a straight line across the page and be unable to complete the sentence.

ASSESSMENT ACTIVITY 2
Give each child a copy of photocopiable page 197 and ask them to draw lines to show how the person on the Earth sees the moonlight. They must show the direction in which the light is travelling.

Answers
There should be a line from the Sun to the Moon and from the Moon to the person on the Earth. Accept answers showing that the child understands that we see the Moon because it reflects light from the Sun.

Looking for levels
Most children will be able to draw the lines required and give a simple explanation of what is happening. Some children may get the lines in the wrong place or be unable to show the direction in which the light is travelling. They may not be able to give an explanation. More able children will draw the lines correctly and give a more detailed explanation of what is happening.

The Sun in the sky

Cut out the pictures and put them in the correct order.

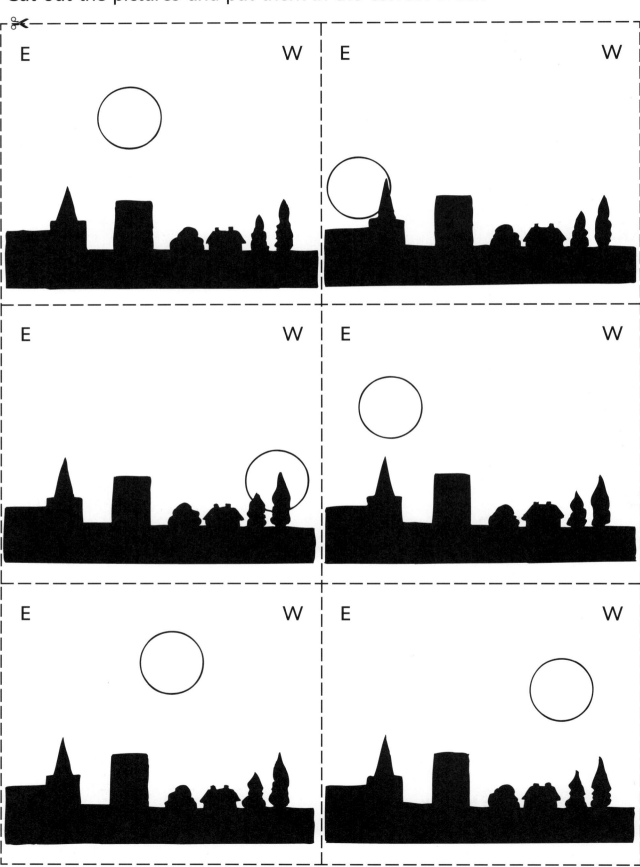

How much light?

Draw the shape of the Moon to match each sentence.

When the Moon looks like this it is only reflecting a little light back to Earth.	When it looks like this it is reflecting all the light back to Earth.	When it looks like this it is only reflecting half the light back to Earth.

Name

Weather data

Season	sunshine			cloud			rain			hail			snow			frost			fog		
	Yr 1	Yr 2	Yr 3	Yr 1	Yr 2	Yr 3	Yr 1	Yr 2	Yr 3	Yr 1	Yr 2	Yr 3	Yr 1	Yr 2	Yr 3	Yr 1	Yr 2	Yr 3	Yr 1	Yr 2	Yr 3
Spring	✓	✓✓	✓✓	✓✓	✓✓	✓	✓✓	✓✓	✓✓	✓						✓	✓		✓✓	✓	✓
Summer	✓✓	✓✓✓	✓✓✓	✓	✓✓	✓	✓	✓✓	✓	✓											
Autumn	✓✓	✓✓	✓✓	✓✓	✓✓	✓✓	✓✓	✓	✓		✓				✓✓	✓✓	✓		✓	✓✓✓	✓✓
Winter	✓	✓	✓	✓✓✓	✓✓✓	✓✓	✓✓	✓✓✓	✓✓				✓✓	✓	✓✓	✓✓ ✓✓✓	✓✓✓	✓✓	✓	✓	✓

Which is the wettest season? _____

Which season has most sunshine? _____

When are we most likely to have frost? _____

When is it most likely to snow? _____

FOG

Name

Weather graph

sunshine				cloud				rain				hail			
spring	summer	autumn	winter	spring	summer	autumn	winter	spring	summer	autumn	winter	spring	summer	autumn	winter

snow				frost				fog				wind			
spring	summer	autumn	winter	spring	summer	autumn	winter	spring	summer	autumn	winter	spring	summer	autumn	winter

The Sun and the seasons

Draw five circles to show how the Sun appears to move across the sky during the day.

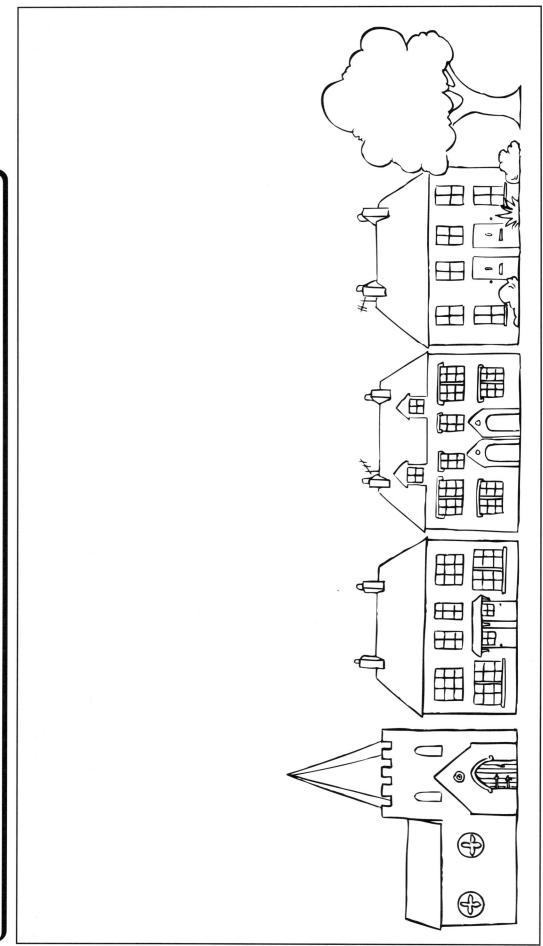

In the summer the Sun is ＿＿＿＿＿＿＿＿＿＿ in the sky than in the winter.

The Sun and the seasons

Draw two arrows to show why we see light from the Moon.

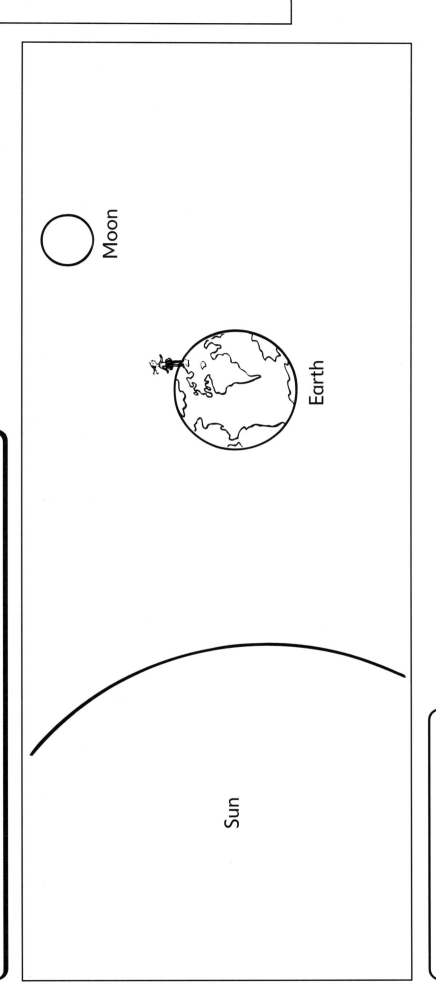

Moon

Earth

Sun

Explain what is happening.

National Curriculum in England

LINKS TO QCA SCIENCE SCHEME OF WORK		Unit 1: Ourselves Keeping healthy **UNIT 2A, 2C**	Unit 2: Animals & Plants Growing up **UNIT 2B, 2C**
SC1 SCIENTIFIC ENQUIRY	**1 Ideas and evidence in science**		
	pupils should be taught that it is important to collect evidence by making observations and measurements when trying to answer a question	4, 5, 14	10, 11
	2 Investigative skills – Planning		
	a ask questions and decide how they might find answers to them		7
	b use first-hand experience and simple information sources to answer questions		7
	c think about what might happen before deciding what to do		7
	d recognise when a test or comparison is unfair		10, 11
	Investigative skills – Obtaining and presenting evidence		
	e follow simple instructions to control the risks to themselves and to others	14	7, 10, 11
	f explore, using the senses of sight, hearing, smell, touch and taste as appropriate, and make and record observations and measurements	5	8, 9, 10, 11
	g communicate what happened in a variety of ways, including using ICT	1, 3, 4, 5, 6, 7	10, 11
	Investigative skills – Considering evidence and evaluating		
	h make simple comparisons and identify simple patterns or associations	1, 2, 9, 10, 11, 12, 16, 17	1, 2, 3, 4, 5, 12, 15
	i compare what happened with what they expected would happen, and try to explain it, drawing on their knowledge and understanding		7, 10, 11
	j review their work and explain what they did to others		(2), 10, 11
SC2 LIFE PROCESSES AND LIVING THINGS	**1 Life processes**		
	a the differences between things that are living and things that have never been alive		
	b that animals, including humans, move, feed, grow, use their senses and reproduce	1, 6, (8)	16
	c to relate life processes to animals and plants found in the local environment		
	2 Humans and other animals		
	a to recognise and compare the main external parts of the bodies of humans and other animals		
	b that humans and other animals need food and water to stay alive	1	
	c that taking exercise and eating the right types and amounts of food help humans to keep healthy	1, 2, 3, 4, (5), (8), 17	
	d about the role of drugs as medicines	9	
	e how to treat animals with care and sensitivity		
	f that humans and other animals can produce offspring and that these offspring grow into adults	12, 13, 16	15, 16
	g about the senses that enable humans and other animals to be aware of the world around them		
	3 Green plants		
	a to recognise that plants need light and water to grow		10, 11, (16)
	b to recognise and name the leaf, flower, stem and root of flowering plants		(5)
	c that seeds grow into flowering plants		(7), (8), (9), 10, 11, 16
	4 Variation and classification		
	a recognise similarities and differences between themselves and others, and to treat others with sensitivity	11, 14, (15), (16)	
	b group living things according to observable similarities and differences	(11)	1, 2, 3, 4, 5, 12, 16
	5 Living things in their environment		
	a find out about the different kinds of plants and animals in the local environment	(11)	6, (13), 14
	b identify similarities and differences between local environments and ways in which these affect animals and plants that are found there		
	c care for the environment		
SC3 MATERIALS & THEIR PROPERTIES	**1 Grouping materials**		
	a use their senses to explore and recognise the similarities and differences between materials		
	b sort objects into groups on the basis of simple material properties		
	c recognise and name common types of material and recognise that some of them are found naturally		
	d find out about the uses of a variety of materials and how these are chosen for specific uses on the basis of their simple properties		
	2 Changing materials		
	a find out how the shapes of objects made from some materials can be changed by some processes, including squashing, bending, twisting and stretching		
	b explore and describe the way some everyday materials change when they are heated or cooled		
SC4 PHYSICAL PROCESSES	**1 Electricity**		
	a about everyday appliances that use electricity		
	b about simple series circuits involving batteries, wires, bulbs and other components		
	c how a switch can be used to break a circuit		
	2 Forces and motion		
	a to find out about, and describe the movement of, familiar things		
	b that both pushes and pulls are examples of forces		
	c to recognise that when things speed up, slow down or change direction, there is a cause		
	Light and sound		
	3 Light and dark		
	a to identify different light sources, including the Sun		
	b that darkness is the absence of light		
	4 Making and detecting sounds		
	c that there are many kinds of sound and sources of sound		
	d that sounds travel away from sources, getting fainter as they do so, and that they are heard when they enter the ear		

Lessons where curriculum content is the main objective are listed below. Lessons where content is included but is not the main focus are shown below in brackets.

Unit 3: The environment Life in habitats	Unit 4: Materials Materials and change	Unit 5: Electricity Making circuits	Unit 6: Forces & motion Making things move	Unit 7: Light & sound Properties and uses	Unit 8: Earth & beyond The Sun and the seasons
UNIT 2B	UNIT 2D	UNIT 2F	UNIT 2E	–	–
(2)	(3)			1, 4, 6	
(10)		7	7, 8, 9	1, 2	
(1)		4	7, 8	2	
	6	3, 4, 5, 7	7, 8, 9, 10	13	
	12		2, 4, 7, 8	4	
4	6	1, 4			
5, 8	1, 2, 7, 8, 9, 10, 11, 13	1	1, 2, 6	2, 3, 10, 11, 12, 13	4
6, (11)	3, (5), 10, 11	3	2, 3, 7, 8, 9	4, 8, 11	5
7		5	4, 5	2, (3), 9	1, 2, 3
(10)	8, 9	6, 7	(2), 4	5	(4)
9, 12, 13	(4)	2	6	3, 5, 7	
2					
13					
13					
3					
1, 5, 8, 9, (10), 11, 14					
4, 6, 7					
12, (13)					
	1, 2				
	1, 2				
	1, 2, 4, 5				
	3, 14				
	6				
	7, 8, 9, 10, 11, 12, (13), 14				
		1, 2, 8			
		3, 4, 5, 7, 8			
		6			
			1		
			2, 3, 4, 5, 7, 8, 10, 11		
			3, 4, 5, 6, 7, 8, 9, 11		
				1, (5)	1, 2, 3, 4, 6
				2, 3, 4, 14	
				6, 7, 8, 10, 13, 14	
				11, 12, 14	
UNIT 2B	UNIT 2D	UNIT 2F	UNIT 2E		

The Northern Ireland Curriculum

			Unit 1: Ourselves Keeping healthy	Unit 2: Animals & Plants Growing up
		Pupils should be encouraged to adopt safe practices when undertaking science and technology activities. They should be made aware of potential hazards and the appropriate actions necessary to avoid risks.		

INVESTIGATING AND MAKING IN SCIENCE AND TECHNOLOGY

Planning
Pupils should have opportunities to participate in practical activities which involve them in talking to the teacher and each other about ideas, predictions and solutions to problems and planning what to make.

		Unit 1	Unit 2
a	respond to questions		
b	talk about what they are going to make and the materials they will use		
c	ask questions, discuss ideas and make predictions		
d	recognise a fair test		10, 11
e	suggest ideas which can be investigated and make predictions		10, 11
f	choose appropriate materials and components when planning what to make		

Carrying out and making
Pupils should have opportunities to participate in practical activities which involve them in exploring familiar objects and materials in their immediate environment and recording what they have done.

		Unit 1	Unit 2
a	make observations using their senses	14	2
b	assemble and rearrange materials		
c	make observations noting similarities and differences	1, 2, 8, 9, 10, 12, 16, 17	3, 4, 5, 8, 9, 12, (14)
d	record observations in a simple form	1, 8	(7), 9
e	explore different ways of joining materials		
f	reinforce measuring skills using non-standard measures and progress to using standard measures		
g	develop manipulative skills using a range of materials and tools		
h	record what they have done or observed using appropriate methods	4, 5	(6), (12)

Interpreting and evaluating
Pupils should participate in practical activities which provide them with opportunities to develop skills in reporting, presenting and interpreting results and evaluating what they have made.

		Unit 1	Unit 2
a	talk to the teacher and others about what happened or about what they have made	(6), (9)	10, 11, 15
b	comment on what happened or what they like or dislike about what they have made		
c	present their findings using appropriate methods	1, 2, 3, 4, 5, 6, 7	1, 10, 11, 13
d	relate what happened to what they predicted		10, 11
e	talk about what they have made in terms of materials, colour, size or shape and make suggestions for improvement	(6), (15)	

KNOWLEDGE AND UNDERSTANDING OF SCIENCE AND TECHNOLOGY

Living things

Ourselves

		Unit 1	Unit 2
a	recognise and name the main external parts of the human body		
b	observe seasonal changes and talk about how these affect themselves		
c	explore similarities and differences between themselves and other children	11, 14, (15)	
d	develop ideas about how to keep healthy, through exercise, rest, diet, personal hygiene and safety	1, 2, 3, 4, 5, 6, 7, 8, 9, 10, 17	
e	be introduced to the main stages of human development	12, 16	
f	find out about themselves including how they grow, move and use their senses	12, (13), 16	

Animals and plants

		Unit 1	Unit 2
a	find out about the variety of animal and plant life both through direct observations and by using secondary sources		4, 5, 6, 10, 11, 13, 14
b	sort living things into the two broad groups of animals and plants		1, 2, 3, 12, 16
c	recognise and name the main parts of a flowering plant including root, stem, leaf and flower		7, 8, (9)
d	sort living things into groups using observable features		1, 2, 3, 4, 5, 16
e	find out about animals and their young		15
f	find out about some animals, including how they grow, feed, move and use their senses		13, 14, 15
g	observe similarities and differences among animals and among plants		1, 2, 3, 4, 5, 12, 13, (14)
h	discuss the use of colour in the natural environment		
i	find out ways in which animal and plant behaviour is influenced by seasonal changes		

Materials

Properties

		Unit 1	Unit 2
a	work with a range of everyday materials in a variety of activities		
b	sort a range of everyday objects into groups according to the materials from which they are made		
c	explore the properties of materials including shape, colour, texture and behaviour		
d	find out some everyday uses of materials		
e	investigate similarities and differences in materials and objects; sort them according to their properties		

Change

		Unit 1	Unit 2
a	find out about the effect of heating and cooling some everyday substances, such as water, chocolate or butter		
b	investigate which everyday substances dissolve in water		

Environment

		Unit 1	Unit 2
a	identify the range of litter in and around their own locality		
b	find out how human activities create a variety of waste products		
c	find out that some materials decay naturally while others do not		

Physical Processes

Forces and energy

		Unit 1	Unit 2
a	explore forces which push, pull or make things move		
b	explore devices, including toys, which move		
c	explore how pushes and pulls make things speed up or stop		
d	find out about the range of energy sources used in school and at home		

Electricity

		Unit 1	Unit 2
a	find out about some uses of electricity in the home and classroom		
b	know that electricity can be dangerous		
c	know about the safe use of mains electricity and its associated dangers		

Sound

		Unit 1	Unit 2
a	listen to and identify sources of sounds in their immediate environment		
b	explore ways of making sounds using familiar objects		
c	investigate how sounds are produced when objects vibrate		

Light

		Unit 1	Unit 2
a	find out that light comes from a variety of sources		
b	explore the use of light including colour in relation to road safety		
c	explore how light passes through some materials and not others		

EMU and Cultural Heritage Pupils should have opportunities to develop an understanding of themselves and others by exploring similarities and differences between thems and other children, and developing a sense of their own individuality. They should appreciate the environment around them, the need to take care of it and how human activi upset the natural environment. They should consider how some toys and devices work and know that the technology which drives them has been developed over a period of t

Lessons where curriculum content is the main objective are listed below. Lessons where content is included but is not the main focus are shown below in brackets.

Unit 3: The environment Life in habitats	Unit 4: Materials Materials and change	Unit 5: Electricity Making circuits	Unit 6: Forces & motion Making things move	Unit 7: Light & sound Properties and uses	Unit 8: Earth & beyond The Sun and the seasons
	1, 2	1, 2	1	1	
	6			2	
6, 7	6		2		
	12		3, 4, 5, 6, 7, 8, 9		
6, 7			3, 4, 5, 6, 7, 8, 9, 10	2, 8, 10	
9				2, 8, 10	
1, 2, 3	1, 2, 3, 7, 10, 11, 13		1, 5, 10	1, 2, 5, 6	
		4, 5, 6, 7		2, 3	
	1, 2, 7		6, 7	4, 9, 11, 12, 13	
1, 4, 5	1, 2, 3		4, 5, 6, 7, 8, 9, 10		
	6		4, 5, 6, 7, 8, 9		
11		(3), 4		3, 8, 10	
7	6		4, 5, 6, 7, 8, 9		
9	8, 10, 11	5, 6, 7	1, 2	3, 5, (7), 13	
10	12			2, 8, 10	4, 5
8, 12, 13	4, 5		4, 5, 6, 7, 8, 9, 10		2, (5)
6, 7	(9), 12		4, 5, 6, 7, 8, 9, 10	9	
9	5			3	1, 3
1, 2, (4), 5, 6, 7, 8, (12), 13, 14					
2, 8					
3					
9, 10					
11					
	1, 2				
	1, 2, 6				
	3, 14				
	1, 2, (4), (5), 6				
	7, 8, 9, 10, 11, 12, (13), 14				
(12)					
(12)					
(12)					
			1, 2, 10		
			3, 6, 7		
			4, 5, 6, 7, 8, 9		
		(3), (4)			
		1, 2, (3), (4), (5), (6), (7)			
		1, 2			
		1, 2			
		8			
				6, 7, (10), (11), (12), (14)	
		(5)		8, 9	
				13	
				1, 5	1, 2, 3, 4
				(4)	
				2, 3, 4, 14	

National Curriculum in Wales

		Unit 1: Ourselves Keeping healthy	Unit 2: Animals & Plants Growing up
SCIENTIFIC ENQUIRY	**1 The nature of science**		
	the link between ideas and information in science		
	1 to ask questions about their ideas in science	(14)	10, 11
	2 to obtain information from their own work and also, on some occasions, from other simple sources	14	
	3 to use their experiences and the information they obtain from their investigations to develop their own scientific ideas		10, 11
	2 Communication in science		
	presenting scientific information		
	1 to describe their work clearly, in speech and in writing, using appropriate vocabulary	6, 7	4
	2 to present scientific information appropriately in a number of ways, through diagrams, drawings, tables and charts	1, 3, 4, 5	
	3 to use ICT to enter and to present different kinds of information, when this is appropriate	(3)	(3), (5)
	4 to use non-standard and standard measures appropriate to their work		
	handling scientific information		
	5 to sort and classify scientific information, using ICT to do so on some occasions	(3)	(3), (5)
	6 to recognise that scientific information can be changed into different forms, and that ICT can help in doing this	(3)	
	3 Investigative skills		
	planning an investigation		
	1 to turn ideas suggested to them, and their own ideas, into a form that can be investigated		
	2 that thinking about, and if possible suggesting, what might happen, can be useful when planning what to do		10, 11
	3 to decide what is to be observed or measured		7
	4 to recognise that a test or comparison may not always be fair		10, 11
	5 to recognise hazards and risks in obtaining information		
	obtaining information		
	6 to explore using appropriate senses		4, 7
	7 to follow instructions to control the risks to themselves	14	7, 10, 11
	8 to make observations and measurements		7, 8, 9, 12, 14
	9 to make an appropriate record of observations and measurements considering information	5	7, 8, (9)
	considering information		
	10 to make simple comparisons	1, 2, 9, 10, 11, 12, 16, 17	1, 2, 3, 4, 5, 12, 15
	11 to use results to say what they found out		10, 11
	12 to try to explain what they found out, drawing on their knowledge and understanding		10, 11, 15
	13 to evaluate their work		(6), (13)
LIFE PROCESSES AND LIVING THINGS	**1 Life processes**		
	1 the differences between things that are living and things that are not		
	2 that humans and other animals have and use senses which enable them to be aware of the world around them		
	3 that animals, including humans, move, need food and water, grow and reproduce	1, 6, (8)	16
	2 Humans and other animals		
	1 to name the main external parts of the human body		
	2 to recognise similarities and differences between themselves and other pupils	11, 14, (15), (16)	
	3 to compare the external parts of human bodies with those of other animals		
	4 that taking exercise and eating the right types and amounts of food helps humans to keep healthy	1, 2, 3, 4, (5), (8), 17	
	5 about the role of drugs as medicines	9	
	6 that humans and other animals can produce offspring and these offspring grow into adults	12, 13, 16	15, 16
	3 Green plants as organisms		
	1 that plants need light and water to grow		10, 11, 16
	2 to recognise and name the leaf, flower, stem and root of flowering plants		(5)
	3 that flowering plants grow and produce seeds which, in turn, produce new plants		(7), (8), (9), 10, 11, 12, 16
	4 Living things in their environment		
	1 to find out about the different kinds of plants and animals in the local environment	(11)	6, (13), 14
	2 that animals and plants can be grouped according to observable similarities and differences		1, 2, 3, 4, 5, 12, 16
MATERIALS & THEIR PROPERTIES	**1 Grouping materials**		
	1 use their senses to explore and recognise the similarities and differences between materials		
	2 sort materials into groups, separating them on the basis of simple properties that con be seen or felt, including texture, shininess, transparency, and on whether they are attracted by a magnet		
	3 recognise and name common types of material, and that some of these materials are found naturally		
	4 find out about the uses made of a variety of common materials		
	2 Changing materials		
	1 that objects made from some materials can be changed in shape by stretching, squashing, bending and twisting		
	2 to describe the way some everyday materials change when they are heated or cooled		
PHYSICAL PROCESSES	**1 Electricity**		
	1 know that many everyday appliances use electricity and that they should be used with care		
	2 to construct and explore simple circuits involving batteries, wires, bulbs, switches and other components		
	3 that electrical devices will not work if there is a break in the circuit, and that a switch in the circuit can be used to control an electrical device.		
	2 Forces and Motion		
	1 to describe the movement of familiar things		
	2 that a push or pull can make something speed up, slow down or change direction		
	3 that both pushes and pulls are examples of forces		
	4 that forces are used in changing the shape of an object or breaking it into parts		
	3 Light and Sound		
	light and dark		
	1 that light comes from a variety of sources, including the Sun		
	2 that darkness is the absence of light		
	making and detecting sounds		
	3 that there are many kinds of sound and many sources of sound		
	4 that sounds travel away from sources, getting fainter as they do so		
	5 that sounds are heard when they enter the ear		

Lessons where curriculum content is the main objective are listed below. Lessons where content is included but is not the main focus are shown below in brackets.

Unit 3: The environment Life in habitats	Unit 4: Materials Materials and change	Unit 5: Electricity Making circuits	Unit 6: Forces & motion Making things move	Unit 7: Light & sound Properties and uses	Unit 8: Earth & beyond The Sun and the seasons
1, 2		1	4, 5, 6, 7, 8, 9, 10	1, 6	
12, 13	1, 6	1, 2	1, 2, 3, 4	1, 2, 3	1, (2), 3
11		4, 6			
6, 7			4	4	5
	6		4		
	1, 4		4, 5	4, 11	5
	1, 4		4, 5	4, 11	5
6, (7), 9, 10	(6)	7	10	12	4
	6	5	5, 6	8	
		4	2, 3	12	
	12		2, 4, 5, 6, 7, 8, 9		
4, 7	(3)	1, 3	2		
3, 10	1, 2, 3, 7, 8, 9, 10, 11, 13		1	4, 10, 13	4
	7, 8, 9, 11	1, 3	4, 5, 6, 7, 8, 9	10	
5			2	10, 11	
5, 8			4, 5, 6, 7	11	
4	1, 2	4	4, 5, 6, 7, 8, 9	2, 9	1, 2, 3, 4
8	6, 12	3		2, 3	(5)
4		5	2	3, 5	
8, 11	5		3	3, 5, 7	
2, 8, (13)					
13					
2, 8					
1, 3, 4, 5, 6, 7, 8, 9, 11, (12), 14					
(3)					
	1, 2				
	(1)				
	1, 2, (3), 4, 5				
	3, 14				
	6				
	7, 8, 9, 10, 11, 12, (13), 14				
		1, 2, 8			
		3, 4, 5, 7, 8			
		6			
			1, 10		
			3, 4, 5, 6, 9, 11		
			1, 2, 3, 6, 7, 8, 9, 10, 11		
			2		
				1, 5	1, 2, 3, 4
				2, 3, 4, 14	
				6, 7, 8, 9, 13, 14	
				11, 12, 14	
				10	

National Guidelines for Scotland

				Unit 1: Ourselves Keeping healthy	Unit 2: Animals & Plants Growing up
SKILLS IN SCIENCE: INVESTIGATING	LEVEL		**Preparing for tasks** Understanding the task and planning a practical activity. Predicting. Undertaking fair testing		
		A	● make simple suggestions and contribute to the planning of simple practical investigations		
		B	● plan simple approaches by asking questions and making suggestions		10, 11
			● make suggestions about what might happen		10, 11
			● recognise when a test or comparison is unfair		10, 11
			Carrying out tasks Observing and measuring. Recording findings in a variety of ways.		
		A	● carry out simple observations and measurements	1, 2, 3, 8, 10, 11, 12, 16	10, 11, 14
			● record observations in a simple form	4, 5, 14	1, 2, 3, 4, 5
		B	● use simple equipment and techniques to make measurements	(14)	10, 11
			● record findings in a range of ways	6, 7, 14, 17	6, 15
			Reviewing and reporting on tasks Reporting and presenting. Interpreting and evaluating results and processes.		
		A	● participate in the presentation of the findings through visual displays and oral reports	3, 6, 9	7, 8, 9, 13
			● answer simple questions about what happened		
		B	● make a short report of an investigation	4, 5, 10, 15	7, 8, 9, 12
			● answer questions on the meaning of the findings		9
			● recognise simple relationships and draw conclusions	(1), (2), (3), (17)	4, 5
EARTH AND SPACE			**Earth and space** Developing an understanding of the position of the Earth in the Solar System and the Universe, and the effects of movement and that of the Moon.		
		A	● identify the Sun, the Moon and the stars		
			● link the pattern of day and night to the position of the Sun		
		B	● associate the seasons with differences in observed temperature		
			● describe how day and night are related to the spin of the Earth		
			Materials from Earth Developing an understanding of the materials available on our planet, and the links between properties and uses.		
		A	● recognise and name some common materials from living and non-living sources		
			● give examples of uses of some materials based on simple properties		
			● give the main uses of water		
		B	● make observations of differences in the properties of common materials		
			● relate uses of everyday materials to properties		
			● explain why water conservation is important		
			Changing materials Developing an understanding of the ways in which materials can be changed.		
		A	● make observations of the ways in which some materials can be changed by processes such as squashing, bending, twisting and stretching		
		B	● describe how everyday materials can be changed by heating or cooling		
			● give examples of everyday materials that dissolve in water		
			● give examples of common causes of water pollution		
ENERGY AND FORCES			**Properties and uses of energy** Developing an understanding of energy through the study of the properties and uses of heat, light, sound and electricity.		
		A	● give examples of sources of heat, light and sound		
			● give examples of everyday uses of heat, light and sound		
			● give examples of everyday appliances that use electricity		
			● identify some of the common dangers associated with use of electricity		
		B	● identify the sun as the main source of heat and light		
			● link light and sound to seeing and hearing		
			Conversion and transfer of energy Developing an understanding of energy conversion in practical everyday contexts.		
		A	● –		
		B	● give examples of being 'energetic'		
			● link the intake of food to the movement of their body		
			Forces and their effects Developing an understanding of forces and how they can explain familiar phenomena and practices.		
		A	● give examples of pushing and pulling, floating and sinking		
		B	● describe the effect that a push and pull can have on the direction, speed or shape of an object		
			● give examples of magnets in everyday use		
			● describe the interaction of magnets in terms of the forces of attraction and repulsion		
LIVING THINGS AND THE PROCESSES OF LIFE			**Variety and characteristic features** Developing an understanding of the characteristic features of the main groups of plants and animals including humans and micro-organisms. The principles of genetics are also considered.		
		A	● recognise similarities and differences between themselves and others	11, 12, 14, (15)	
			● sort living things into broad groups according to easily observable characteristics		1, 2, 3, (4), (5)
		B	● give some of the more obvious distinguishing features of the major invertebrate groups		(12), (13), (14)
			● name some common members of the invertebrate groups		(12), (13), (14)
			The processes of life Developing an understanding of growth and development and life cycles, including cells and cell processes. The main organs of the human body and their functions are also considered.		
		A	● name and identify the main external parts of the bodies of humans and other animals		
			● describe some ways in which humans keep themselves safe	9, 10, 17	
			● give the conditions needed by animals and plants in order to remain healthy	1, 2, 3, 4, 5, 6, 7, 8, 17	10, 11
		B	● give examples of how the senses are used to detect information		
			● recognise the stages of the human life cycle	12, 13, 16	
			● recognise stages in the life cycles of familiar plants and animals	12	(6), 7, 8, 9, (12), (13), (14), 15
			● identify the main parts of flowering plants		(6), 7

Lessons where curriculum content is the main objective are listed below. Lessons where content is included but is not the main focus are shown below in brackets.

Unit 3: The environment Life in habitats	Unit 4: Materials Materials and change	Unit 5: Electricity Making circuits	Unit 6: Forces & motion Making things move	Unit 7: Light & sound Properties and uses	Unit 8: Earth & beyond The Sun and the seasons
4	6	7	1, 3, 4, 5, 6, 7, 8	2	
9			2, 10	8	
6	6		4, 5, 6, 7, 8	2, 4, 8, 10, 12	
	12		3, 4, 5, 6, 7, 8, 9		
1, 3	1, 2, 3, 7, 8, 9, 10, 11	1	2, 3, 4, 5, 6, 7, 8, 9, 10	2	
4	1, 2, 3, 12		4, 6, 8, 10	11	4
	6	3, 4, 5, 6, 7	3, 4, 5, 6, 7, 8, 9	11	
6	6		3, 4, 5, 6	11	
4, 5, 8, 11	4, 5	2	1, 2, 10	1, 3, 5, 6, 7, 9, 13	1, 3
9, 10	6, 7, 8, 9, 10		2, 4, 6	4	2, 4
2, 7, (12), (13)	1, 2, 3, 4, 13	4, 5, 6	7, 8, 9	5	
7	7		5, 9	11	5
	12		9	(3)	5
					1, 2, 3, 4
					(1), (2), (3)
					5
					(1), (2), (3)
	1, 2, (4), (5)				
	3				
	1, 2				
	3, 14				
	6				
	7, 8, 9, 10, 11, 12, (13), 14				
	13			1, 6, 7, 8, 9, 11, 12, 14	
	13				
		1, 2, 3, (4), (5), (6), (7)			
		1, 2			
				(1), 5	
				2, 3, 4, 8, 9, 10, 11, 12, 13, 14	
		(4), (5)			
			1, 2, 3, 4, 5, 6, 7, 8, 9, 10, 11		
			2, 3, 4, 5, 6, 7, 8, 9, 10, 11		
		(5)			

Living things and the processes of life continued overleaf

National Guidelines for Scotland

			Unit 1: Ourselves Keeping healthy	Unit 2: Animals & Plants Growing up
LIVING THINGS AND THE PROCESSES OF LIFE	**LEVEL**	**Interaction of living things with their environment** Developing an understanding of the interdependance of living things with the environment. The conservation and care of living things are also considered.		
	A	● recognise and name some common plants and animals		(6), 13
		● give examples of how to care for living things and the environment		(10), (11)
		● give some examples of seasonal changes in the appearance of plants		
	B	● give examples of feeding relationships found in the local environment		
		● construct simple food chains		
		Developing informed attitudes Pupils should be encouraged to develop an awareness of, and positive attitudes, to:		
		A commitment to learning		
		● the need to develop informed and reasoned opinions on the impact of science in relation to social, environmental moral and ethical issues		
		● working independently and with others to find solutions to scientific problems		
		Respect and care for self and others		
		● taking responsibility for their own health and safety	1, 2, 3, 4, 5, 6, 7, 8, 9, 10	
		● participating in the safe and responsible care of living things and the environment		10, 11
		● the development of responsible attitudes that take account of different beliefs and values		
		Social and environmental responsibility		
		● thinking through the various consequences for living things and the environment of different choices, decisions and courses of action		
		● the importance of the interrelationships between living things and their enviroment		
		● participating in the conservation of natural resources and the sustainable use of the Earth's resources		
		● the need for conservation of scarce energy resources and endangered species at local and global level		

Lessons where curriculum content is the main objective are listed below. Lessons where content is included but is not the main focus are shown below in brackets.

Unit 3: The environment Life in habitats	Unit 4: Materials Materials and change	Unit 5: Electricity Making circuits	Unit 6: Forces & motion Making things move	Unit 7: Light & sound Properties and uses	Unit 8: Earth & beyond The Sun and the seasons
1, 2, 3, 4, 5, 6, 7, 8, 9, 10, 14					
12, 13					
(10), 11					
2					
8					
		1, 2			
12, 13					
12					
12					
	(13)				
	(13)				

Unit 3: The environment Life in habitats	Unit 4: Materials Materials and change	Unit 5: Electricity Making circuits	Unit 6: Forces & motion Making things move	Unit 7: Light & sound Properties and uses	Unit 8: Earth & beyond The Sun and the seasons

Series topic map

Year/Primary	YR/P1	Y1/P2	Y2/P3	Y3/P4	Y4/P5	Y5/P6	Y6/P7
Unit 1: Ourselves	This is me!	Me and my body	Keeping healthy	Teeth and food	How I move	Growing up healthy	New beginnings
Unit 2: Animals & plants	Looking at animals and plants	Growing and caring	Growing up	The needs of plants and animals	Different sorts of skeletons	Life cycles	Variation
Unit 3: The environment	Out and about	Environments and living things	Life in habitats	How the environment affects living things	Habitats and food chains	Water and the environment	The living world
Unit 4: Materials	Exploring materials	Properties of materials	Materials and change	Natural & manufactured materials	Warm liquids, cool solids	Gases, solids and liquids	Reversible and non-reversible changes
Unit 5: Electricity	Making things work	Using and misusing electricity	Making circuits	Electricity and communication	Switches and conduction	Making and using electricity	Changing circuits
Unit 6: Forces & motion	Pushing and pulling	Introducing forces	Making things move	Magnets and springs	Friction	Exploring forces and their effects	Forces and action
Unit 7: Light & sound	Looking and listening	Sources of light and sound	Properties and uses	Sources and effects	Travelling and reflecting	Bending light and changing sound	Light and sound around us
Unit 8: Earth & beyond	Up in the sky	Stargazing	The Sun and the seasons	The Sun and shadows	The Sun and stars	Sun, Moon and Earth	The Solar System